TRENDS IN BIODIVERSITY RESEARCH

TRENDS IN BIODIVERSITY RESEARCH

A.R. BURK
EDITOR

Nova Science Publishers, Inc.
New York

LIBRARY OF CONGRESS CATALOGING-IN-PUBLICATION DATA

Trends in biodiversity research / A.R. Burk, (editor).
p. cm.
Includes bibliographical references and index.
ISBN 1-59454-385-2 (hardcover)
1. Biological diversity. 2. Biological diversity--Research. I. Burk, A. R.
QH541.15.B56T74 2005
333.95'16--dc22 2005005425

Published by Nova Science Publishers, Inc. ✣ New York

CONTENTS

PREFACE

Biological diversity, or "biodiversity," refers to the variety of all life on earth, and the complex relationships among living things, and between living things and their environment. Biodiversity includes genetic variety, species diversity, and variability in communities, ecosystems and landscapes. Biodiversity sustains the environments in which we live and on which our lives and those of every other living creature on Earth depend. Thanks to biodiversity, we are able to obtain such necessary goods as food, clothing, medicine, and fuel. Equally important are the ecosystem services that biodiversity provides, such as clean air and drinkable water. Conservation scientists have identified a number of universal threats to biodiversity: habitat loss and degradation, invasive species, pollution, overpopulation, overexploitation and consumption, and global climate change. This new book examines critical issues in this field from researchers around the globe.

Five species of reptiles present in tropical Australia are considered in chapter 1. These are the hawksbill turtle (*Eretmochelys imbricata)*; the northern long-necked turtle (*Chelodina rugosa)*; the taipan snake (*Oxyuranus scutellatus)*; the freshwater crocodile *(Crocodylus johnstoni)*; and the saltwater crocodile *(Crocodylus porosus)*. Background information is provided on the ecological status of each of these species and after outlining their human use (including commercial use) and management in Australia, an experimental survey method is introduced and results from its application are reported and analysed. The survey method involves two serial surveys of a sample of 204 Brisbane (Australia) residents. The first survey is based on the initial knowledge of the respondents of the reptile species and for the subsequent survey the knowledge available to participants about these species is experimentally increased. These surveys provide information on the amount of knowledge possessed by this sample of the public about the relevant reptile species, the respondents' attitudes to these species (including their attitudes to commercial use), respondents' support for the survival of these reptiles and for their conservation. Furthermore, data is gathered from the surveys on the comparative amount respondents' state they would be prepared to contribute to support the conservation of each of these focal reptile species. Respondents are asked to assume that they are given $1,000 and that this can only be allocated to the conservation of these reptiles. Later, however, they are also given the option to donate this money to any charity concerned with human welfare. The contingent valuation data for each of the reptile species are used to isolate factors that influence the comparative allocation of conservation funds to each of the relevant reptile species. Factors considered include the extent of the respondents' knowledge of the species, the stated degree to which respondents' reported that they liked or disliked the species, and ethical views of the respondents. Implications of the findings for the theory of economic valuation of wildlife species and for the focal reptile species in Australia are discussed in concluding this chapter.

As demonstrated in various recent investigations the signs of climate change are already evident. In a rapidly changing environment a management strategy to strengthen biodiversity is urgently required. Chapter 2 shows how such a strategy might be achieved by understanding the effects of global climate change for three major Australian ecosystems - rainforest, mangroves and savannah. A risk assessment for these ecosystems that considers the impacts of past climate change lays the basis for understanding how these ecosystems might be managed under a rapidly changing climate. This is demonstrated by a case study for the wet tropics bioregion. To retain a wide range of flora and fauna, core habitats of target species at risk from climate change are to be identified by using a combination of modelling scenarios and field work. Only by concentrating on the potential refuge areas, with a joint effort of social, governmental and scientific bodies, can we expect to maximise the chances of regionally endemic species surviving climate change. This issue is discussed with regard to ecosystem complexity and the likely difficulties that will be incurred in implementing a conservation strategy for at risk species.

To test the hypothesis that the contaminated landscapes around a big polluter represent a sink habitat for birds and mammals, the authors of chapter 3 quantified population densities and estimated biomass of birds and mammals at ten sites located within 65 km distance from the nickel-copper smelter at Monchegorsk, NW Russia, and used relative densities of burying beetles as an index reflecting mortality of vertebrates from factors other than predation. Biomass of birds (estimated from transect counts) and large mammals (estimated from snow-tracking) declined monotonously with increase in pollution, while biomass of small mammals (estimated from snap-trapping) peaked in moderately polluted areas. Population densities of vertebrates in industrial barrens were 10-50% of densities observed in unpolluted forests, depending on the group studied. Population density of burying beetle *Nicrophorus vespilloides*, measured by bait-trapping, peaked 15-30 km from the polluter, indicating increased mortality rate of vertebrates in moderately polluted forest habitats. The increase in mortality, in absence of compensatory increase in reproduction (as reported in earlier studies), suggests that populations in the polluted (low quality) habitats are supported by migration from the surrounding unpolluted territories, and that migrants are not able to assess habitat quality in terms of toxic contamination before breeding. Moderately polluted habitats may be attractive for the dispersing birds and mammals not only because of permanent vacation of territories due to high mortality, but also because some resources are more abundant there than in surrounding unpolluted forests. We concluded that the contaminated area of about 1000 km^2 works like a death trap for dispersing birds and mammals, and the moderately contaminated forested part of this area can possibly be classified as an attractive sink habitat.

The authors of Chapter 4 reviews that natural resource management decisions are complicated by multiple property rights, management objectives, and stakeholders with varying degrees of influence over the decision making process. In order to make efficient decisions, managers must incorporate the opinions and values of the involved stakeholders as well as understand the complex institutional constraints and opportunities that influence the decision-making process. Involved federal, state, local, private and public stakeholder groups have diverse values and preferences about the use and management of public resources. Underlying institutional factors give certain stakeholders a greater level of influence over the policy outcome. How stakeholders use their influence can greatly effect the time, effort and costs of the decision making process. The overall result of an individual stakeholder or stakeholder group's influence on a negotiation will depend both on their relative power and their level of conviction for a particular outcome.

Chapter 5 highlights the importance of maintaining low-intensity farming systems for preserving European biodiversity, particularly in the Mediterranean region. The European Directives 79/409/EEC (Birds directive) and 92/43/EEC (Habitats directive) are the main political instruments for nature conservation in Europe. They identify and list the habitats, flora and fauna species of higher conservation concern in Europe, for which a network of protected areas, named Natura 2000, is being implemented. The objective of this paper is to quantify the importance of low-intensity agriculture to maintaining Natura 2000 values in Mediterranean countries, using Portugal as a case study. Each protected species of fauna and flora, as well as each protected habitat, occurring in the country were ranked according to the degree of dependence on low-intensity farming systems, using a set of criteria. For vertebrates, 46.8% of the 96 species listed in EU directives and occurring in Portugal depended on low-intensity agriculture. Most of these consist of bird species associated with low-intensity arable and pastoral systems, particularly pseudosteppes and "montados". For plants, 34.7% of the 72 species also depended on extensive farming systems, particularly grazed grasslands. Finally, 20.8% of the 91 habitats occurring in the country corresponded to early or intermediate phases of vegetation succession (e.g. hay meadows, scrublands) benefiting from disturbance originating from grazing, ploughing or burning associated with low-intensity arable and pastoral systems. We end up identifying the main farming systems holding relevant biodiversity values occurring in Portugal and discussing the importance of low-intensity farming for the whole Mediterranean region.

As described in chapter 6, intensive agricultural practices have resulted in a strong decline of biodiversity in agricultural landscapes, which may result in the deterioration of ecosystem functions, such as pest regulation by natural enemies. Non-crop habitats play an essential role in maintaining biodiversity and the biological control of pest populations in crops because these habitats are relatively undisturbed areas that provide essential (food) resources for natural enemies and their prey. The area, configuration and composition of non-crop habitats in the landscape are important factors that affect the pest regulation function. Simulations and empirical studies suggest that pest pressure decreases in a non-linear way with an increasing area of non-crop habitats in landscapes. This implies that the area of non-crop habitat should exceed a threshold value in order to acquire notable biological control. A fine-meshed distribution of non-crop habitats, which may be encountered in extensively managed, small-scale landscapes, allows an effective colonization of crops by natural enemies and is likely to result in improved crop protection. Forests and other robust undisturbed natural habitats are identified as habitats that are generally associated with improved impact of natural enemies and suppressed pest populations in surrounding crops. In conclusion, improving and expanding the area of non-crop habitats in agricultural landscapes has good potential to improve the pest regulation function in agroecosystems and may therefore contribute to a transition towards sustainable agriculture.

Multi-nutrient fertilization can be an effective management tool to enhance conifer production and economic returns in the inland Northwest. Given that a greater emphasis has been placed on multiple-resource management, it is important to quantify how these silvicultural treatments for overstory vegetation affect understory vegetation to provide a picture of overall ecosystem health, and for wildlife habitat and range quality. Chapter 7 reports on the response of understory vegetation Ca and P concentrations following the addition of other nutrients through multi-nutrient fertilization treatments. Vegetation was separated into three lifeforms (grasses and grass-likes, forbs, and shrubs). A selected number of individual species were also analyzed. Based on this study, P concentrations appear to be more affected by multi-nutrient fertilization with other nutrients than Ca concentrations across all lifeforms. Optimum animal growth is highly dependent on these two nutrients. However, the proper ratio between them is also important because extreme amounts of Ca can interfere with P metabolism. Ca/P ratios showed variability across lifeforms and sites following treatment.

In: Trends in Biodiversity Research
Editor: A. R. Burk, pp. 1-40
ISBN 1-59454-385-2

Chapter 1

AUSTRALIAN TROPICAL REPTILE SPECIES: ECOLOGICAL STATUS, PUBLIC VALUATION, ATTITUDES TO THEIR CONSERVATION AND COMMERCIAL USE

Clem Tisdell and Hemanath Swarna Nanth
School of Economics, The University of Queensland, Brisbane, Australia
Clevo Wilson
School of Economics and Finance, Faculty of Business
Queensland University of Technology, Brisbane, Australia

ABSTRACT

Five species of reptiles present in tropical Australia are considered in this study. These are the hawksbill turtle (*Eretmochelys imbricata)*; the northern long-necked turtle (*Chelodina rugosa)*; the taipan snake (*Oxyuranus scutellatus)*; the freshwater crocodile *(Crocodylus johnstoni)*; and the saltwater crocodile *(Crocodylus porosus)*. Background information is provided on the ecological status of each of these species and after outlining their human use (including commercial use) and management in Australia, an experimental survey method is introduced and results from its application are reported and analysed. The survey method involves two serial surveys of a sample of 204 Brisbane (Australia) residents. The first survey is based on the initial knowledge of the respondents of the reptile species and for the subsequent survey the knowledge available to participants about these species is experimentally increased. These surveys provide information on the amount of knowledge possessed by this sample of the public about the relevant reptile species, the respondents' attitudes to these species (including their attitudes to commercial use), respondents' support for the survival of these reptiles and for their conservation. Furthermore, data is gathered from the surveys on the comparative amount respondents' state they would be prepared to contribute to support the conservation of each of these focal reptile species. Respondents are asked to assume that they are given $1,000 and that this can only be allocated to the conservation of these reptiles. Later, however, they are also given the option to donate this money to any charity concerned with human welfare. The contingent valuation data for each of the reptile species are used to isolate factors that influence the comparative allocation of conservation funds to each of the relevant reptile species. Factors considered include the extent of the respondents' knowledge of the species, the stated degree to which respondents' reported that they liked or disliked the species, and ethical views of the respondents. Implications of the findings for the theory of economic valuation of wildlife species and for the focal reptile species in Australia are discussed in concluding this chapter.

INTRODUCTION

A large portion of Australia (approximately 40% of it) is located in the tropical zone, above the Tropic of Capricorn. This study focuses on five species of reptiles that occur in the Australian Tropics. The two species of crocodile considered, the saltwater crocodile (*Crocodylus porosus*) and the Australian freshwater crocodile (*Crocodylus johnstoni*), occur in Australia mainly in the tropics. The two species of taipan snakes are discussed of which one (*Oxyuranus scutellatus*) occurs mainly in the Australian tropics. Two species of turtles are assessed; the northern long-necked turtle (*Chelodina rugosa*) and the marine hawksbill turtle (*Eretmochelys imbricata*). The former occurs only in the Australian tropics and the latter occurs mainly in tropical waters but is sometimes found in subtropical waters.

After considering the ecological status of these species in Australia, we outline the use made of them in Australia by indigenous Australians, their potential uses and their commercial uses, giving particular attention to the saltwater crocodile. The saltwater crocodile is one of the least liked of the Australian reptiles but is commercially very valuable. It obtains the greatest commercial use of the reptile species considered here.

We then draw upon the results of a survey of a sample of 204 Brisbane (Australia) residents. This provides information about the sampled public's awareness of each of the focal reptile species and the extent to which they state that they like or dislike each of these species. From the latter, a 'likeability' index is calculated for each of the species based on the attitudes of the whole sample of respondents.

It is hypothesised that likeability is a major factor influencing the attitudes of the public to the survival of individual species, their support for the commercial harvesting of species and for their comparative willingness to allocate funds for the conservation of different species. This is tested using the likeability index for each of those reptile species and the results from the sample.

Note that the sample of reptile species was selected on the premise that they would reveal significant differences in awareness of them by the public and also in their likeability. As will be found later, this condition is satisfied.

Now let us consider the ecological status in Australia of the five focal reptile species. Strictly, this should be six species because there are two species of Taipan snake present in Australia, the western taipan and the coastal taipan. The western taipan only occurs below the tropics. However, both species were mentioned, and referred to commonly in the survey as 'taipan snake'.

ECOLOGICAL STATUS IN AUSTRALIA OF THE FOCAL REPTILE SPECIES

Saltwater Crocodile

Description

The saltwater crocodile (*Crocodylus porosus*) (Figure 1), along with the Indian gharial, is the world's largest crocodilian species and reptile (Grenard, 1991; Ross, 1998). Generally, adults are 5 metres long and around 400 to 500 kg in weight, but adult males can reach sizes of up to 6 or 7 metres and weigh more than 1,000 kg (Ross, 1998). It is a large-headed crocodilian species with a shorter and broader snout than the Australian freshwater crocodile, and has a heavy set of jaws capable of crushing the bones of mammals as large as a buffalo (Ross, 1998; Cronin, 2001; EPA, 2002). Juveniles are normally pale tan in colour while mature adults are generally grey, brown to almost black, with creamy yellow bellies (Ross, 1998; Cronin, 2001). It has a fierce disposition and is known to injure or kill humans (Webb and Manolis, 1993, p. 250; Britton, 2002a).

Figure 1. A saltwater crocodile in northern Queensland

Distribution and Habitat

Saltwater crocodiles are the most widely distributed of the crocodilians, ranging from southern India, Southeast Asia to Papua New Guinea and Australia (Ross, 1998). In Australia, they are distributed in the coastal regions of northern Australia, from Broome in Western Australia through the Northern Territory to Gladstone in Queensland (see Figure 2).

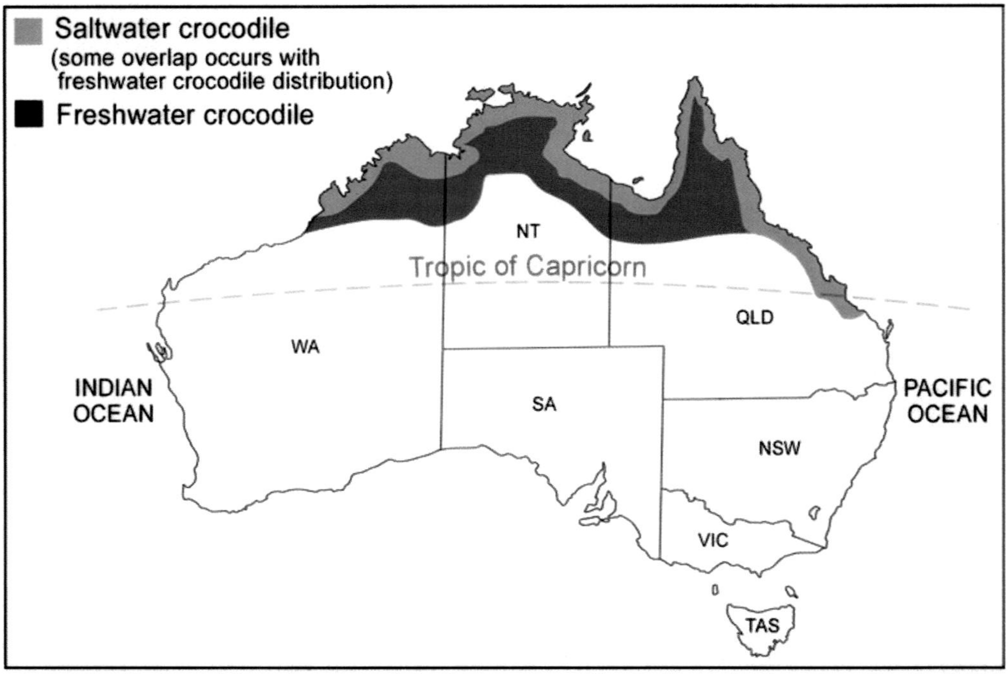

Figure 2. Distribution of the saltwater and freshwater crocodiles in Australia (based on Cronin, 2001)

The saltwater crocodile lives in coastal brackish water habitats and tidal sections of rivers (Ross, 1998). It is also found in freshwater sections of rivers and in freshwater swamps (Ross, 1998). It is known to frequent inland lakes, and can be encountered at sea, usually around the coasts (Webb et al., 1987; Messel and Vorlicek, 1989; Webb and Manolis, 1993).

Life History and Ecology

The saltwater crocodile breeds during the wet season (from November to March) (Cronin, 2001; EPA, 2002). Breeding and recruitment is established in the freshwater areas of rivers and freshwater swamps. Females become mature at lengths of 2.2 to 2.5 metres (about 12 years of age) and lay 40 to 60 eggs in mound nests about 45 centimetres high to prevent losses of eggs from flooding during rainfall (Webb et al., 1987; Cronin, 2001; Britton, 2002a). Incubation lasts around 90 days (Ross, 1998). The sex of the hatchling is determined by the incubation temperature in its nest, a phenomenon known as temperature-dependent sex determination (TSD) (Britton, 2002a). Low and high temperatures produce females while temperatures between 31 and 33°C produce males (EPA, 2002). This feature is much researched because it is of value for captive breeding programs to ensure the desired sex ratio (Britton, 2002a). TSD is manipulated to produce males for farming purposes because male saltwater crocodiles have faster growth rates than the females (Britton, 2002a).

The saltwater crocodile is reported to be territorial. The growing male encounters competition from larger individuals for area, and is sometimes forced to move to marginal habitats like higher salinity rivers (Ross, 1998; Webb, 2002). This competition results in high mortality among intermediate-sized crocodiles (Ross, 1998; Webb, 2002). The survival of juveniles is sometimes threatened by large individuals who will kill and eat them (Britton,

2002a; Webb, 2002). Intraspecific competitive behaviour appears to be one of the main factors limiting the population size of this species in many areas (Britton, 2002a).

The diet of young saltwater crocodiles consist of small animals such as crabs, prawns, fish, frogs and insects. Larger crocodiles take bigger prey such as rodents, birds, pigs, wallabies that come close to the water's edge and even other crocodiles (Cronin, 2001; EPA, 2002).

Abundance, Survival Status, Threats and Conservation Overview

In Australia, intensive commercial harvesting for saltwater crocodile skins occurred in 1945 when the population of saltwater crocodiles in the Northern Territory numbered around 100,000 individuals (Webb et al., 1984; Webb et al., 1987; Webb et al., 2000). Protection was accorded to the crocodile in Australia beginning in the late 1960s (Western Australia in 1969, the Northern Territory in 1971 and Queensland in 1974) (Letts, 1987) when, after thirty years of unregulated hunting, the saltwater crocodile population became severely depleted (Webb et al., 2000). In the Northern Territory, for example, adult crocodiles were rare and the total population, consisting mostly of young juveniles, was thought to be no more than 5,000 individuals (Messel, 1977; Webb, 1997). Over the next thirty years, the population level of saltwater crocodiles rebounded to pre-exploitation levels (Webb et al., 1986; Webb et al., 1994) and this crocodile now occupies its complete historical range (Webb, 2002). Their estimated population size in Western Australia, Northern Territory and Queensland is now considered to be at least 100,000 to 150,000 adults (Britton, 2002a). It is considered to be at low risk or of least concern according to the IUCN Red List (IUCN, 2003). Highly threatened in many parts of the world, it is nonetheless considered unlikely to become extinct because its population is numerous and secure in Australia and Papua New Guinea (Ross, 1998). Other threats include predation of eggs by pigs and goannas and the destruction of nests from seasonal flooding (EPA, 2002). The saltwater crocodile is a CITES-listed species, and comes under Appendix II for controlled trade in Australia, Papua New Guinea and Indonesia and under Appendix I prohibiting trade in all other countries (Ross, 1998). This reflects the success of crocodile management strategies in Australia in ensuring effective conservation and subsequently successful sustainable farming and wild harvesting programs (Ross, 1998; Webb, 2000a).

Possible Implications of Territoriality and Intraspecific Competition for Sustainable Harvest Levels of Wild Crocodiles

The chief form of competition the saltwater crocodile faces in its habitat in several areas in Australia is intraspecific competition (i.e., competition within species). Interspecific competition on the other hand is low or negligible for the saltwater crocodile because the species is located at the top of the food chain in its ecosystem (EPA, 2003b) and has little extra-species competitors or predators (if predation of eggs and the very young are excluded). Interspecific competition occurs with its sympatric species, the freshwater crocodile, where as Webb et al. (1983) point out saltwater crocodile competitively exclude or prey upon freshwater crocodiles at overlapping habitat areas. Therefore, a significant ecological relationship exists between sustainable use or harvesting and intraspecific competition of saltwater crocodiles.

The territorial behaviour saltwater crocodiles exhibit is a form of intraspecific competition (Webb and Manolis, 1989; Begon et al., 1996, p. 253). In the tidal waterways of northern Australia, the saltwater crocodile occupies year-round territories where breeding and nesting occur (Lang, 1987). Territories are established and maintained by dominant males, from which other males are excluded but females are tolerated (Lang, 1987). A male's territory may encompass the nesting sites of several females (Lang, 1987). Females are also territorial with nesting sites. The energy spent defending and maintaining territories results in gains in terms of increased survival or productivity of the territorial animal (Bolen and Robinson, 2003). Given that suitable area is a limiting factor, it is a zero-sum game: the animal that has failed to secure a territory for itself loses out in terms of access to resources such as food, favourable habitat and potential mates. These individuals frequently do not reproduce and suffer higher mortality rates than the owners of territories (*cf.* Jenkins et al., 1963; Begon et al., 1996, p. 253). These difficulties have been observed among the smaller, subadult saltwater crocodiles that have been disadvantaged by larger adults. Territory formation thereby restricts breeding, setting a limit on the sizes of breeding populations (Bolen and Robinson, 2003). The rate at which the population expands is thus regulated.

Evidence of intraspecific competition in saltwater crocodiles exists. In a study of saltwater crocodile population sizes in the Blyth-Cadell River system in the Northern Territory during the years of protection between 1974 and 1990, Webb and Manolis (1992) found that while overall crocodile population size showed an increasing trend, there was also a negative correlation between the numbers of juveniles (2, 3 and 4 year olds) with increasing density of larger crocodiles (6 years old and above). The decreasing abundance of smaller crocodiles is thought to be evidence of direct predation on juveniles by larger crocodiles and/ or the exclusion of juveniles by larger crocodiles (Webb et al., 1996).

However, currently ongoing studies of Queensland saltwater crocodile populations seem to show that saltwater crocodile territories in the wild overlap to quite a degree, suggesting that the high competitive exclusion usually assumed may have been overestimated (Mark Read, personal communication, 22nd July 2004). Possibly competitive territoriality varies from place to place depending on biological and natural conditions. There are comparatively greater saltwater crocodile densities in the Northern Territory than in Queensland, and abundant suitable landscape features in the Northern Territory (e.g. long meandering river systems that provide good habitat for the crocodiles) compared to the Queensland east coast (where development may have also had some effect). Environmental factors control saltwater crocodile populations more in Queensland than in the Northern Territory where intraspecific competition is possibly more controlling, according to preliminary findings by Mark Read (personal communication, 22nd July 2004). This may explain the possibly stronger territoriality of saltwater crocodiles in the Northern Territory than in Queensland.

At first blush, the idea of harvesting adult crocodiles possesses intuitive appeal because it can be envisaged that through population regulation other competing adults or subadults will rapidly take the place of the removed (or dead) territory holder (*cf.* Begon et al., 1996, p. 253). However, the wisdom in harvesting territory-holding saltwater crocodiles is unclear. Lang (1987) for instance contends that although some territory holders or large adult animals that are not breeding may appear to be "surplus" animals, the removal of the larger animals with high reproductive potential can destabilise long-standing social relations in a population and decrease in the long-term the population's overall reproductive success (Lang, 1987). Studies of other territorial animals inform that enough males should be left in the adult age or size class that are developing territoriality so that the annual supply of physically and socially mature males is not undermined (see Wilson and Franklin, 1985; Franklin and Fritz, 1991, p. 329).

It is thus hypothesised, based on the theory of compensatory mechanism (Errington, 1946, 1967), that the harvesting of the non-breeding segment of the population (particularly the subadult males) that would perish in any case through competition would be favourable and ensure minimal net loss to the population. Despite the evidence presented by Webb et al. (1996) from their Blyth-Cadell River system studies of decreasing abundance of smaller crocodiles, they point out that recruitment into the older age classes is continuing and expect harvesting to be sustainable. This would suggest that in areas like the Northern Territory where wild populations are closer to carrying capacity and contain more larger-sized animals, the populations could sustain a substantial harvesting rate without significant decline in population size. Population growth rates may increase because of higher per capita resource availability, increased juvenile or subadult survivorship and increased fecundity (Thorbjarnarson, 1991, p. 231).

The situation may be different in Queensland where the environmental factor is the limiting factor in many areas, holding population densities and size classes at lower levels and rendering sustainable harvesting not very feasible. The effects of harvesting are being investigated in the trial harvests conducted in the Northern Territory (Webb et al., 1996). Similarly, the harvesting of eggs that would otherwise be destroyed by flooding appears to leave recruitment unaffected; the number of non-hatchlings counted in the Adelaide River has steadily increased even with the harvesting of 22,823 eggs over a period of twelve years (Webb et al., 1996).

Consider the possible relevance of standard theories of the population dynamics of wild vertebrates to the net recruitment and level of harvestable biomass of saltwater crocodiles. This relationship is commonly assumed to be of a symmetric inverted U-shape, usually quadratic, as a function of the population of the species. If this is so, the maximum sustainable yield (MSY) or maximum sustainable harvest of the species occurs at half the population level that corresponds to the carrying capacity of its environment (Caughley and Sinclair, 1994).

However, when considerable intraspecific competition occurs (as it does for some population of crocodiles), the net recruitment curve or curve of net change in biomass of a species as a function of population density is likely to be skewed or asymmetric as illustrated in Figure 3 (*cf.* Begon et al., 1996, p. 221). This implies that MSY corresponds to a population closer to carrying capacity than in the symmetric case. It also indicates that because of intraspecific competition, the species can withstand a high level of harvesting pressure when its population level is near carrying capacity without greatly reducing its sustainable level of population. Basically this is because harvesting pressure reduces intraspecific competition.

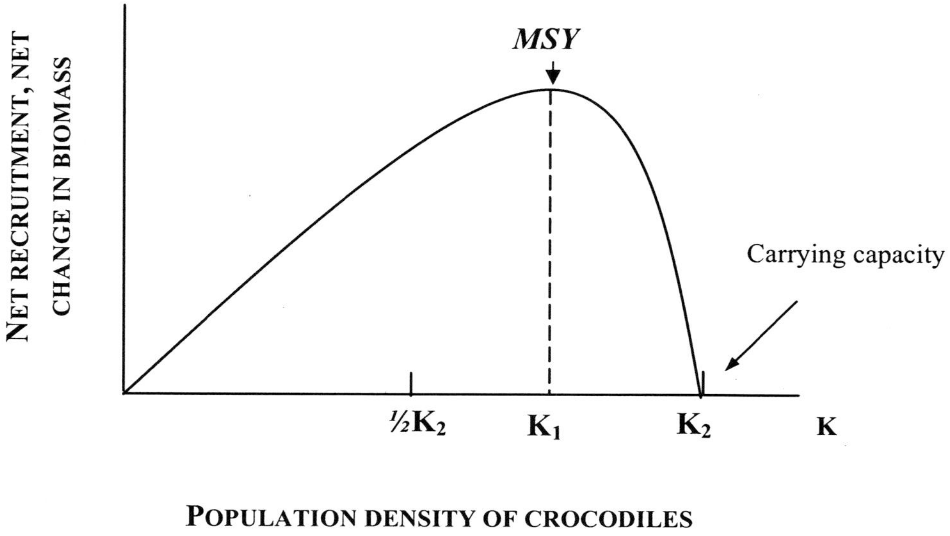

Figure 3. As a result of intraspecific competition, the net recruitment or net change in biomass of populations of saltwater crocodiles may be a skewed or asymmetric curve like the above one (adapted from Begon et al., 1996)

It should, nevertheless be borne in mind that the situation illustrated in Figure 3 is based on highly simplified theory. It does not, for example, take into account the age classes harvested of the population. The above discussion of saltwater crocodiles indicates that this can be a relevant consideration when assessing the sustainability of net recruitment or harvest. Furthermore, in one environment intraspecific competition may be an important influence on the population levels of a species, such as the saltwater crocodile, but not in others. As suggested above, intraspecific competition of saltwater crocodiles may be a much more important factor influencing their population levels in the Northern Territory than in Queensland, Australia.

Freshwater Crocodile

Description

The freshwater crocodile (*Crocodylus johnstoni*) is a small- to medium-sized freshwater crocodile unique to Australia (Ross, 1998). It is similar to other Asian freshwater crocodilian species but is morphologically distinct because of its long, unusually narrow and tapering snout (Ross, 1998; Cronin, 2001; Britton, 2002b). Adult males can grow to sizes of up to 2.5 to 3 metres and can have bodyweights of 70 to 80 kg (Webb and Manolis, 1993; Ross, 1998; Britton, 2002b). Their powerful jaws can crush turtle shells, and have very sharp teeth that intermesh when the jaws are closed (Cronin, 2001). The freshwater crocodile has grey to olive brown body colour, with darker bands forming across the back and sides (Cronin, 2001; Britton, 2002b). Though it occasionally bites swimmers during the courtship season, this species is generally considered harmless to man (Webb and Manolis, 1993).

Distribution and Habitat

The freshwater crocodile is restricted to the tropics of Western Australia, Northern Territory and Queensland (see Figure 2) (Ross, 1998). It inhabits permanent freshwater areas such as floodplain lakes, billabongs and swamps, including less saline upstream areas of river systems and creeks (Ross, 1998). The freshwater crocodile is generally not found near the coast, where prohibitive high salinity and competition with the more dominant saltwater crocodile renders this habitat far less favourable (Britton, 2002b). However, they may be found in some tidal estuaries where the saltwater crocodile is absent (Cronin, 2001).

Life History and Ecology

Freshwater crocodiles breed during the dry season (from August to September) (Cronin, 2001; EPA, 2002). The female freshwater crocodile lays its eggs in moist holes dug into sand bars that become exposed in the dry season (Ross, 1998, Cronin, 2001). Clutch size averages 13 eggs, but range from 4 to 20 (Britton, 2002b). The incubation period is usually 75 to 85 days (Webb et al., 1983). Temperature-dependent sex determination is also evident in the freshwater crocodile (Britton, 2002b). Feral pigs and goannas are major predators of eggs (Britton, 2002b). Often only 1% of hatchlings survive to reach maturity, and in some years predation pressures are so great that it is unlikely that any contribution is made to the adult population pool (Britton, 2002b).

The freshwater crocodile eats fish; the shape of its snout itself suggests primary adaptation to a piscivorous diet (Britton, 2002b). They feed on a variety of other prey too, such as invertebrates and small, young vertebrates, lizards, turtles, bats and birds (Britton, 2002b; EPA, 2002). Larger individuals may even take small terrestrial species that come close to the water's edge (Britton, 2002b).

Abundance, Survival Status, Threats and Conservation Overview

Freshwater crocodiles have survived long-term traditional hunting by Australian Aborigines for food. At the end of the 1950s as saltwater crocodile populations declined, commercial hide-hunters targeted freshwater crocodiles, causing widespread reduction of their populations (Britton, 2002b). The freshwater crocodile has since been accorded protection (Western Australia in 1962 and the Northern Territory in 1964) (Letts, 1987). Populations are said to have recently recovered to a significant extent (Britton, 2002b). The wild population size of the Australian freshwater crocodile is estimated at between 50,000 to 100,000 (Britton, 2002b). According to Britton (2002b), the IUCN Red List ranks this species as at 'low risk' and of 'least concern'. Threats to the species still exist in the form of habitat destruction, and possibly some mortality caused by an invasive species, the cane toad (*Bufo marinus*) (Britton, 2002b). Under CITES, it is included in Appendix II, which allows legal but controlled trade (CITES, 2003). There are now small-scale farming and ranching programs for the freshwater crocodile in Australia, and monitoring and management studies that have been in place since the 1970s continue (Britton, 2002b).

Taipan Snake

Description

Australia's two species of taipan snakes, the coastal taipan (*Oxyuranus scutellatus*) and the western taipan (*Oxyuranus microlepidotus*), are among the continent's largest snakes and probably the most dangerous venomous snakes in the world (Shine and Covacevich, 1983; Cogger, 2000). Mature adults of both species measure on average 2 metres in length (Cogger, 2000). The coastal taipan is uniform light to dark brown above, paling on the sides to creamy-brown while the western taipan is rich brown or olive-brown above and scales with dark brown or black anterior edges sometimes forming obscure cross-bands (Cogger, 2000).

Distribution and Habitat

The coastal taipan is found in the Kimberley Division of Western Australia, the northern part of the Northern Territory and along the coasts of eastern Queensland (see Figure 4) (Cogger, 2000). It is also found in the extreme north-eastern corner of New South Wales (Cogger, 2000). The habitats of the coastal taipan are tropical wet and dry sclerophyll forests, open savannah woodlands and cultivated areas such as sugarcane fields (Cogger, 2000; Queensland Museum, 2003a). The western taipan on the other hand is distributed further inland, in western and south-western Queensland, north-eastern South Australia and western New South Wales (Cogger, 2000). Its habitats are in arid to semi-arid drainage regions of inland river systems, in sparsely-vegetated sites, on flood plains with deep cracking soils, on lateritic gibber plains and on sand dunes and rocky outcrops (Cogger, 2000; Cronin, 2001). It occurs only below the Tropic of Capricorn.

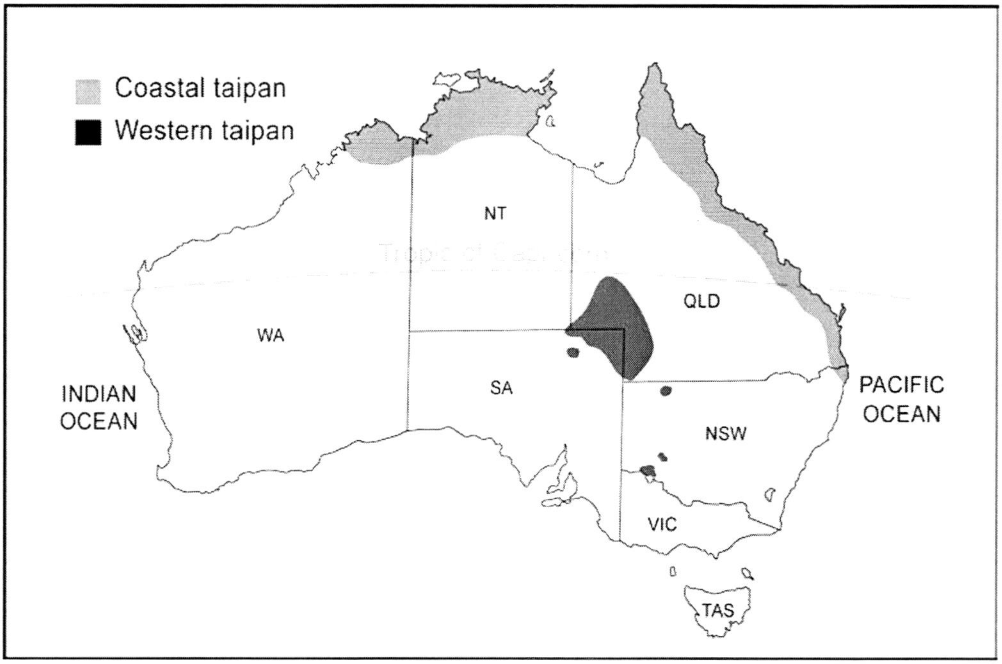

Figure 4. Distribution of taipan snakes in Australia (based on Queensland Museum, 2003a, 2003b; Cogger, 2000).

Life History and Ecology

Taipan snakes are mostly diurnal, though the coastal taipan is sometimes nocturnal (Cogger, 2000). Egg-layers, the coastal taipan and western taipan breed between July and December and have recorded clutches of about 3 to 20 eggs (Cogger, 2000) and 12 to 20 eggs respectively (Cogger, 2000; Cronin, 2001). Taipans are unique among Australian elapid snakes because they specialise in mammalian prey. They feed on rats (*Rattus* spp.), house mice (*Mus musculus*), bandicoots (*Isoodon macrourus, Perameles nasuta*) and quolls (*Dasyurus hallucatus*). The coastal taipan is also known to consume some birds (Shine and Covacevich, 1983; Shine, 1991). The coastal taipan has a notable method of killing its prey: it bites and then usually releases the victim immediately, knowing the prey will not go far before dying (Shine and Covacevich, 1983; Gow, 1989). This is an energy-saving response.

Abundance, Survival Status, Threats and Conservation Overview

There have been records of elapid snake deaths and decrease in populations in Australia since the introduction of an exotic and toxic species, the cane toad (*Bufo marinus*) (Shine and Covacevich, 1983). Consumption of these toads kill snakes that eat them. This is especially so in places where the toads have invaded, like the cane-growing areas of Queensland (Shine and Covacevich, 1983). The numbers of taipan snakes however have shown no apparent decline over the same period (Shine and Covacevich, 1983). It is presumed that the widespread establishment of sugarcane farms provided habitat for and increased the densities of rats, which in turn allowed the taipan snake to thrive whilst other elapid species that are dependent on uncleared forested areas were disadvantaged (Shine and Covacevich, 1983). The taipan snake populations, though sparsely distributed, are presently considered secure (Cronin, 2001).

Northern Long-Necked Turtle

Description

The northern long-necked turtle (*Chelodina rugosa*) is a tropical freshwater turtle (see Figure 5) distinguished by its flattened head and very long neck that when extended exceeds the length of its shell (Cronin, 2001). It has nostrils at the tip of its snout, enabling it to breathe while submerged (Cronin, 2001). Its shell is broadly oval and is wider towards the rear (Cogger, 2000; Cronin, 2001). It is usually dark brown to black in colour above with darker flecks and blotches; its ventral area is whitish (Cogger, 2000; Cronin, 2001). Adults weight up to 4 kg and their shell length measures about 40 centimetres long (Cogger, 2000; Cronin, 2001; Kennett, 2004).

Figure 5. The northern long-necked turtle

Distribution and Habitat

The northern long-necked turtle probably occurs in all rivers running to the sea, from the Kimberly district in Western Australia, across the coastal regions of the northern Territory to Cape York in Queensland (see Figure 6) (Cann, 1998; Cogger, 2000). Apart from large slow-flowing rivers, the habitats of the northern long-necked turtle include freshwater lagoons and lakes, billabongs and swamps (Cann, 1998; Cronin, 2001).

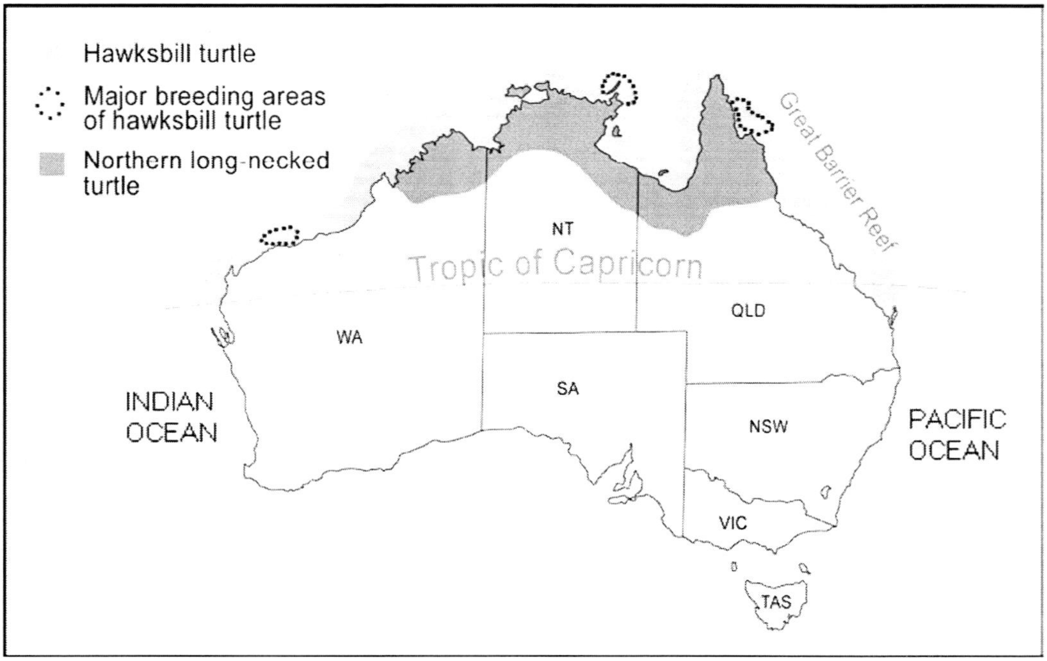

Figure 6. Distribution of the hawksbill and northern long-necked turtles in Australia (based on Cann, 1998; Cogger, 2000; Cronin, 2001; DEH, 2004a)

Life History and Ecology

Among Australia's freshwater turtles, the northern long-necked turtle is unique in that it nests and lays its eggs under water (Reader's Digest, 1997; Kennett, 1999). Nesting occurs in the wild during the dry season, from March to September (Cann, 1980; Kennett et al., 1993; Cronin, 2001). The female produces on average two clutches a season (sometimes up to four clutches per season) of 12 to 20 eggs (Cann, 1998; Cronin, 2001).

Unlike all known reptiles, the eggs are laid in moist soil rather than on dry land, in holes dug in banks by the water's edge where they incubate under the sun's heat (Cann, 1998). The eggs hatch at the beginning of the next wet season, from December to January (Cronin, 2001).

The northern long-necked turtle survives drought periods by aestivating, the summer equivalent of hibernating (Kennett, 2004). They do this by burying themselves in drying mud and do not emerge until the return of the wet season (Kennett, 2004).

The turtle is a very efficient carnivorous predator (Cann, 1998). With its long neck it strikes and captures its prey swiftly (Kennett, 2004). They feed primarily on fish, crustaceans, tadpoles, frogs and aquatic insects but even eat snakes (Cann, 1998; Cronin, 2001).

Abundance, Survival Status, Threats and Conservation Overview

The populations of the northern long-necked turtle are considered secure (Cronin, 2001). The turtle is a traditional food and its flavoursome meat is a significant protein source of the Australian Aborigines (Kennett, 2004; Fordham, undated). They have been consumed by the Aboriginal people for tens of thousands of years and is considered to represent one of the "world's longest-running and ecologically sustainable wildlife harvests" (Kennett, 2004).

Hawksbill Turtle

Description

The hawksbill turtle (*Eretmochelys imbricata*) is a medium-sized marine turtle that is distinctive for its sharp beak-like upper jaw and beautiful shell that is highly sought after for ornamental trade (see Figure 7) (Cronin, 2001; NMFS, 2001). The shell is olive-green or dark brown in colour with streaks and marbles of amber, yellow or reddish-brown (Kemf et al., 2000; Cronin, 2001). The shell is narrowly heart-shaped and serrated at the rear, with 4 overlapping plates on each side (Cronin, 2001). Its ventral area is cream (Cronin, 2001). It grows to about almost 90 centimetres in length and weighs 60 to 80 kg on average (NMFS, 2001; WWF, 2004).

Figure 7. A hawksbill turtle in a pen at Crocodylus Park near Darwin, Northern Territory

Distribution and Habitat

The hawksbill turtle occurs in tropical and subtropical seas and nests in more than 60 countries (WWF, 2002; NMFS, 2001). In Australia, its distribution is along the tropical and warm temperate coastal waters and islands of Western Australia, the Northern Territory and Queensland, even extending as far south as northern New South Wales (see Figure 6) (Cronin, 2001; DEH, 2004a). Their common habitats are tidal and sub-tidal coral and rocky reefs (DEH, 2004a). In Australia, hawksbills feed in rocky areas and on coral reefs (GBRMPA, 1996). There are three main breeding areas in Australia: the northern Great Barrier Reef and the Torres Straits region (internationally significant area for hawksbill turtle nesting), the archipelagos of the Northern Territory and Western Australia (GBRMPA, 1996; DEH, 2004a).

Life History and Ecology

The female hawksbill turtle breeds in 2 to 5 year cycles and produces 3 to 5 nests at about bi-weekly intervals in a single breeding season (WWF, 2002). The female comes ashore at night and usually lays clutches of 50 to 130 eggs, in nest chambers dug into the sand of the beaches beyond the high tide line (Cronin, 2001; Lutz and Musick, 1997, p. 65). Eggs hatch 52 to 57 days later, the male-female proportion of hatchlings determined by incubation temperature (Cronin, 2001). Hatchlings emerge and they dash to the water under cover of darkness (Cronin, 2001). Small turtles spend their first years of life carried by the currents of the open ocean, then move to near-shore waters, reef habitats and areas with hard, sandy bottoms (WWF, 2002). In the wild, they reach maturity late at between 20 to 50 years of age (WWF, 2002). A major part of the hawksbill turtle's diet is made up of sea sponges, although they also eat seagrasses, algae, sea cucumber, shellfish, some crustaceans and molluscs (GBRMPA, 1996; Cronin, 2001; WWF, 2002).

Abundance, Survival Status, Threats and Conservation Overview

The global population of the hawksbill turtle is believed to have declined by 80% over the past few decades (Red List Standards & Petitions Subcommittee, 1996). Intense national and international trade in hawksbill shell has led to widespread concerns that the species is seriously overexploited (Meylan, 1998; Bjorndal, 1999; WWF, 2002). Other threats worldwide include hunting for meat and eggs, loss of nesting beaches and feeding areas, fisheries by-catch, and marine pollution and debris (Cronin, 2001; WWF, 2002). Threats within Australia include death by ingestion of synthetic materials, drowning in shark control nets and fishing gear, and fox and goanna (*Varanus* lizard) predation of eggs along Queensland coast (GBRMPA, 1996). The hawksbill turtle is listed in IUCN's Red List (2003) as critically endangered. It has been listed in Appendix I under CITES since 1977, prohibiting its commercial international trade (WWF, 2002; CITES, 2003). Under Australia's *Environment Protection and Biodiversity Conservation Act 1999*, it is protected and listed as vulnerable (DEH, 2003). Various other State-level conservation legislations provide the hawksbill turtle protection and have spurred successful conservation effort (DEH, 2003). For example, some of the hawksbill turtle's major breeding and feeding sites in Australia are protected in the Great Barrier Reef Marine Park (DEH, 2003).

However, given the current level of protection in Australia, the hawksbill turtle seems secure in Australia (Grahame Webb, August 2004, personal communication), although there may be some threats to those turtles that migrate out of Australian waters, for example, to Indonesia. Furthermore, considerable doubt has been raised by Mrosovsky (2003) about the adequacy of the IUCN Red List classification of the hawksbill turtle. It is listed as critically endangered but "is not expected to become extinct in the foreseeable future" (see Mrosovsky, 2003, p. 31). Only the IUCN's critically endangered status of the hawksbill was conveyed to participants in our survey. So they would have perceived the hawksbill turtle as being at high risk of extinction in the wild in the near future. This should be borne in mind later when interpreting survey results.

HUMAN USE IN AUSTRALIA, INCLUDING COMMERCIAL USE, OF THE REPTILE SPECIES UNDER CONSIDERATION

All of the reptile species considered here have human use, some of them having considerably more human use value than others. In the past, this was a serious threat to the populations of some when combined with open access to harvesting them. The high commercial use values of the saltwater crocodile, the freshwater crocodile and the hawksbill turtle resulted in serious declines in their populations and a prospect of the species becoming extinct. The northern long-necked turtle has had modest commercial demand quite recently in the domestic pet market. The taipan snake, besides being used to obtain snake bite antidote, has the lowest commercial value of the reptilians in this study but may have considerable potential commercial value due to the other properties of its highly poisonous venom. In this section, we review the various consumptive and non-consumptive human uses of these reptile species, historic and current, and discuss prospects for sustainable use into the future.

Saltwater and Freshwater Crocodiles

Historic and Current Uses

Australia's Aborigines have utilised crocodiles for 20,000 to 40,000 years (McBryde, 1979; Flood, 1983). Their eggs and meat are eaten by many Aboriginal people. The crocodile has also been used for ceremonial purposes by certain Aboriginal tribes to whom it is culturally significant and a sacred symbol (Lanhupuy, 1987). For the most part, Aboriginal use of the crocodiles in Australia has been essentially cultural and subsistence-based.

It was not until around the middle of the twentieth century that commercial consumptive use of Australia's crocodiles took off and resulted in widespread hunting (*cf.* Webb et al., 1987; PWC, 1999) fuelled by high American and European demand for leather products (Thorbjarnarson, 1999, p. 465). The saltwater crocodile's skin is considered to be the most valuable of crocodilian skins and highly sought after because it produces the highest quality leather (Peucker, 1997; Department of Primary Industries and Fisheries, 2004). It is used to produce various types of fashion apparel and accessories like shoes, bags, wallets, watchstraps, belts and luggage bags (Ashley and David, 1987; Brazaitis, 1987). Export market demand for freshwater crocodile skin on the other hand is low because of its comparatively lower quality (PWC, 1999; Warfield et al., 2000).

The saltwater crocodile is consequently the main crocodilian species farmed in Australia and the main variety whose skin is commercially exported (Warfield et al., 2000) although a small, but negligible amount of freshwater crocodile skin is also exported (Love and Langenkamp, 2003, p. 123). With 11,849 saltwater crocodile skins exported in 2001 (accounting for about 43% of total saltwater crocodile skin trade), Australia is one of the leading exporters of saltwater crocodile skin in the world (Caldwell, 2003). The major markets for skins are France, Italy, Japan and Singapore (Department of Primary Industries and Fisheries, 2004). Australian crocodile farms also produce and sell trophy skins, and jewellery made out of crocodile feet and teeth (Darwin Crocodile Farm, 2003).

Another consumptive use of the crocodile is the commercial consumption of its meat. The saltwater crocodile meat is regarded as a tasty white meat with a delicate flavour, and has nutritional values that compare favourably with traditional meats (Mitchell et al., 1995; Castaldo, 2001; Department of Primary Industries and Fisheries, 2004). The supply of crocodile meat is dictated by the demand for skins (Peucker, 1998; Department of Primary Industries and Fisheries, 2004). In 2000, Australia produced 66,480 kg of crocodile meat (Department of Primary Industries and Fisheries, 2004). Crocodile meat consumption is mainly in the domestic Australian market, through restaurants, specialty meat outlets and some large foodchain stores (Peucker, 1998). The retail price of the meat is between $15 and $40 per kg (in Australian dollars* as of 2001 and 2002) (see Bodger and Goulding, 2003, p. 5). It is therefore relatively expensive compared, for example, with chicken. Export demand for Australian crocodile flesh has been growing over the last few years, with major markets in the United Kingdom, Denmark, Japan, Korea, China and New Zealand (Peucker, 1998; Department of Primary Industries and Fisheries, 2004). It has also been an alternative choice of meat during meat-related disease outbreaks like the avian influenza in parts of Asia (Castaldo, 2004).

---

* All values in this chapter are in Australian dollars unless otherwise stated.

While consumptive use of the saltwater crocodile is still the primary form of human use, non-consumptive use is also popular. Non-consumptive use includes viewings of crocodiles in the wild, and captive displays in zoos and crocodile farms. Wild and captive crocodilians have become primary tourist attractions in places like Queensland, the Northern Territory and Western Australia, generating wealth and employment (Webb et al., 2000, p. 223). A privately owned company called Adelaide River Queen Cruises in the Northern Territory is well known for its 'Famous Jumping Crocodiles': tourists are taken on boat cruises on the Adelaide River to view crocodiles making spectacular leaps out of the water when receiving feed (see Figure 8) (Adelaide River Queen Cruises, 2004). Several other tour companies also operate similar cruises on the Adelaide River. At Crocodylus Park near Darwin, captive displays of crocodiles in various habitats and museum displays of crocodile history are available for tourists (WMI, 2004). In Queensland, the Australia Zoo, which features shows of daring human-crocodile interaction, recently won the Australian Tourism Award 2003/2004 for best major tourist attraction (Queensland Tourism Industry Council, 2004; Australia Zoo, undated). Many Australian crocodile farms also cater for tourists.

Figure 8. Saltwater crocodile leaping out of the water to receive meat lowered from a deck of a tourist cruise boat on the Adelaide River, Northern Territory, Australia

Annual earnings (in Australian dollars) from the sales of meat and skins in Australia has been estimated to be \$5 million (\$4 million for skins and \$1 million for meat) (Stubbs, 1998), while revenue from crocodile cruises for tourists in the Northern Territory amounted to at least \$2 million annually in the late 1990s (Australian Senate, 1998).

Management Practices

Crocodile management in Australia currently involves crocodile farming and ranching programs, wild egg and animal harvest programs and research and monitoring programs (Webb, 2000a; Webb et al., 2000). In the Northern Territory, where the largest crocodile enterprises are, private entities manage farming and ranching programs whereas relevant government departments maintain a regulatory role that includes the setting of quotas and provision of permits, monitoring, analysis or results and egg harvest reporting (PWC, 1999; PWC, undated; Webb et al., 2000, p. 224).

Crocodile farming in Australia first began in Queensland in 1969 with the dual aim of conserving the saltwater crocodile and providing employment for the local community (Department of Primary Industries and Fisheries, 2004). However, it was not until the 1980s that viable commercial farming commenced following growing international market demand for crocodile leather goods and apparel, population recovery, and CITES endorsement of the Australian proposal to move the Australian population of the saltwater crocodile from Appendix I to Appendix II (Webb et al. 1984; Stubbs, 1998; Stirrat et al., 2001; PWC, undated).

In strict terms, crocodile farming is the husbandry or closed-cycle captive breeding of adult animals taken from the wild which then lay eggs that form the farm's stock (Thorbjarnarson, 1999; EPA, 2003a; see also CITES, undated). The hatchlings that are raised in captivity are killed for meat and skins in 3 to 4 years or are retained for breeding in 10 years (Webb et al., 1996). Some of the advantages of closed-cycle farming are that the production of eggs and hatchlings is more reliable and predictable than in the wild; the eggs can be obtained on the day of laying thereby reducing mortality; and commercial gains are totally detached from the status of wild populations (Webb et al., 1996).

Alternatively, crocodile ranching is an open-cycle procedure that involves the removal of eggs or hatchlings from the wild and their incubation and rearing in farms (EPA, 2003a; CITES, undated). Crocodile ranching is commercially advantageous because it has lower infrastructure costs than crocodile farming since breeding pens do not have to be constructed, breeding stocks do not have to be maintained (Magnusson, 1984; Porosus Pty. Ltd., 2003) and the 'costs of obtaining eggs and/ or juveniles from the wild are generally less than those of producing them through captive breeding' (Webb et al., 1996). Ranching also allows the removal of eggs or hatchlings that would otherwise have very low chances of survival in the wild due to mortality (Porosus Pty. Ltd., 2003). Mean egg survivorship in the wild is estimated to be about 25% of eggs laid (Webb et al., 1984) and 54% of hatchlings survive to one year in the wild (Webb et al., 1987). Once taken from the wild and ranched, hatch rates rise to about 70-80% and rates are of similar magnitude for subsequent survival (Porosus Pty. Ltd., 2003). However, commercial viability ranching enterprises are dependent on the conservation status of the wild population and thus resources may need to be expended to ensure that key habitats and populations are monitored and protected (Webb et al., 1996).

Crocodile farms (see Figure 9) usually run farming and ranching operations in combination. This is practiced in the Northern Territory and Western Australia, where the law permits farming and ranching. In Queensland, however, ranching is prohibited (DEH, 2004b); crocodiles are protected wildlife in Queensland and capturing wild crocodiles is illegal unless a license has been granted under Queensland's *Nature Conservation Act 1992* (DEH, 2004b). In 1998, there were 20 crocodile farms in Australia with a combined stock level of 60,000 crocodiles (Stubbs, 1998). Current estimates are that there are about 12 to 14 crocodile farms

(Warfield et al., 2000; MacNamara et al., 2003), six each in the Northern Territory and Queensland and two in Western Australia (Love and Langenkamp, 2003, p. 123).

Figure 9. Juvenile saltwater crocodiles in a pen on a crocodile farm in northern Queensland

The main purpose of wild egg harvesting is to provide stock for ranching. Harvesting requires a permit and harvesters are to report details of all stocks removed from the wild (PWC, 1999). The total number of eggs collected annually in the Northern Territory has increased broadly from 2,320 eggs in 1984 to 17,536 eggs in 2002, with a maximum of 29,044 gathered in 1995/1996 (PWC, 1999; PWC, undated; Williams et al., 2001, p. 75). The number of eggs collected depends on the timing and extent of rainfall because nest flooding greatly influences egg survival and availability (PWC, 1999).

Management programs in the Northern Territory also include annual quotas for the harvesting of hatchlings, juveniles, and adults to stock farming operations with breeding animals. Only 67 juveniles and adult crocodiles were removed from the wild over the two decades to 1999 for farming purposes (PWC, 1999). Problem crocodiles removed from native habitats in areas of recreational use because of public safety concerns have often been used to supplement breeding stocks on farms (PWC, 1999). Since 1997 in the Northern Territory, a few adult crocodiles have been harvested from the wild for direct skin and meat production. The number of such crocodiles harvested increased from 17 individuals in 1997 to 138 individuals in 2002 (PWC, undated).

Overall, harvests of crocodile eggs and crocodiles have been sustained at a conservative level (below maximum sustainable yield), allowing populations of crocodiles to increase and stabilise over the years (Webb et al., 2000, Webb, 2000a; Webb, 2000b). Sustainable harvesting of crocodiles and their eggs for ranching provides landowners and people living in remote and rural communities (particularly indigenous communities) with an opportunity to benefit economically from this wildlife with minimal capital investment (PWC, undated; Ross, 1995), and can consequently (in particular circumstances) induce the conservation of crocodiles and their habitat (Thorbjarnarson, 1991, p. 221). Interestingly, it has been argued that ranching and harvesting in the wild can be more effective as a means for conservation than closed-cycle farming, because the latter is not naturally linked with the maintenance of wild populations and their habitat, and does not provide the economic incentives for conservation in the wild that forms the basis of sustainable-use programs (Thorbjarnarson, 1999).

Overall, saltwater crocodile research and management strategies in Australia continue to promote sustainable use and conservation of crocodilians. Current approaches have been billed as involving a "sound model of pragmatic, effective conservation" (Webb et al. 2000, p. 224).

Hawksbill Turtle

Historic and Current Uses

People of different cultures have hunted and used hawksbill turtles for many centuries (Parsons, 1972; Groombridge and Luxmoore, 1989; Meylan, 1999; Kemf et al., 2000).

Hawksbill turtle has been exploited chiefly for its highly valued ornate shell, sometimes referred to also as *carey* or *bekko* (in Japanese), and there has never been significant international trade in other hawksbill turtle products (although other uses such as for leather and oils for cosmetics exist) (TRAFFIC, undated; Ottenwalder, 1996; NMFS, 2001). The hawksbill turtle shell has been used to make household items like combs, brushes and spectacle frames and expensive ornamental products like rings and necklaces and works of art such as exquisite carvings in Japan (TRAFFIC, undated). The need for turtle shell products declined worldwide with the advent of plastics, but it has retained a niche at the high end of the luxury market (Groombridge and Luxmoore, 1989).

Over the past few decades, the greatest market for hawksbill turtle shells has been from Japan, where the commercial production and consumption of *bekko* products is a multi-million dollar industry and involves an ancient and culturally significant tradition (Meylan and Donnelly, 1999; Kaneko and Yamaoka, 1999; TRAFFIC, undated). Between 1970 and 1992, Japan imported about 754 tonnes of hawksbill shell, representing approximately 712,000 hawksbills turtles (Meylan, 1998). Since the CITES's trade ban, the *bekko* industry in Japan has continued to operate on existing stockpiles (CITES, undated). Because it is a luxury item in Japan, hawksbill shell prices rise with increasing rarity, motivating illegal harvesting and trade in places like Vietnam and Indonesia (Bjorndal, 1999; van Dijk and Shepherd, 2004).

The hawksbill turtle has also long been a supplemental source of food protein for some people. Hawksbill turtle meat and egg harvesting have been carried out at the subsistence level by fishing and coastal communities in the Caribbean and is sometimes used for medicinal purposes (CITES, undated). In some indigenous communities, for example, in the Torres Straits off the north of Australia, hawksbill turtle meat is considered to be poisonous and is rarely eaten but the eggs are considered highly palatable (Hobson, 1988; Limpus and Parmeter, 1988).

Management Practices

It has been suggested that the introduction of hawksbill turtle farming and ranching to satisfy the demand of a well-regulated market, such as in Japan, can alleviate or eliminate illegal harvest pressures on wild populations (Anonymous, 1995a; Anonymous, 1995b; Ross, 1995; Ross, undated). To date, hawksbill turtle farming and ranching activities have been experimental and a response to Cuba's recent efforts to re-open trade in hawksbill turtle shells (Gray, 1998; Grahame Webb, personal communication, 25th June 2004). In Australia, Crocodylus Park near Darwin is trying to rear hawksbill turtles in captivity and establish a closed cycle. Some critics have argued that there could be drawbacks to hawksbill turtle farming and ranching: increased availability of products on the legal international market might stimulate demand, which existing farms will be unable to satisfy, thereby increasing pressure on wild populations and trade through illegal channels (*cf.* Tisdell, 1986; Ross, undated). Ross (undated) says that although objective evidence on the reality of such a scenario is contradictory, it merits objective testing.

Northern Long-Necked Turtle

Historic and Current Uses and Management Practices

The northern long-necked turtle has been traditionally harvested by the indigenous people of Australia, particularly the Aboriginal people of the Northern Territory, as a source of food over a long period in history with little or no negative impact on the overall survival of the species (Kennett, 2004). Evidence of the sustainability of northern long-necked turtle use is manifest in its relatively secure and abundant populations throughout its Australian range of distribution.

Traditional knowledge of northern long-necked turtle harvesting coupled with scientific research and support may help in meeting the dual aim of sustaining the survival of the species while providing economic benefit to Aboriginal people. Support agencies like the Bawinanga Aboriginal Corporation in Maningrida, Northern Territory enable the Aboriginal people to employ their wealth of knowledge of wildlife, such as that about the northern long-necked turtle, to achieve these aims. Currently, the Bawinanga Aboriginal Corporation in collaboration with the University of Canberra and Charles Darwin University in Darwin is trying to promote increased economic self-sufficiency of Aboriginal people by developing a sustainable indigenous enterprise involved in harvesting northern long-necked turtles and incubating their eggs for hatchlings to be reared and sold in the pet trade (Applied Ecology Research Group, 2003). The possibility of the commercial use of such turtles for meat is also being trialled.

Taipan Snake

Current Uses

Taipan snake venom is used to produce antivenom to treat snake bites. But snake venoms, due to their chemical properties, are known to promise a range of other medical benefits too, such as treatment for cancer, stroke, heart ailments, Parkinson's disease and Alzheimer's disease (Ferrer, 2001). The highly poisonous venom of the taipan snakes is no exception. Taipan snake venom is being studied for medical applications in screening for lupus, an autoimmune disorder (ABC Radio National, 1995; Marsh, 2001; Moore et al., 2003).

Public Attitudes to Conservation and Commercial Use Towards Focal Reptile Species and their Comparative Willingness to Allocate Funds for Species Conservation

Survey Methodology

Having outlined the ecological status and uses of the focal reptilians in Australia, let us now consider attitudes of the Australian public to them. Attitudes to their survival, for their commercial use, and willingness to support their conservation financially are amongst the issues considered.

Two questionnaire-based surveys provided the data for this study. The surveys were conducted from July to September 2002. These surveys were designed to elicit information about the following: (i) the Brisbane public's knowledge and attitude towards ('likeability'of) tropical Australian reptile species, (ii) their degree of support for the survival of these species and willingness to pay for the conservation of these species, and (iii) their attitude towards the commercial use of the reptilians.

A survey sample of 204 responding participants was drawn from various suburbs of Brisbane with differing socio-economic characteristics. They were also selected on a first-come-first-served basis according to the age and gender distribution of Brisbane city so that the sample would be reasonably representative of Brisbane residents. Potential respondents were initially reached by means of 1500 letterbox-dropped circulars distributed in the Brisbane area. The circular was an invitation to participate in the series of surveys on the conservation and use of Australia's tropical resources, to be conducted at The University of Queensland. In the circular, it was mentioned that participants would be offered \$20, a public presentation, refreshments and a chance to win \$200. The real nature and objectives of the experimental survey were withheld from the participants to avoid bias.

The participants were divided into groups of five consisting of about 40 individuals each to attend survey sessions of about two hours with a 15-minute tea break. Four groups were asked to attend sessions held at the University of Queensland— two during the working week and two during the weekend. The remaining group was requested to attend a Sunday session at a church hall. The survey sessions were arranged as such to accommodate the participation of employed persons and provide flexibility of attendance for others.

In the survey sessions, participants filled out a structured questionnaire (Survey I) to gather participant's background information, and their initial knowledge, attitude and support for the conservation of 24 Australian wildlife species made up of mammals, birds and the five reptilians addressed in this study. In the survey, the participants were also asked to allocate among the reptilians a hypothetical sum of $1,000 to fund conservation work for the species. This fixed-pie valuation approach has the benefit of overcoming problems relating to income differences and reduces strategic bias.

After completing the above task, the participants were given a tea break. A public presentation followed, presented by Dr. Steve Van Dyck, the Curator of Vertebrates at the Queensland Museum. This lecture dealt mostly with birds and mammal species. The participants were then given coloured photo brochures containing descriptions of all the species concerned including the reptilians, their geographical range, life history and current status. In the brochures, approximately the same amount of factual background information was provided on each species and normative statements were avoided. The participants were asked to take the brochure home and read it before completing and returning (in postage pre-paid envelope) the second questionnaire, Survey II, which contained several overlapping questions with Survey I. This overlap of questions was planned to provide us information on changes in the respondents' knowledge of the various species, and alterations in their attitudes and support for the conservation of species.

Aims

Tisdell and Wilson (2004) hypothesised that important factors in influencing individuals' willingness to contribute to schemes to conserve particular wildlife species might be: (i) judgement of respondents about the effectiveness of the scheme; (ii) perceived degree of threat to the survival of the species; (iii) the likeability of the species; (iv) ethical considerations; and (v) degree of knowledge of the species, which can affect (ii), (iii) and possibly (i). Here we use results from the surveys to consider the relationships between the respondents' stated likeability of each of the focal reptile species and their support for survival of each of the reptile species and for commercial use of these. Also, their allocation of funds for conserving each of these species is considered in a similar manner.

To reduce the influence of the knowledge factor, we concentrate on the results from Survey II for analytical purposes. In that survey, respondents had reasonably balanced information about the nature and status of the various reptile species. In Australia, none of the reptile species considered is threatened by imminent extinction. However, the hawksbill turtle had been listed in the IUCN Red List (IUCN, 2003) as critically endangered and respondents were made aware of this status and this would have been an influence on their response in Survey II. Therefore, we assume that the major influences on the dependent variables to be investigated in relation to results from Survey II are likeability, threat to survival of species and ethical considerations.

The importance of likeability as a factor to strongly influencing support for conservation of wildlife species is suggested by the analysis of Metrick and Weitzman (1996, 1998) of the public funding of conservation of endangered species in the USA. They suggest that 'charismatic megafauna' effects dominate allocations of public funds for the conservation of such species (Metrick and Weitzman, 1998, p. 33), or that 'visceral' characteristics are the main determinant rather than scientific characteristics such as 'degree of endangerment' and 'taxonomic uniqueness' (Metrick and Weitzman, 1996, p. 1). We consider that 'likeability' ratings capture the visceral or charismatic aspects of wildlife species.

Note that our study differs from that of Metrick and Weitzman (1996, 1998) because it is based upon stated preferences of individual respondents rather than the revealed public spending decisions. It is possible that the latter are to some extent 'corrupted' by political processes and may not be an entirely accurate reflection of the preferences of individuals for conserving species. Given this background, we shall investigate to what extent likeability of the various species is important for support for the survival and funding of conservation of reptile species in our selected group.

Results

Knowledge of Species and their Likeability Ratings

Respondents were asked to state in Survey I whether they knew the species or not. Less than half the respondents said they knew the hawksbill turtle while at least 95% said they knew the crocodiles (see Table 1). Species dangerous to man were better known than the turtles, which posed no danger to man.

Table 1. The percentage of respondents who said they knew the reptile species in Survey I

	Hawksbill turtle	Northern long-necked turtle	Taipan snake	Freshwater crocodile	Saltwater crocodile
Percentage of respondents who said they knew the species	42	65	82	95	96

Respondents were asked in the surveys to indicate how much they knew about each species and the extent to which they liked the species according to the rating possibilities shown in the first row of Tables 2 and 3 respectively. We assigned the weights shown in the second row of these tables to these ratings.

Table 2. Knowledge rating

Rating	Very good	Good	Poor	Non-existent
Knowledge weights	3	2	1	0

Table 3. Likeability rating

Rating	Strongly like	Like	Uncertain	Dislike	Strongly dislike
Likeability weights	2	1	0	-1	-2

The knowledge and likeability weights shown in Table 2 and 3 respectively were used to calculate a knowledge index and a likeability index for each of the species. Each of these is a simple average of the weights determined for each of the respondents. The results are shown in Table 4.

Table 4. Knowledge and likeability indices (Survey I and Survey II) for the focal species

	Hawksbill turtle	Northern long-necked turtle	Taipan snake	Freshwater crocodile	Saltwater crocodile
Survey I					
Knowledge index	0.55	0.81	1.22	1.51	1.66
Likeability index	1	1.07	-0.31	0.4	0.3
Survey II					
Knowledge index	1.49	1.51	1.51	1.69	1.77
Likeability index	1.21	1.08	-0.15	0.32	0.18

We note from Table 4 that the knowledge indices of the species in Survey I is consistent with the data in Table 1 and that the least liked species are those most dangerous to man whereas the turtles (not dangerous to man) are the most liked. The ordering of likeability of the species is broadly similar in Survey I and Survey II but some differences are apparent. The differences are due to extra information being provided to survey participants about the individual species. As a result of this, knowledge about all the species increased (compare rows 1 and 3 in Table 4) and became more even or balanced; knowledge of the more poorly known species increased relatively more than for the best known species. As a result, the hawksbill turtle displaced the northern long-necked turtle as the most liked species, but the latter remained a highly liked species. The taipan snake remained the least liked species but it improved its likeability rating in Survey II, possibly because respondents became aware of its possible use value in medicine. The saltwater crocodile and the freshwater crocodile displayed some likeability reduction, but the freshwater crocodile continued to be the least disliked of the two. Both had low likeability indices, but not negative ones.

In order to reduce the possible influence of uneven knowledge of wildlife species on the responses of survey participants, we shall concentrate on analysis using responses given in Survey II. Linear regression analysis will be used to consider whether preference for the survival of species is associated with its likeability, whether support for commercial harvesting of species is associated with its likeability, and whether individuals are more likely to want to allocate more funds to the conservation of a species if they like it more than others.

Likeability and Support for Survival of Species

Comparing likeability to the percentage of respondents who said they are in favour of a species' survival, the relationship shown in Figure 10 emerges. The species are identified as follows: Northern long-necked turtle (Lt), hawksbill turtle (Ht), freshwater crocodile (Fc), saltwater crocodile (Sc) and taipan snake (Ts).

From the relationship shown in Figure 10, it can be seen that there is a positive relationship between the stated likeability of a wildlife species and the percentage of respondents in favour of its survival. The linear regression line when fitted by ordinary least squares is

$$y = 88.9 + 6.0x \quad (1)$$

It is a relatively good fit ($R^2 = 0.88$) and using the t-test the slope factor is significant at 95% confidence level ($P = 0.02$).

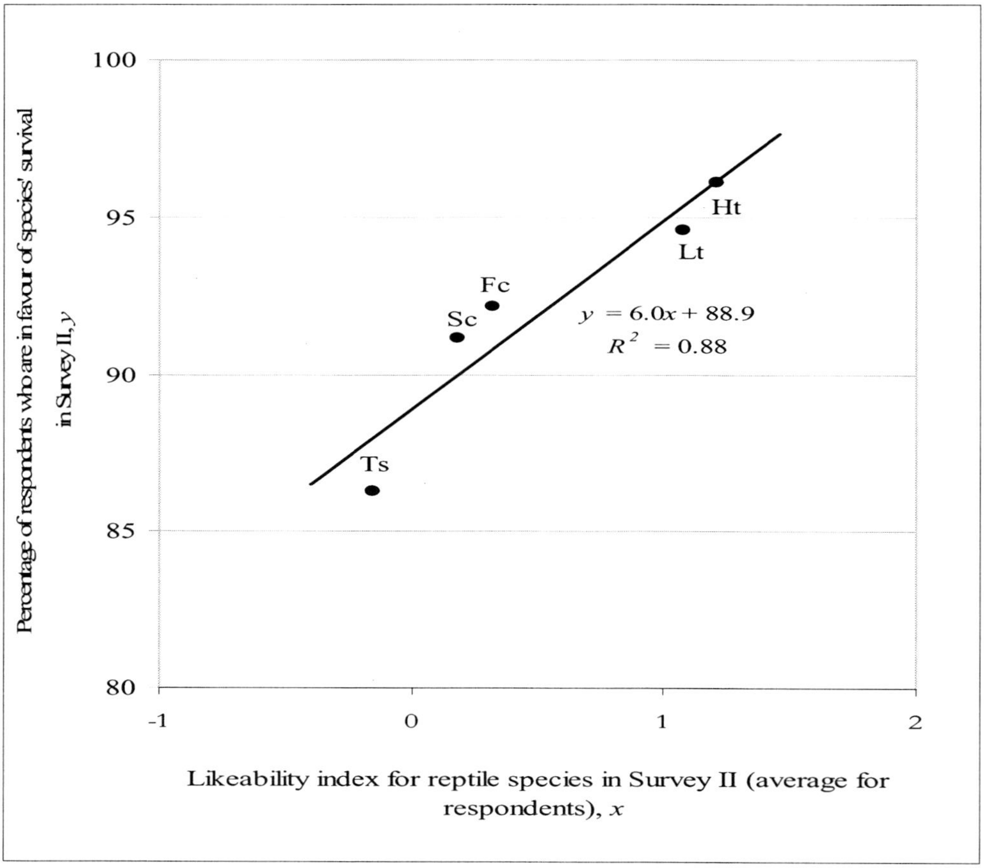

Figure 10. Likeability versus percentage of respondents in favour of survival of the reptile species in Survey II

It should be noted that most individuals supported the survival of all the reptile species in the set, even the most disliked species. For example, more than 85% of respondents favoured the survival of taipan snakes. The reason frequently given was that all species have a right to exist.

Likeability and Attitude Towards Sustainable Commercial Harvesting of Species

We assessed the relationship between the likeability of reptile species and the percentage of respondents supporting their sustainable commercial harvesting. It was thought likely that a negative relationship would exist.

The scatter of observations shown in Figure 11 emerges. This indicates that a negative relationship does exist. Fitting a linear regression line by ordinary least squares, the line

$$y = 49.9 - 16.8x \quad (2)$$

provides the best fit. However, the fit is not close (R^2 = 0.49) and the slope is statistically significant only at 80% confidence level (P = 0.19).

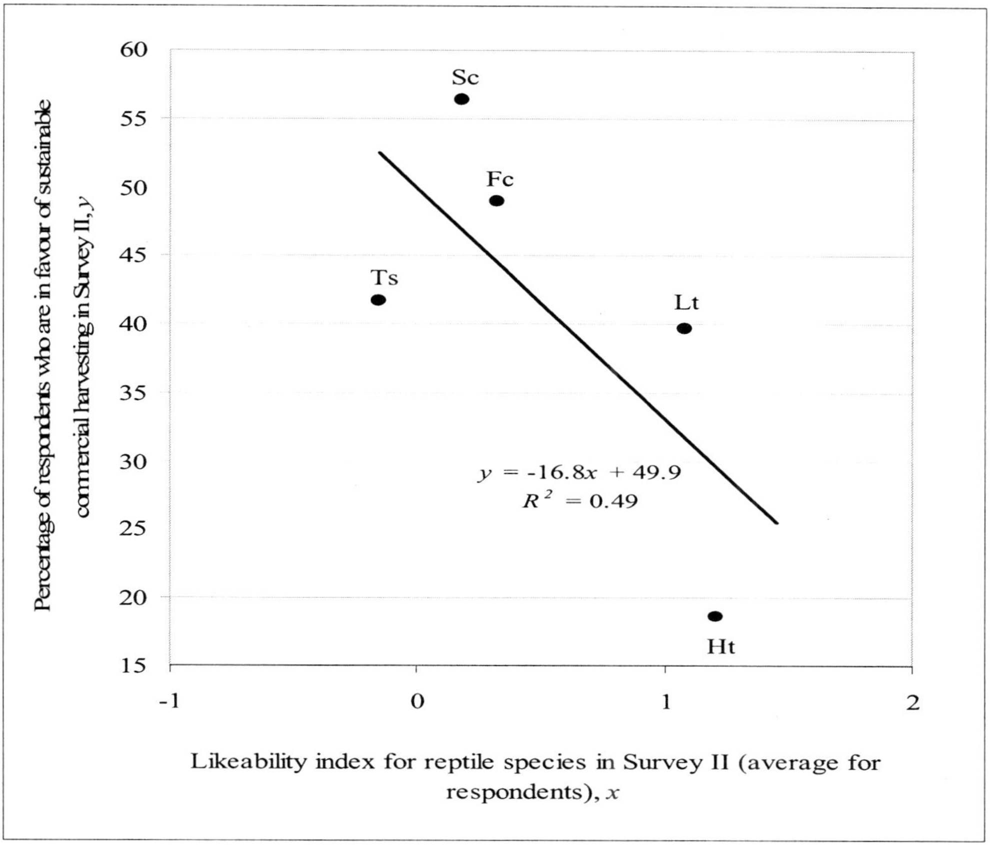

Figure 11. Likeability versus percentage of respondents in favour of commercial harvesting of the reptile species in Survey II

Comparative Willingness to Respondents to Allocate Funds for the Conservation of the Reptile Species

Respondents were asked to complete the following exercise:

> "Suppose that you are given Aus $1,000, but you can only use it to donate funds to support the conservation of the reptiles in Australia listed below. Suppose that a reliable organisation were to carry out the conservation work and your money would supplement other funds for this purpose. What percentage of your $1,000 would you contribute for the conservation of each of the reptiles listed below? Your total should add up to 100%."

Reptiles	**(%)**
Saltwater crocodiles	
Freshwater crocodiles	
Hawksbill sea turtles (a marine species with a beautiful shell)	
Northern long-necked turtle (freshwater) turtle	
Taipan snakes (also known as Fierce snakes)	
	100

The scatter of average allocations that emerged is shown in Figure 12 for Survey II and is plotted against the likeability index for each species. A positive association exists between the percentage of funds allocated for the conservation of each of the species and their likeability. However, the hawksbill turtle is an outlier. This seems to reflect its reported critically endangered status. The association between the likeability index and funds allocated for conservation of the other four species is quite close. None of these other species was reported as being under threat.

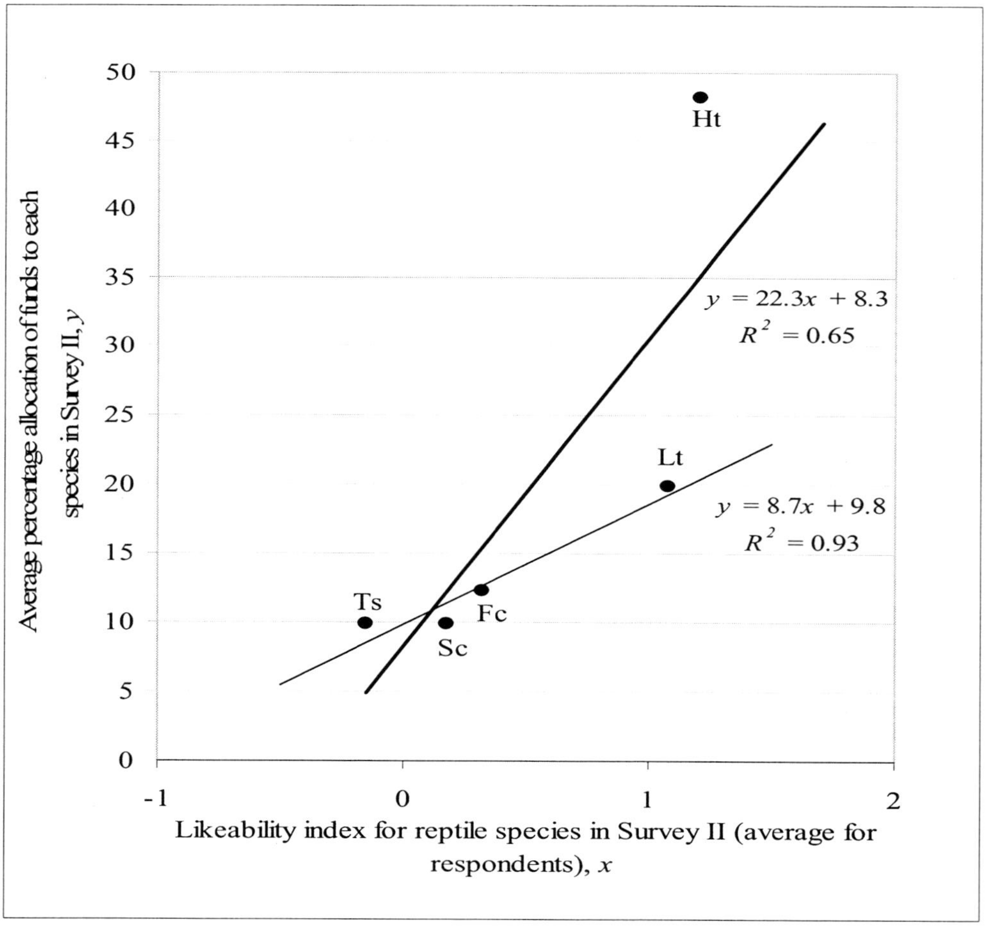

Figure 12. Likeability versus average percentage allocation of funds for the conservation of the reptile species in Survey II

None of the other species are endangered in Australia. Likeability is the major influence on allocation of funds for their conservation. Fitting a linear regression to the four observations for these other species yields the regression line

$$y = 9.8 + 8.7x \quad (R^2 = 0.93) \tag{4}$$

The relationship is close and is statistically significant at the 95% level. It suggests that if likeability is the only influence on the relative allocation of funds for conserving species, the hawksbill turtle would be allocated 20.3% of available funds for its conservation. However, in fact 48.2% of funds are allocated for its conservation. Thus more than half the allocation of funds for conservation of the hawksbill turtle (28%) may be accounted for by its IUCN critically endangered status, which suggested to respondents that it is in imminent danger of extinction.

Fitting a linear regression to all the observations by ordinary least squares, the following is the result:

$$y = 8.3 + 22.3x \quad (R^2 = 0.65) \tag{3}$$

The slope value is significant at 80% confidence interval ($P = 0.097$).

This linear relationship is not very close. This is mainly because of the high allocation of funds for conservation of hawksbill turtle. This is probably a result of its being reported to be critically endangered. The observation for Ht, therefore, is influenced by a combination of its likeability and its reported high level of endangerment.

None of the other species are endangered in Australia. Likeability is the major influence on allocation of funds for their conservation. Fitting a linear regression to the four observations for these other species yields the regression line

$$y = 9.8 + 8.7x \quad (R^2 = 0.93) \tag{4}$$

The relationship is close and is statistically significant at the 95% level. It suggests that if likeability is the only influence on the relative allocation of funds for conserving species, the hawksbill turtle would be allocated 20.3% of available funds for its conservation. However, in fact 48.2% of funds are allocated for its conservation. Thus more than half the allocation of funds for conservation of the hawksbill turtle (28%) may be accounted for by its IUCN critically endangered status, which suggested to respondents that it is in imminent danger of extinction.

Respondents were also asked their reasons for choosing the reptile (the hawksbill turtle in this case) for the largest allocations of funds for their conservation. The reasons respondents provided include:

> 'they are harmless and beautiful' and 'they are gentle creatures'
> 'this appears to be the only one of the reptiles that is endangered' and 'more danger facing the animal'

The reasons offered for giving the largest amount of funds for conserving the hawksbill turtle boil down essentially to the following factors: likeability (attractiveness of species, benign nature of species) and perceived endangerment of species. To a lesser extent, some respondents said that ecological and tourism values of the species were important as an influence. Respondents who decided to give equal allocations for all species justified their decision by giving the following reasons: 'do not have enough knowledge about species', 'all species have intrinsic values' or 'all have the right to exist' and the desire to protect 'the balance of nature'.

The results tend to support the view of Metrick and Weitzman (1996, 1998) that visceral factors play an important role in support for conservation of wildlife species. However, the degree of endangerment also seems to be important as illustrated by the case of the hawksbill turtle. Furthermore, even species that are not very much liked (taipan snakes and crocodiles in this case) were allocated at least 10% of funds available for allocation to conservation of reptiles in the selected set. This seems to reflect the importance of moral or ethical sentiments e.g. all species have a right to exist, mentioned by several respondents. The importance of such sentiments may have grown in recent times. We can conclude that although likeability of species is very important, it is far from being the sole arbiter of human support for conservation of wildlife species.

Allocation of Funds from a $1,000 Fund to Different Causes (Conservation of Reptiles Versus Funds for Charity)

It is also interesting to find from our research that human interests (humanitarianism) do not eliminate support for reptile conservation when the option exists for reducing support for conservation of reptiles to benefit humans in need.

The following proposition was presented to participants in Survey I and Survey II:

> Suppose you have a choice of donating your Aus $1,000 to support conservation of the above reptiles or donating it or a part of it to support a charity of your choice to help people in need (e.g. Lifeline, Smith Family, Salvation Army, St Vincent de Paul). What percentage would you allocate to each of the following:
>
> Support for conservation of the above reptile species %
>
> Support for charity to help people in need %

The average response in Survey I and Survey II is shown in Figure 13. In Survey I, on average, respondents allocated 53.4% of the fund to charity and 46.6% to the conservation of the focal reptile species. The difference is significant at the 85% confidence level (according to a paired t-test). In Survey II, having learnt more about the species, allocation of funds were on average 50.1% to charity and 49.9% to reptile conservation. The t-test performed on the results from Survey II showed no significant difference between both averages at the 95% confidence level.

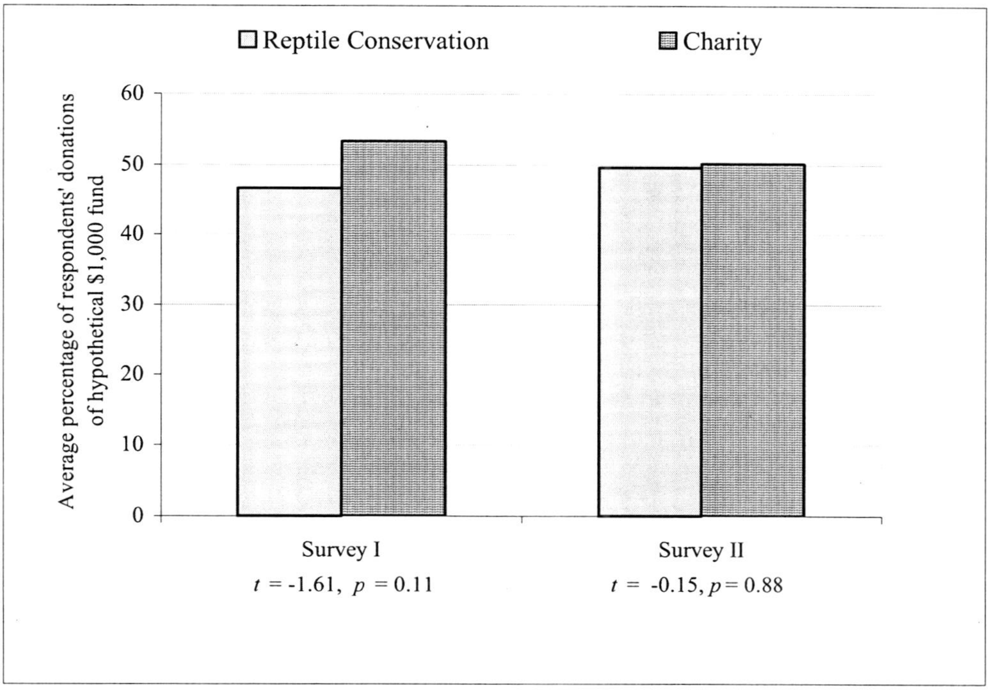

Figure 13. Respondents' allocation of hypothetical $1,000 fund between charity and the conservation of the focal reptile species

Thus the focal set of reptiles (a group with which most humans have limited empathy) managed to retain a considerable proportion of funds for their conservation even when respondents had an opportunity to allocate these funds instead for human charitable help.

Reasons given in favour of a positive allocation of funds to the conservation of reptiles in the set included the following:

> 'Reptiles are endangered due to human mismanagement' and 'humans are plundering wildlife, we need to protect wildlife'
> 'Some reptiles are endangered, humans are not'
> 'Both causes are of equal concern to me' and 'both equally need help'
> 'A lot of financial support is available to charities'

Although most respondents remained supportive in providing fund for conserving reptiles, when the above trade-off was possible some were not supportive. Their comments included the following:

> 'Human life is more important' and 'people in need come before animals'
> 'I suppose I value people more than animals'
> 'Problems of people seem more pressing' and 'I see the suffering of people more and thus understand this more'

Although views of participants varied on average, it is clear that considerable support exists for conserving reptiles, despite some species not being liked very much.

Concluding Comments

The ecological status and use values of several species of reptiles present in tropical Australia has been reviewed. The coverage includes two species of turtles (a marine one and a freshwater one), two crocodilian species and taipan snakes. None of these are considered to be endangered in Australia. However, the anomaly exists that the hawksbill turtle is considered by the IUCN to be critically endangered globally. This is not because it lacks protection in Australia but possibly because it is migratory and faces lack of effective protection outside Australia. The IUCN classification was reported to participants in the survey. Therefore, the hawksbill would have been regarded by them as in imminent danger of extinction, even though this seems not to be the case in reality.

Of the reptile species considered, the saltwater crocodile has the greatest commercial value in Australia. It has consumptive economic use values (for leather and meat) and non-consumptive use value (e.g. for tourism). It is both farmed and ranched. The hawksbill turtle has significant commercial potential as a farmed animal and Crocodylus Park near Darwin is experimenting with the possibility of closed-cycle farming of it. Limited commercial use of the northern long-necked turtle has developed in the Northern Territory (mainly sales of animals for the pet trade) based on ranching by the Aboriginal people of Maningrida. No significant commercial use of taipan snakes has occurred but their venom has potential applications in medicine.

Based on a sample of 204 members of the Australian public living in Brisbane (located below the Australian tropics), it was found that their stated knowledge of the focal reptile species varied greatly. They are much more aware of reptile species dangerous to man rather than benign species, in this case the turtle species.

Associations between the stated likeability of each of the reptile species and respondents' attitudes to their survival, commercial use and respondents' willingness to allocate funds for their conservation were considered. While there is a negative relationship between support for commercial use of a species and their likeability, the relationship is a weak one. On the other hand, the probability of respondents favouring the survival of species rises with the likeability of a species, and the relationship is relatively close and significant. This is also mirrored in respondents' proposed allocation of funding for the conservation of the various reptile species (allocations are higher for species that are more liked) but the result is confounded by the endangered status of the hawksbill turtle.

Those results are consistent with the findings of Metrick and Weitzman (1996, 1998) in a different context. However, the results suggest that likeability is not the only factor that influences the proposed financial support of humans for conserving wildlife. For example, the degree of perceived endangerment plays a role, possibly a very important role, as for instance illustrated above by support for conservation of the hawksbill turtle. However, the sample of reptile species is too small and the variation in their degree of endangerment is too little to test confidently for the general relative influence of likeability and endangerment of these reptile species on the willingness of respondents to pay for their conservation. The experiment should be re-run with a greater number of species displaying more variation in their degree of endangerment. Furthermore, moral sentiment is also important (*cf.* Kotchen and Reiling, 2000). For example, more than 85% of the sampled public supported the survival of the taipan snakes, even though they were the most disliked species. Respondents as a whole allocated some funds to conserve all the focal reptile species. Several respondents stated that even the most disliked species have a right to exist.

In addition, it was found that humanitarian considerations by the sampled public did not completely override support for conservation of reptiles. When respondents were given a chance to allocate funds to a charity helping people in need rather than having the funds used to conserve the focal reptiles, they opted to allocate about half of the funds, on average, for the conservation of the reptiles. The desire to help humans in need did not extinguish funding support for conserving reptiles. Non-anthropocentric values in modern societies are stronger than is often recognised.

REFERENCES

ABC Radio National. (1995). The Health Report: Medical benefits of snake venom. Radio National Transcripts. Australian Broadcasting Corporation. Available from: http://www.abc.net.au/rn/talks/8.30/helthrpt/hstories/hr140804.htm

Adelaide River Queen Cruises. (2004). The Famous Jumping Crocodiles. Available from: http://www.jumpingcrocodilecruises.com.au

Anonymous. (1995a). Legal briefs. *Marine Turtle Newsletter,* 69, 25-28. Available from: http://www.seaturtle.org/mtn/archives/mtn69/mtn69p25b.shtml

Anonymous. (1995b). Sea turtle ranching guidelines. *Marine Turtle Newsletter,* 69, 2-3. Available from: http://www.seaturtle.org/mtn/archives/mtn69/mtn69p2.shtml

Applied Ecology Research Group. (2003). Research flier: Aboriginal harvest of long-necked turtles. Canberra: University of Canberra. Available from: http://www.maningrida.com/mac/wwwmedia/newsletter.pdf

Ashley, D. and David, D.N. (1987). Marketing crocodilian skins. In G.J.W. Webb, S.C. Manolis and P.J. Whitehead (Eds.), *Wildlife Management: Crocodile and Alligators* (pp. 397-403). Chipping Norton, Australia: Surrey Beatty and Sons in association with the Conservation Commission of the Northern Territory.

Australian Senate. (1998). Report of the Rural and Regional Affairs and Transport References Committee: Commercial utilisation of Australian native wildlife. Canberra: Parliament of Australia. Available from:
http:// www.aph.gov.au/senate/committee/rrat_ctte/wild/report/contents.htm

Australia Zoo. (Undated). The Crocodile Hunter. Available from: http://www.crocodilehunter.com/australia_zoo/welcome/index.html

Begon, M., Harper, J.L. and Townsend, C.R. (1996). *Ecology: Individuals, Populations and Communities* (3rd Edition). Osney Mead, England: Blackwell Science.

Bjorndal, K.A. (1999). Conservation of Hawksbill sea turtles: Perceptions and realities. *Chelonian Conservation and Biology*, 3, 174-176. Available from: http://www.turtles.org/bjorndal.htm

Bodger, J. and Goulding, B. (2003). Distribution of Meat Products from Prospective Australian Animal Industries: Crocodiles, Emus, Game birds, Rabbits, Hares and Snails. ACT, Australia: RIRDC (The Australian Government Rural Industries Research and Development Corporation). Available from: http://www.rirdc.gov.au/reports/NAP/03-023sum.html

Bolen, E.G. and Robinson, W.L. (2003). *Wildlife Ecology and Management* (5th Edition). Upper Saddle River, New Jersey: Prentice Hall.

Brazaitis, P. (1987). The identification of crocodilian skins and products. In G.J.W. Webb, S.C. Manolis, P.J. Whitehead (Eds.), *Wildlife Management: Crocodile and Alligators* (pp. 373-386). Chipping Norton, Australia: Surrey Beatty and Sons in association with the Conservation Commission of the Northern Territory.

Britton, A. (2002a). Crocodilian species list: *Crocodylus porosus* (Schneider, 1801). Available from: http://www.flmnh.ufl.edu/natsci/herpetology/brittoncrocs/csp_cpor.htm

Britton, A. (2002b). Crocodilian species list: *Crocodylus johnstoni* (Krefft, 1873). Available from: http://www.flmnh.ufl.edu/natsci/herpetology/brittoncrocs/csp_cjoh.htm

Caldwell, J. (2003). *World Trade in Crocodilian Skins, 1999-2001*. Cambridge, UK: UNEP World Conservation Monitoring Centre.

Cann, J. (1980). Notes on the reproduction of the northern long-necked tortoise (*Chelodina rugosa*). *Northern Territory Naturalist*, 1, 4-5.

Cann, J. (1998). *Australian Freshwater Turtles*. Singapore: Beaumont Publishing.

Castaldo, D. (2001). Ostrich: The other red meat? *MEATNEWS*, 3 (39), article no. 38. Available from: http://www.meatnews.com/index.cfm?fuseaction=issue&issNum=107&Status=Archive

Castaldo, D. (2004). Thailand going organic. *MEATNEWS*, 6 (12), article no. 37. Available from: http://www.meatnews.com/index.cfm?fuseaction=issue&issNum=235&Status=Archive

Caughley, G. and Sinclair, A.R.E. (1994). *Wildlife Ecology and Management*. Boston: Blackwell Scientific Publications.

Choquenot, D. (1996). The ecological basis of wildlife harvesting. In M. Bomford and J. Caughley (Eds.), *Sustainable Use of Wildlife by Aboriginal Peoples and Torres Strait Islanders* (pp. 48-59). Canberra: Australian Government Publishing Service.

CITES. (Undated). CITES glossary. Available from: http://www.cites.org/eng/resources/glossary.shtml

CITES. (2003). Appendices I, II and III. Available from: http://www.cites.org/eng/append/index.shtml

Cogger, H.G. (2000). *Reptiles and Amphibians of Australia*. Sydney: Reed New Holland.

Cronin, L. (2001). *Australian Reptiles and Amphibians*. Annandale, NSW: Envirobook.

Darwin Crocodile Farm. (2003). Products: Others. Available from: http://www.crocfarm.com.au/other.asp

DEH (Australian Government Department of Environment and Heritage). (2003). Recovery Plan for Marine Turtles in Australia. Available from: http://www.deh.gov.au/coasts/species/turtles/recovery/index.html

DEH (Australian Government Department of Environment and Heritage). (2004a). Marine Turtles in Australia: Hawksbill Turtle (*Eretmochelys imbricata*). Available from: http://www.deh.gov.au/coasts/species/turtles/hawksbill.html

DEH (Australian Government's Department of the Environment and Heritage). (2004b). Approved farming operations for crocodiles in Queensland. Available from: http://www.deh.gov.au/biodiversity/trade-use/sources/captive/crocodile-farms.html

Department of Primary Industries and Fisheries (Government of Queensland). (2004). Crocodile farming: A general overview. Available from: http://www.dpi.qld.gov.au/crocodiles/12600.html

EPA (Queensland Environmental Protection Agency). (2002). Wildlife information: Crocodiles in Queensland. Brisbane, Queensland: Environmental Protection Agency.

EPA (Queensland Government Environmental Protection Agency). (2003a). *Code of Practice – Crocodile Farming*. Brisbane, Queensland: Environmental Protection Agency. Available from: http://www.epa.qld.gov.au/publications?id=65

EPA (Queensland Government Environmental Protection Agency). (2003b). Crocodiles. Available from: http://www.epa.qld.gov.au/nature_conservation/wildlife/living_with_wildlife/crocodiles

Errington, P.L. (1946). Predation and vertebrate population. *Quarterly Review of Biology,* 21, 144-177, 221-245.

Errington, P.L. (1967). *Of Predation and Life*. Ames, Iowa: Iowa University Press.

Ferrer, E. (2001). Snake venom: The pain and potential of poison. *The Monitor, Newsletter of the Hoosier Herpetological Society,* 12 (2). Available from: http://coloherp.org/cb-news/Vol-28/cbn-0103/Venom.html

Flood, J. (1983). *Archeology of the Dreamtime*. Sydney: Collins.

Fordham, D. (Undated). Aboriginal harvest of the northern long-necked turtle (*Chelodina rugosa*) – modelling population dynamics in support of a sustainable industry. PhD Thesis Proposal, University of Canberra. Available from: http://www.wildlife.ntu.edu.au/postgrad/downloads/Damien%20Fordham%20WebPage.pdf

Franklin, W.L. and Fritz, M.A. (1991). Sustained harvesting of the Patagonia guanaco: Is it possible or too late? In J.G. Robinson and K.H. Redford (Eds.), *Neotropical Wildlife Use and Conservation* (pp. 317-336). Chicago; London: University of Chicago Press.

GBRMPA (Great Barrier Reef Marine Park Authority). (1996). Hawksbill turtles– *Eretmochelys imbricata*. Available from: http://www.gbrmpa.gov.au/corp_site/key_issues/conservation/threatened_species/turtles/hawksbill_turtles.html

Gow, G. (1989). *Graeme Gow's Complete Guide to Australian Snakes*. London: Angus and Robertson Publishers.

Gray, J. (Ed.). (1998). Proposals for Amendment of Appendices I and II: Hawksbill Turtle *Eretmochelys imbricata*. Report of the Tenth Meeting of the Conference of the Parties to CITES. *TRAFFIC Bulletin,* 17. Available from: http://www.traffic.org/factfile/cop10/cop10_37.html

Grenard, S. (1991). *Handbook of Alligators and Crocodiles*. Malabar, Florida: Krieger Publishing Company.

Groombridge, B. and Luxmoore, R. (1989). *The Green Turtle and Hawksbill* (Reptilia: Cheloniidae)*: World Status, Exploitation and Trade*. Lausanne, Switzerland: CITES Secretariat.

Hobson, I. (1988). Traditional knowledge within the communities. In F. Gray and L. Zann (Eds.), *Traditional Knowledge of the Marine Environment in northern Australia: Proceedings of a Workshop held in Townsville, Australia, 29 and 30 July 1985* (pp. 42-53). Townsville, Queensland: The Great Barrier Reef Marine Park Authority. Available from: http://www.gbrmpa.gov.au/corp_site/info_services/publications/workshop_series/ws008

IUCN. (2003). *2003 IUCN Red List of Threatened Species*. Available from: http://www.redlist.org

Jenkins, D., Watson, A. and Miller, G.R. (1963). Population studies on red grouse, *Lagopus lagopus scoticus* (Lath.) in north-east Scotland. *Journal of Animal Ecology,* 32, 317-376.

Kaneko, Y. and Yamaoka, H. (1999). Traditional use and conservation of Hawksbill turtles: From a Japanese industry's perspective. Report of the Proceedings of the 2nd Symposium on Sustainable Use of Wildlife Resources, Chengdu, China, 22-26 November, 1999. Lausanne, Switzerland: IMWC (World Conservation Trust). Available from: http://www.iwmc.org/sustain/2ndSymposium/aquatic/aquatic-22-1.htm

Kemf, E., Groombridge, B., Abreu, A. and Wilson, A. (2000). *Marine Turtles in the Wild: A WWF Species Status Report.* Gland, Switzerland: WWF (World Wildlife Fund for Nature). Available from: http://www.wwf.be/online_publications/species/wanted_alive_turtles.pdf

Kennett, R. (1999). Reproduction of two species of freshwater turtle, *Chelodina rugosa* and *Elseya dentata*, from the wet-dry tropics of northern Australia. *Journal of Zoology,* 247, 457-473.

Kennett, R. (2004). Turning turtle. *Nature Australia Magazine,* 27, 46-51.

Kennett, R., Georges, A. and Palmer-Allen, M. (1993). Early developmental arrest during immersion of eggs of a tropical freshwater turtle, *Chelodina rugosa* (Testudinata: Chelidae), from Northern Australia. *Australian Journal of Zoology,* 41, 37-45.

Kotchen, M.J. and Reiling, S.D. (2000). Environmental attitudes, motivation, and contingent valuation of non-use values: A case study involving endangered species. *Ecological Economics*, 32, 93-107.

Lang, J.W. (1987). Crocodilian behaviour: Implications for management. In G.J.W. Webb, S.C. Manolis and P.J. Whitehead (Eds.), *Wildlife Management: Crocodiles and Alligators* (pp. 273-294). Chipping Norton, Australia: Surrey Beatty and Sons in association with the Conservation Commission of the Northern Territory.

Lanhupuy, W. (1987). Australian Aboriginal attitudes to crocodile management. In G.J.W. Webb, S.C. Manolis and P.J. Whitehead (Eds.), *Wildlife Management: Crocodile and Alligators* (pp. 145-147). Chipping Norton, Australia: Surrey Beatty and Sons in association with the Conservation Commission of the Northern Territory.

Letts, G.A. (1987). The management of crocodilians in Australia— introductory comments. In G.J.W. Webb, S.C. Manolis and P.J. Whitehead (Eds.), *Wildlife Management: Crocodile and Alligators* (pp. 103-105). Chipping Norton, Australia: Surrey Beatty and Sons in association with the Conservation Commission of the Northern Territory.

Limpus, C.J. and Parmeter, C.J. (1988). The sea turtle resources of the Torres Strait region. In F. Gray and L. Zann (Eds.), *Traditional Knowledge of the Marine Environment in northern Australia: Proceedings of a Workshop held in Townsville, Australia, 29 and 30 July 1985* (pp. 149-163). Townsville, Queensland: The Great Barrier Reef Marine Park Authority. Available from: http://www.gbrmpa.gov.au/corp_site/info_services/publications/workshop_series/ws008

Love, G. and Langenkamp, D. (2003). *Australian Aquaculture: Industry Profile for Selected Species.* Canberra: ABARE (Australian Bureau of Agricultural and Resource Economics).

Lutz, P.L. and Musick, J.A. (1997). *The Biology of Sea Turtles.* Boca Raton, Florida: CRC Press.

MacNamara, K., Nicholas, P., Murphy, D., Riedel, E., Goulding, B., Horsburgh, C., Whiting, T. and Warfield, B. (2003). *Markets for Skins and Leather from the Goat, Emu, Ostrich, Crocodile & Camel Industries.* ACT, Australia: RIRDC (The Australian Government

Rural Industries Research and Development Corporation). Available from: http://www.rirdc.gov.au/reports/NAP/02-142.pdf

Magnusson, W.E. (1984). Economics, developing countries and the captive propagation of crocodilians. *Wildlife Society Bulletin*, 12, 194-197.

Marsh, N.A. (2001). Diagnostic uses of snake venom. *Haemostasis*, 31, 211-217.

McBryde, I. (1979). Archeology. In D. Barwich, M. Mace and T. Stannage (Eds.), *Handbook for Aboriginal and Islander History*. Canberra: Aboriginal History Publishers.

Messel, H. (1977). Chapter 13— The crocodile programme in Northern Australia: Population surveys and numbers. In H. Messel, and S. Butler (Eds.), *Australian Animals and their Environment* (pp. 207-236). Sydney, Australia: Shakespeare Head Press.

Messel, H. and Vorlicek, G.C. (1989). Ecology of *Crocodylus porosus* in northern Australia. In IUCN, *Crocodiles: Their Ecology, Management and Conservation. A Special Publication of the IUCN/SSC Crocodile Specialist Group* (pp. 164-183). Gland, Switzerland: IUCN.

Messel, H., Vorlicek, G.C., Wells, A.G., Green, W.J., Curtis, H.S., Roff, C.R.R., Weaver, C.M. and Johnson, A. (1981). *Surveys of Tidal Waterways on Cape York Peninsula, Queensland, Australia, and their Crocodile Populations. Monograph 16.* Oxford, England; Sydney, Australia: Pergamon Press Ltd.

Metrick, A. and Weitzman, M.L. (1996). Patterns of behaviour in endangered species preservation. *Land Economics*, 72, 1-16.

Metrick, A. and Weitzman, M.L. (1998). Conflicts and choices in biodiversity preservation. *Journal of Economic Perspectives*, 12, 21-34.

Meylan, A. (1998). Hawksbill turtles still endangered. *Nature*, 391, 117-117.

Meylan, A.B. (1999). Status of the hawksbill turtle (*Eretmochelys imbricata*) in the Caribbean region. *Chelonian Conservation and Biology*, 3, 177-184.

Meylan, A.B. and Donnelly, M. (1999). Status justification for listing the hawksbill turtle *(Eretmochelys imbricata*) as Critically Endangered on the 1996 IUCN Red List of Threatened Animals. *Chelonian Conservation and Biology*, 3, 200–224.

Mitchell, G.E., Reed, A.W. and Houlihan, D.B. (1995). Composition of crocodile meat (*Crocodylus porosus* and *Crocodylus johnstoni*). *Food Australia*, 47, 221-221.

Moore, G.W., Smith, M.P. and Savidge, G.F. (2003). The Ecarin time is an improved confirmatory test for the Taipan snake venom time in warfarinized patients with lupus anticoagulants. *Blood Coagulation & Fibrinolysis*, 14, 307-312.

Mrosovsky, N. 2003. Predicting extinction: Fundamental flaws in IUCN's Red List system, exemplified by the case of sea turtles. Available from: http://members.seaturtle.org/mrosovsky

NMFS (National Marine Fisheries Service). (2001). Hawksbill Sea Turtle. Available from: http://www.nmfs.noaa.gov/prot_res/species/turtles/hawksbill.html

Ottenwalder, J. A. (1996). The current status of sea turtles in Haiti. In R. Powell and R.W. Henderson (Eds.), *Contributions to West Indian Herpetology*, 12, 381-393.

Parsons, J.J. (1972). The hawksbill turtle and the tortoiseshell trade. In *Etudes de Géographie Tropicale Offertes à Pierre Gourou* (pp. 45-60). Mouton, Paris: La Haye.

Peucker, S. (1998). The crocodile industry. In K. Hyde (Ed.), *The New Rural Industries: A Handbook for Farmers and Investors*. ACT, Australia: RIRDC (The Australian Government Rural Industries Research and Development Corporation). Available from: http://www.rirdc.gov.au/pub/handbook/croco.html

Porosus Pty. Ltd. (2003). Australia's crocs: Farming in Australia. Available from: http://www.crocfarm.com.au/farming_in_australia.asp

PWC (Parks and Wildlife Commission of the Northern Territory). (1999). *A Management Program for* Crocodylus porosus *and* Crocodylus johnstoni *in the Northern Territory of Australia*. Darwin, Northern Territory: Northern Territory Parks and Wildlife Commission. Available from: http://www.deh.gov.au/biodiversity/trade-use/sources/management-plans/approved/crocodile-nt/

PWC (Parks and Wildlife Commission of the Northern Territory). (Undated). *A Draft Management Plan for* Crocodylus porosus *in the Northern Territory*. Darwin, Northern Territory: Northern Territory Parks and Wildlife Commission. Available from: http://www.deh.gov.au/biodiversity/trade-use/sources/management-plans/draft/croc

Queensland Museum. (2003a). Queensland Museum Explorer: Coastal Taipan (*Oxyuranus scutellatus*). Available from: http://www.qmuseum.qld.gov.au/features/snakes/snakedetail.asp?TaxName=Oxyuranus+scutellatus

Queensland Museum (2003b). Queensland Museum Explorer: Western Taipan (*Oxyuranus microlepidotus*). Available from: http://www.qmuseum.qld.gov.au/features/snakes/snakedetail.asp?TaxName=Oxyuranus+microlepidotus

Queensland Tourism Industry Council. (2004). 16 February 2004 - Queenland A Big Winner at the Australian Tourism Awards. Available from: www.qtic.com.au/ATAstory.htm

Reader's Digest. (1997). *Encyclopedia of Australian Wildlife*. Sydney: Reader's Digest.

Red List Standards & Petitions Subcommittee. (1996). *Eretmochelys imbricata*. In: IUCN, *2003 IUCN Red List of Threatened Species*. Available from: http://www.redlist.org

Ross, J.P. (Undated). Ranching and captive breeding. Special programmes: Hawksbill turtle in CITES. Available from: http://www.cites.org/eng/prog/HBT/intro.shtml

Ross, J.P. (1995). C.I.T.E.S. Approves Marine Turtle Ranching Guidelines. *Marine Turtle Newsletter*, 69, 1-2. Available from: http://www.seaturtle.org/mtn/archives/mtn69/mtn69p1.shtml

Ross, J.P. (1995). La Importancia del Uso Sustentable para la Conservación de los Cocodrilos. In A. Larrieta and L.M. Verdade (Eds.), *La Conservación y el Manejo de Caimanes y Cocodrilos de América Latina. Vol. 1* (pp. 19-32). Santo Tome, Argentina: Fundación Banco Bica.

Ross, J.P. (Ed.). (1998). *Crocodiles. Status Survey and Conservation Action Plan* (2nd Edition) [Online]. IUCN/SSC Crocodile Specialist Group. Gland, Switzerland; Cambridge, UK: IUCN. Available from: http://www.flmnh.ufl.edu/natsci/herpetology/act-plan/plan1998a.htm

Shine, R. and Covacevich, J. (1983). Ecology of highly venomous snakes: the Australian genus *Oxyuranus* (Elapidae). *Journal of Herpetology*, 17, 60-69.

Shine, R. (1991). *Australian Snakes: A Natural History*. New South Wales, Australia: Reed.

Stirrat, S.C., Lawson, D., Freeland, W.J. and Morton, R. (2001). Monitoring *Crocodylus porosus* populations in the Northern Territory of Australia: A retrospective power analysis. *Australian Wildlife Research*, 28, 547-554.

Stubbs, A. (1998). *Information Systems for New Animal Industries*. RIRDC (Rural Industries Research and Development Corporation) – Publication No. 98/139. Canberra: RIRDC. Available from: http://www.rirdc.gov.au/fullreports/nap.html

Thorbjarnarson, J.B. (1991). An analysis of the spectacled caiman (*Caiman crocodilus*) harvest program in Venezuela. In J.G. Robinson and K.H. Redford (Eds.), *Neotropical*

Wildlife Use and Conservation (pp. 217-235). Chicago; London: University of Chicago Press.

Thorbjarnarson, J. (1999). Crocodile tears and skins: International trade, economic constraints, and limits to the sustainable use of crocodilians. *Conservation* Biology, 13, 465-470.

Tisdell, C. (1986). Conflicts about living marine resources in Southeast Asian and Australian waters: Turtles and dugong as cases. *Marine Resource Economics*, 3, 89-109.

Tisdell, C.A. and Wilson, C. (2004). Information and wildlife valuation: Experiments and policy. A paper presented at WEAI 79th Annual Conference, Vancouver, 28th June to 3rd July, 2004.

TRAFFIC. (Undated). Status of trade in hawksbill turtles. Available from: http://www.cites.org/eng/prog/HBT/bg/trade_status.shtml

van Dijk, P.P. and Shepherd, C.R. (2004). *Shelled Out? A Snapshot of Bekko Trade in Selected Locations in South-east Asia*. Selangor, Malaysia: TRAFFIC Southeast Asia. Available from: http://www.traffic.org/news/press-releases/bekko_trade_report.pdf

Warfield, B., Twyford-Jones, P. and MacNamara, K. (2000). Identification of market opportunities for skins and leather products of newly emerging animal industries – crocodile. *Crocodile Capers*, 7. Available from: www.dpi.qld.gov.au/croc/11813.html

Webb, G.J.W. (1997). Crocodiles. *Australian Biologist*, 1, 31-39.

Webb, G.J.W. (2000a). Crocodiles and sustainable use in the Northern Territory. Lausanne, Switzerland: IWMC World Conservation Trust. Available from: http://www.iwmc.org/reptiles/010322.htm

Webb, G.J.W. (2000b). Sustainable use of large reptiles – an introduction to issues. In *Proceedings of the 15th Working Meeting of the IUCN-SSC Crocodile Specialist Group, Varadero, Cuba, 15-20 January, 2000* (pp. 413-430). Gland, Switzerland: IUCN.

Webb, G.J.W. (2002). Conservation and sustainable use of wildlife— an evolving concept. *Pacific Conservation Biology*, 8, 12-26.

Webb, G.J.W., Bayliss, P.G. and Manolis, S.C. (1986). Population research on crocodiles in the Northern Territory, 1984-1996. In *Crocodiles. Proceedings of the 8th Working Meeting of the IUCN-SSC Crocodile Specialist Group, Quito, Ecuador* (pp. 22-59). Gland, Switzerland: IUCN.

Webb, G.J.W., Britton, A.R.C., Manolis, S.C., Ottley, B. and Stirrat, S. (2000). The recovery of *Crocodylus porosus* in the Northern Territory of Australia: 1971-1998. In *The Proceedings of the 15th Meeting of the IUCN-SSC Crocodile Specialist Group, Varadero, Cuba, 15-20 January, 2000* (pp. 195-234). Gland, Switzerland: IUCN.

Webb, G.J.W. and Manolis, S.C. (1989). *Crocodiles of Australia*. Frenchs Forest, New South Wales: Reed Books.

Webb, G.J.W. and Manolis, S.C. (1992). Monitoring saltwater crocodiles (*Crocodylus porosus*) in the Northern Territory of Australia. In D.R. McCullough and R.H. Barrett (Eds.), *Wildlife 2001: Populations* (pp. 404-418). Essex, England: Elsevier Science Publishers.

Webb, G.J.W. and Manolis, S.C. (1993). Conserving Australia's crocodiles through commercial incentives. In D. Lunney and D. Ayers (Eds.), *Herpetology in Australia: A Diverse Discipline* (pp. 250-256). Sydney: Surrey Beatty and Sons.

Webb, G.J.W., Manolis, S.C. and Buckworth, R. (1983). *Crocodylus johnstoni* in the McKinlay river area, N.T. I. Variation in the diet, and a new method of assessing the relative importance of prey. *Australian Journal of Zoology*, 30, 877-899.

Webb, G.J.W., Manolis, S.C. and Ottley, B. (1994). Crocodile management and research in the Northern Territory: 1992-1994. In *Crocodiles. Proceedings of the 12th Working Meeting of the Crocodile Specialist Group* (pp. 167-180). Gland, Switzerland: IUCN.

Webb, G.J.W., Manolis, S.C. and Sack, G.C. (1983). *Crocodylus johnstoni* and *C. porosus* coexisting in a tidal river. *Australian Wildlife Research*, 10, 639-650.

Webb, G.J.W., Manolis, S.C., Whitehead, P.J. and Letts, G.A. (1984). A proposal for the transfer of the Australian population of *Crocodylus porosus* Schneider (1801), from Appendix I to Appendix II of CITES. Conservation Commission of the Northern Territory, Tech. Report No. 21.

Webb, G.J.W., Missi, C. and Cleary, M. (1996). Sustainable use of crocodiles by Aboriginal people in the Northern Territory. In M. Bomford and J. Caughley (Eds.), *Sustainable Use of Wildlife by Aboriginal Peoples and Torres Strait Islanders* (pp. 176-185). Canberra: Australian Government Publishing Service.

Webb, G.J.W., Whitehead P.J. and Manolis, C.S. (1987). Crocodile management in the Northern Territory of Australia. In G.J.W. Webb, S.C. Manolis and P.J. Whitehead (Eds.), *Wildlife Management: Crocodile and Alligators* (pp. 107-124). Chipping Norton, Australia: Surrey Beatty and Sons in association with the Conservation Commission of the Northern Territory.

Williams, J., Read, C., Norton, A., Dovers, S., Burgman, M., Proctor, W. and Anderson, H. (2001). *Biodiversity: Australia State of the Environment Report 2001 (Theme Report)*. Canberra, ACT: CSIRO Publishing on behalf of the Department of the Department of Environment and Heritage.

Wilson, P. and Franklin, W.L. (1985). Male group dynamics and inter-male aggression of guanacos in southern Chile. *Zoological Tierpsychology*, 69, 305-528.

WMI (Wildlife Management International). (2004). Crocodylus Park: Wildlife Research and Education Centre. Available from: http://wmi.com.au/crocpark/

WWF (World Wildlife Fund). (2002). Hawksbill Turtles. Species Programme May 2002. UK: WWF International Species Programme.

WWF (World Wildlife Fund). (2004). Marine Turtles: Hawksbill. Available from: http://www.worldwildlife.org/turtles/species/ht.cfm

ACKNOWLEDGEMENTS

This contribution has been completed as part of a research project on 'The Economics of Conserving Australia's Tropical Widlife' and we are grateful to the Australian Research Council for financial support for this project.

In: Trends in Biodiversity Research
Editor: A. R. Burk, pp. 41-80
ISBN 1-59454-385-2

Chapter 2

CHANGE UNDER CLIMATE CHANGE – A STRATEGY TO STRENGTHEN AUSTRALIAN ECOSYSTEMS

Jan-Olaf Meynecke *

Department of Ecology and Environmental Chemistry,
Faculty of Environmental Studies, University of Lüneburg, Lüneburg, Germany;
School of Environmental and Applied Sciences, Griffith University, Gold Coast, Queensland, Australia

ABSTRACT

As demonstrated in various recent investigations the signs of climate change are already evident. In a rapidly changing environment a management strategy to strengthen biodiversity is urgently required. This chapter shows how such a strategy might be achieved by understanding the effects of global climate change for three major Australian ecosystems - rainforest, mangroves and savannah. A risk assessment for these ecosystems that considers the impacts of past climate change lays the basis for understanding how these ecosystems might be managed under a rapidly changing climate. This is demonstrated by a case study for the wet tropics bioregion. To retain a wide range of flora and fauna, core habitats of target species at risk from climate change are to be identified by using a combination of modelling scenarios and field work. Only by concentrating on the potential refuge areas, with a joint effort of social, governmental and scientific bodies, can we expect to maximise the chances of regionally endemic species surviving climate change. This issue is discussed with regard to ecosystem complexity and the likely difficulties that will be incurred in implementing a conservation strategy for at risk species.

Key words: Global climate change; modelling; rainforest; mangroves; savannah; management strategy.

---

* Corresponding author. Tel.: +61(0)7 5552 8983; Fax: +61(0)7 5552 8067. *E-mail address:* j.meynecke@griffith.edu.au

INTRODUCTION

The prospect of global climate change is well known and generally considered the direct result of anthropogenic emissions of the so-called "greenhouse gases" (Houghton *et al.*, 1995). In the past decade lines of evidence of global climate change have consolidated. Numerous models have been developed to predict future climate trends. An important role with regard to this challenge is taken by the Intergovernmental Panel on Climate Change (IPCC). Its investigations are used by numerous organisations and institutes.

In the year 2001 the IPCC completed a report (IPCC, 2001a, b) documenting expected greenhouse gas emissions and climate change. Six scenarios the so called "IS92" from the year 1992 were replaced. The new scenarios cover the period of 1990 to 2100 and also include socio-economic factors such as demographic change and population growth. Thus it is expected that greenhouse gas emission in the industrialised countries in the northern hemisphere could rise from 40ppb in the year 2000 up to 70ppb in the year 2100 and the Carbon Dioxide concentration could increase from 478ppm up to 1.099ppm with an expected global temperature rise of 1.4 - 5.8°C by the year 2100 (Figure 1).

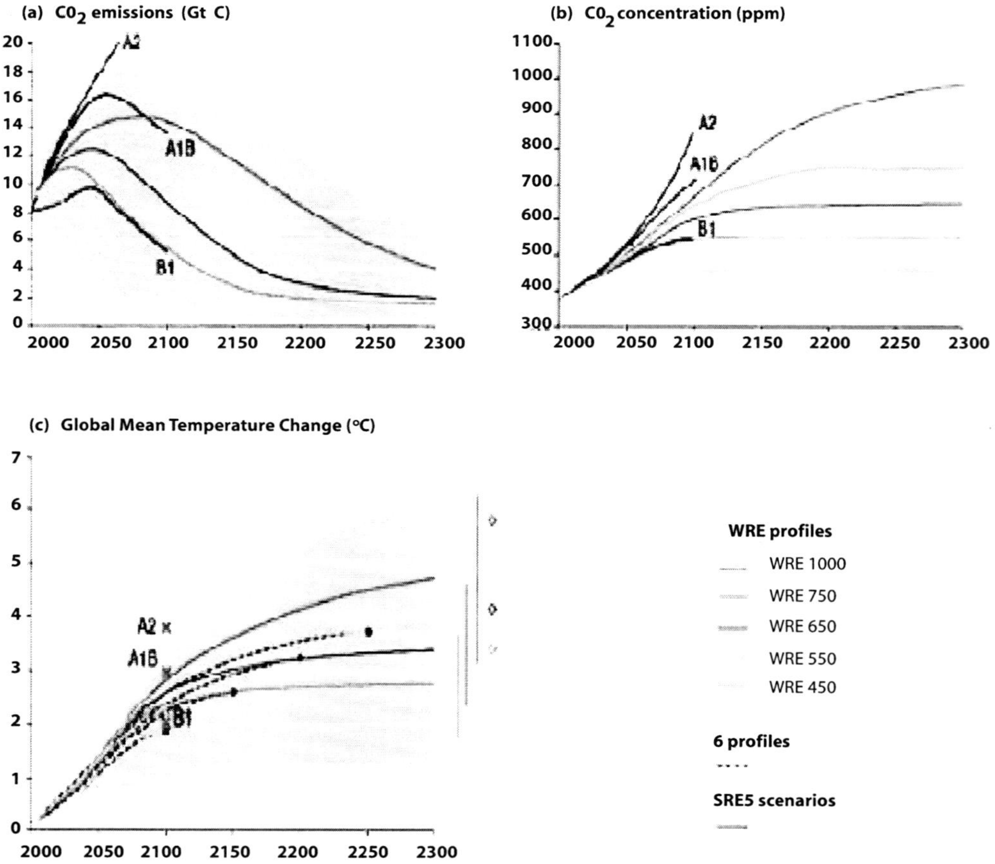

Figure 1. Stabilisation Pathways. Source: IPCC (2001b).

Future climate changes induced by greenhouse gases are expected to lead to regional climate shifts and sea level rise. Even small changes can have dramatic consequences for ecological systems. For example the seasonality of precipitation, precipitation frequency and intensity as well as soil moisture status can be modified rapidly. With increasing temperature the frequency of cyclones (starting from +27°C sea temperature) will increase. Extreme precipitation events, and with it intense erosion episodes, may occur more often (Goldammer & Price, 1998).

The complex character of the climate system leads to different scenarios despite the same experimental data (Palmer, 1993; Cubasch *et al.*, 1994). Therefore, results of global climate models may have limited use, particularly when they include predictions on future emissions and aerosols. In addition many models do not consider the Earth's orbit parameters such as the Milankovitch's orbital theory (Berger, 1984) and insulation changes (Lindzen, 1994).

However, according to Houghton *et al.* (1995) the expected climate change is faster than any comparable event in the past 10,000 years. Its effects on nature are already evident as shown in various investigations (Post *et al.*, 1997; Parmesan *et al.*, 1999; Sparks *et al.*, 1999; Wilkinson, 2000; Hughes, 2000; McCarty, 2001; Walther *et al.*, 2001; Thomas *et al.*, 2004a). Predictions exist for individual species and for different habitats (for example Loehle & LeBlanc, 1996; Parmesan, 1996; Allen & Breshears, 1998; Lindgren, 1998; Visser *et al.*, 1998; Iverson *et al.*, 1999). Research on amphibians in the mountains of Costa Rica reported by Pounds *et al.* (1999), showed that recent climate change led to shifts in species' distributions in highland rain forests of Monteverde (Costa Rica). Frog and toad species richness collapsed from 50 to 20 in the 30 km^2 investigation area. One reason could be a reduction of cloud frequency in the dry season since the mid 70s - most likely resulting from a warmer sea surface caused by climate warming (Graham, 1995). Still *et al.* (1999) showed in three simulations with a resolution of 3.75° longitude that worldwide many mountain species could become extinct under warmer climatic conditions. Although the dimensions of possible effects of climate change on certain species were analysed in detail (for example Crowley, 2000), the likely effects on biodiversity for a whole ecosystem are mostly unknown.

Australia and Climate Change

Climate change already affects Australia. Consistent with global trends, Australia has warmed ~0.8°C over the last century with minimum temperatures warming faster than maxima (CSIRO Report, 2000) (Figure 2). There have also been significant regional trends in rainfall. The northern, eastern and southern parts of the continent receive greater rainfall whereas the western region received less. However, the amount of warming since 1910 has not been uniform throughout the country, nor has it been the same for maximum and minimum temperatures. The largest increase in minimum temperatures has been in the northeast quadrant of Australia while the largest increase in maximum temperatures has been in the northwest. The last two decades have been particularly warm with many of the warmest years on record having occurred during the 1980s and 1990s (data based on Lavery *et al.*, 1997; Plummer *et al.*, 1995; Torok & Nicholls, 1996).

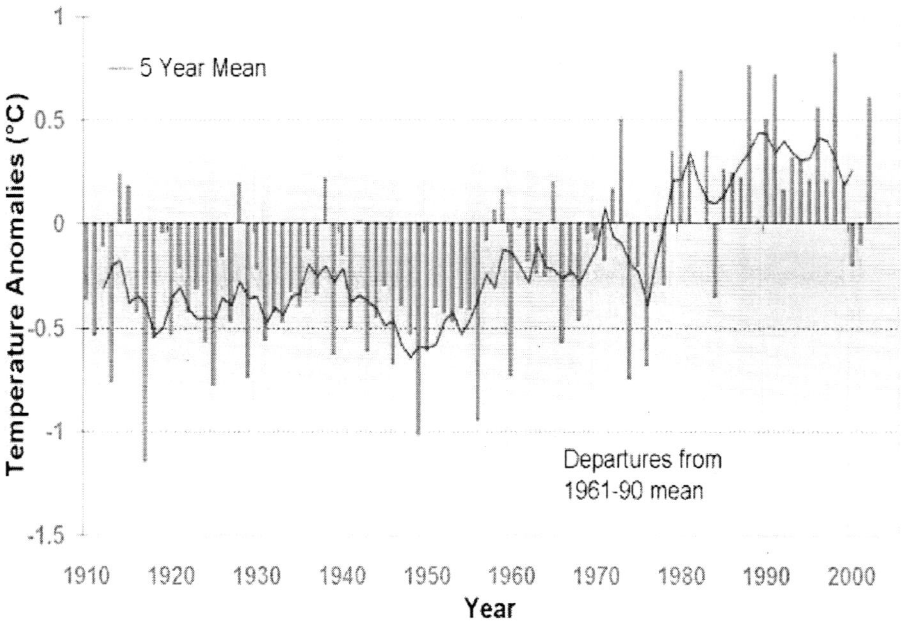

Figure 2. Annual mean temperature time-series for the four quadrants of Australia divided by the lines 135°E and 26°S. Source: Commonwealth of Australia 2004, Bureau of Meteorology.

Heavy rainfall events have been associated with a general higher rainfall and an increase in the number of rain days. Sea surface temperatures on the Great Barrier Reef have increased and are associated with an increase in the frequency and severity of coral bleaching and mortality. Sea level rises have been variable, and less than the global average (Hughes, 2003).

The climatic analysis of the IPCC Report for Australia resulted in a trend to larger dryness in the next 50 to 100 years and a clear increase in temperature. An average temperature increase of 1°C would affect many species, especially for those which live at the upper limit of their temperature range and are sessile (e.g. coral) or cannot migrate due to topographic barriers and/or anthropogenic landscape change (IPCC Report, 2001). The climate change results are based on general Circulation Models (GCM`s) and Limited Area Models (LAM`s). On a global scale these models have a large resolution and tend to underestimate the intensity of precipitation as well the frequency. Therefore, the establishment of regional models is more and more common (IPCC, 2001b).

CSIRO projections for future climatic changes predict an increase in annual average temperatures of 0.4–2.0°C by 2030 (relative to 1990) and 1.0–6.0°C by 2070. Hulme and Viner (1998) expect an increase in temperature of +0.2 °C per decade with 560 ppm CO_2 (55% more than 1998) for 2060. Considerable uncertainty remains as to future changes in rainfall, El Niño Southern Oscillation events and tropical cyclonic activity. Overall increases in potential evaporation over much of the continent are predicted as well as continued reductions in the extent and duration of snow cover (Hughes, 2003; CSIRO Report, 2001)

Reflection on Past Climate Changes

In order to understand the effects of future climate change for Australia, it is essential to look at historical climate alterations. Historic climate change can be revealed by evidence from ice cores, sea and lake sediments and continental records. Past changes in the global climate resulted in major shifts in species ranges and marked reorganisation of biological communities, landscapes, and biomes.

The present global biota was influenced by fluctuating Pleistocene (last 1.8 million years) such as varying concentrations of atmospheric carbon dioxide, temperature, and precipitation. Some species developed the ability to survive in small patches of favourable habitat (refugia). Throughout the past one million years a series of changes from glacial periods to interglacial periods about every 100,000 years and other variations with periods of about 40,000 and 20,000 years are evident. These coincide with variations in the Earth's orbit - the "Milankovitch" cycles - that affect the amount and the distribution of solar radiation reaching the Earth (CSIRO, 2000).

According to Anklin *et al.* (1993), who examined the climate stability of the last interglacial period, comparatively stable and warm temperatures existed 125 to 115 thousand years ago. Investigations on the basis of ice core drills from central Greenland and measurements of the concentration of Mg, Cl, SO_4 and NO_3 compared with other results have shown the following results. The Eem Interglacial indicated the existence of three warmer intermediate periods within a time scale of 10 to 30 years. These were probably similar climate shifts as expected in the future according to the oceanic and atmospheric circulation. It is difficult to determine which species went extinct during this time on a local scale. First attempts were the palaeontological investigations on climate warming and marine bivalves by Kaustuv *et al.* (2001).

For Australia Moss and Kershaw (2000) report major stepwise decreases in araucarian rainforest taxa around 135ka and around 45ka. This period coincides with the most prominent charcoal peaks within all records. These changes resulted from a sustained increase in fire (Singh & Geissler, 1985), which has most likely initiated the replacement of araucarian forest by eucalypt woodland for example on the Atherton Tableland. A process completed in about 12,000 years (Kershaw, 1986).

It is clear that the later part of the Quaternary has witnessed long term changes in the distribution of vegetation. Many of the long term time series data sets of paleo-vegetation are not static, but demonstrate that there have been sustained alternations in vegetation through the late Quaternary period (Hope *et al.*, 2004). Therefore past distribution of plant communities can give indications which areas might be important for the future management strategies.

IMPORTANCE AND ROLE OF BIODIVERSITY

A ''protected area'' has been defined by the World Conservation Union (IUCN) as ''an area of land and/or sea especially dedicated to the protection and maintenance of biological diversity, and of natural and associated cultural resources, and managed through legal or other effective means'' (IUCN, 1994). In conservation management, biodiversity is often a very important indicator to identify habitats of high conservation value.

However, species diversity can be measured through out the number of species describing the species richness or the relationship of species to their taxonomic diversity. Whittaker (1960, 1965) defined alpha diversity as the number of species in a sample from particular communities and beta diversity, relating to the types of species contained and not to the number of species. Ecosystem diversity is difficult to measure because the "boundaries" of communities - associations of species - and ecosystems are elusive. A set of criteria is to be used to define communities and ecosystems (WRI *et al.*, 1992).

In the Global Biodiversity Assessment, a key recent document Hengeveld (1997) defined the so- called gamma diversity (Whittaker, 1960) as the overall diversity within a region. Overall, I support Rosenzweig's (1995) definition of gamma diversity as pertaining to a biogeographical province and relating a large area to a functional evolutionary unit. Such an evolutionary unit is seen in this study as a landscape and thus follows the spatial scaling studies in terrestrial ecology. However, I like to emphasise that the optimisation procedures used in biodiversity conservation should reflect a joint integration of a species evaluation by, for example, vulnerability to climate change, with a multi-species risk analysis. Estimates of extinction probabilities have certain advantages. First, through their use we can calculate the expected loss of species diversity due to climate change. Secondly, the use of extinction probabilities allows us to account for both direct and indirect species interactions. The minimisation of the expected loss of species vulnerable to global climate change defines an objective for conservation biology. This objective is fulfilled at the global minimum when no species is expected to become extinct within the time-frame of interest. It differs from that defined by traditional optimisation procedures, which aims to collect as many species as possible into reserve systems independently of whether the collected species are vulnerable or not (Witting & Loeschke, 1995).

Behind the definition of biodiversity lies also a certain philosophy. Beattie (1995) identified three overlapping reasons for the support of biodiversity: beauty, utility and profit. Other values include spiritual enrichment and the intrinsic right of species to exist. Biodiversity contributes to the continued existence of a healthy planet, our physical, mental and economic wellbeing. Accordingly, the conservation of biodiversity is now legally mandated in many places throughout the world, including Australia. (Davis *et al.,* 1995; Myers *et al.,* 2000; Weston & Goosem, 2004).

The biodiversity within Australia is unique and Australia is also known as a "Megadiverse Country" (Conservation International, 1999). Although two-thirds of the continent is dry, a large span of latitude provides for a variety of climatic zones from the tropical north to the cool temperate south. This has allowed a rich variety of plant habitats to develop. For example there are 252 mammal species, of which are 198 endemic and 65 threatened. There is an increasing trend (1996: 58 of total species and 2000: 65 of total *species)* towards threatened as well (Groombridge & Jenkins, 1994; IUCN, 2000).

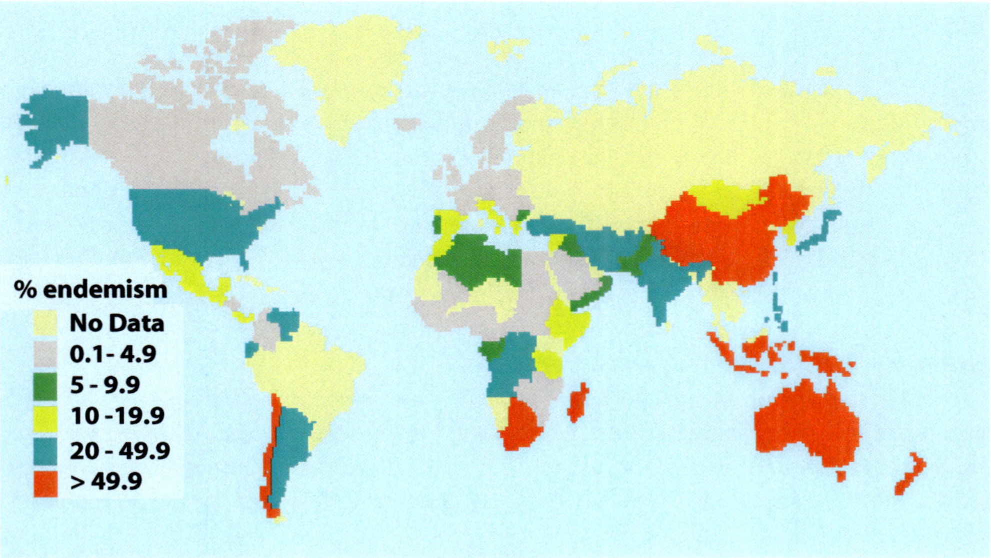

Figure 3. Endemism world wide. Source: WCMC, 1992.

Australia has an estimated 21-23 000 native species of vascular plants, some 85 per cent of which are unique to Australia (Figure 3). There are 19 endemic families of flowering plants (angiosperms) - the most for any country in the world. Acacias (Mimosaceae; 950 species) and eucalypts (Myrtaceae; 600 species) dominate the landscape and are adapted to almost every habitat. Australia has the greatest diversity of the family Proteaceae in the world with 42 genera (860 species) from a world total of 72. Thirty-five genera are endemic to Australia (including banksias, grevilleas, hakeas, macadamias and waratahs) (Williams *et al.*, 2001).

The rainforests of Australia, especially in northern Queensland, harbour some of the world's most important links in plant evolution (Department of the Environment and Heritage, 2004), demonstrating the importance of historical developments to understand todays biodiversity. The origins of some of Australia's plants can be traced back about 175 million years ago. Fossils of the kauri pine (*Agathis jurassica*) and a cycad species (*Williamsonia sewardiana*) have been found in fossil beds in New South Wales (White, 1994). The origin of other species can be traced to a time when the southern landmass of Gondwana split from Pangaea (Kershaw *et al.*, 2003). For example the family Proteaceae, southern beeches and acacias.

POTENTIAL CLIMATE CHANGE RISKS FOR THREE MAJOR ECOSYSTEMS IN AUSTRALIA

Three major ecosystems with a wide range of biodiversity (Adam, 1992; Medina & Huber, 1992; Ley *et al.*, 2002) covering almost 30% of Australia's land mass can be identified. These are mangroves, rainforest and savannah. (Orchard, 1999; Beadle, 1981). They should therefore be a major focus for research on climate change effects to allow sufficient conservation management in these ecosystems.

Mangroves

Mangroves occur within tropical and subtropical sheltered coastal environments are commonly defined as either a plant or plant community associated with intertidal areas such as saltmarshes, representing a number of plant communities (Claridge & Burnett, 1993; Hogarth, 1999). Their global distribution is controlled by the 20°C isotherm, with diversity, forest height and productivity declining with increasing latitude from the equator (Green *et al.*, 2003). Australia has the third largest area of mangroves in the world, totalling about 12,000 km^2 (22%) of the total coastline covered in mangrove forest.

Importance of Australian Mangrove Forests

Over 40 species of mangrove trees occur within Australia (Spalding *et al.*, 1997), representing approximately 50% of the world's total mangrove species. Although mangroves extend from the northern tip of Australia to the southern boundary of NSW (Galloway, 1982; Tomlinson, 1986; Claridge & Burnett, 1993), the greatest diversity of species is found in the tropics (Hartey & Cheng, 2003).

Mangroves can provide important services for adjacent ecosystems such as breeding and nursery ground for aquatic organisms, sediment trapping to sustain offshore water quality for coral reefs, protection for inland sites from storm surges and flooding, and also supply products to human societies e.g. traditional medicines (Department of Environment and Planning, 1983; Hutchings & Saenger, 1987; Underwood & Chapman, 1995; Hartey & Cheng, 2002). Mangroves are biologically productive natural systems providing high economic value. For example mangroves have been valued at AUS$8380 in terms of marketable fish/ha/yr in Moreton Bay, Queensland and are a habitat for many species of birds, which use them for feeding, roosting and/or breeding (Hutchings & Saenger, 1987; Morton, 1990).

Potential Risks Due to Climate Change Effects

It is widely believed that climate change will result in increased temperature, raised sea level, increased CO_2 and changed rainfall patterns – relative to current conditions (IPCC, 2001a). Already different opinions arise when estimating the sea level rise from anthropogenic climate change between 1910 to 1990. The estimated rate of sea level rise (from modelling studies of thermal expansion, glaciers and ice sheets) ranges from 0.3 to 0.8mm/yr. It is very likely that 20th century warming has contributed significantly to the observed sea level rise, through thermal expansion of sea water and widespread loss of land ice (IPCC, 1996).

Based on geological data, global average sea level may have risen at an average rate of about 0.5mm/yr over the last 6,000 years and at an average rate of 0.1 to 0.2mm/yr over the last 3,000 years (Church *et al.*, 2001). According to this, a projected sea level increase of 0.9 and 8.8mm/year can be a major threat in terms of sediment erosion, inundation stress and increased salinity at landward zones (McInnes *et al.*, 2002). These problems will be exacerbated for mangrove stands, where landward migration is restricted by topography or human developments (Green *et al.*, 2003). Dramatic changes in the vegetation distribution of the humid tropics occurred in the last 250,000 years as pollen records have shown. Mangrove values were high at marine transgressions (Grindrod *et al.*, 1999; Kershaw *et al.*, 2003).

Recent shifts in the distribution of mangroves and saltmarshes have been related to sea level rise (Saintilan & Williams, 1999). Other authors argue that in the longer-term, a sea level rise of 1 - 2m could see a return of the "big swamp" conditions of 2000 - 3000 years BP when most of the freshwater wetlands for example in the Alligator River Region in the Northern Territory were saline and supported mangrove communities (Woodroffe *et al.*, 1986).

Mangrove ecosystems may react in different ways to climate change depending on a number of factors, including current tidal range, sedimentology, salinity regime, community composition and shore profile (see Semeniuk, 1994 for a detailed discussion). Mangroves are in general adapted to extreme and changing environments. Although mangroves can tolerate high salinity they require a minimum of constant freshwater access. Stress increase by reduced freshwater flow, reduced rainfall, high evapotranspiration and sea level change can obviously poses a threat to this unique ecosystem. There are several factors important in determining patterns of mangrove advance or retreat; studies have shown that mangroves are closely controlled by sea level elevation at their seaward margin. For example, the macrotidal shores of King Sound, in north-western West Australia, are eroding naturally at 1 - 3cm/year. This rate could reflect the effect of a rising sea level with the mangrove species in this area are migrating landwards. A sea-level rise in a system such as King Sound would most likely result in the migration of mangroves. By contrast, in microtidal locations a predicted rise of 50cm will inundate the existing mangrove zones such as those around Shark Bay and Exmouth Gulf (Semeniuk, 1994). The outlined assumptions can put fisheries at risk as mangroves are potentially important contributors to fish stocks (Suppiah *et al.*, 1998). Loss of these areas through rising sea levels may also lead to declining catches (Williams *et al.*, 2001).

There is evidence that climate change will also be experienced through extreme weather events, areas of susceptibility such as coastal regions will particularly be under threat (Bijlsma, 1997; WRI, 1995). Suggested increased cyclone frequency is likely to threaten and destroy some mangrove stands along the coast (Bayliss *et al.*, 1997). Any decrease in rainfall leading to a reduction in freshwater flow can reduce mangroves vitality (Duke *et al.*, 1998) and destroy mangrove stands. Predictions of increased drought frequency (Kothavala, 1999; Walsh *et al.*, 2000) and reduced river flows for many Australian rivers (Schreider *et al.*, 1997; Arnell, 1999), have serious implications for inland wetlands but also for tidal wetlands. For example for the Macquarie Valley area, regional scenarios of reduced rainfall and increased evaporation indicate that mean annual runoff to a local dam may be reduced by 12 - 32% by 2030, resulting in an annual reduction in water flow to the Macquarie Marshes (Herron *et al.*, 2002; see also Hassall & Associates, 1998). Assuming that water allocation practices do not change, Johnson (1998) suggested that this will reduce both semipermanent and ephemeral wetland vegetation.

As yet, the effect of elevated CO_2 on mangroves is not clear (Ball *et al.*, 1997). Some investigations indicate an increase of growth of mangrove species, although experimental studies by Ball *et al.* (1997) have indicated that these effects may occur only when mangrove species are not limited by either humidity or salinity. Most species ranges lie between 1ppt to 30 ppt salinity concentration (Bulger *et al.*, 1993). Elevated CO_2 is therefore unlikely to allow mangroves to expand into areas where salinity is currently too extreme to support growth.

Overall, evidence arises that mangrove species composition and distribution will be threatened under climate change and therefore all their vital functions. Further research should focus on potential mangrove distribution under climate change especially at the northern and southern end of their distribution.

Savannah

Savannah may be widely defined as any tropical or subtropical grassland characterized by scattered trees or shrubs, a pronounced dry season, and periodic bush fires. The climate generally shows distinct seasons: cool and dry, hot and dry, warm and wet, in this order. Soils are generally porous with a thin humus layer and rapid water drainage (University of Maryland, 2002). Savannah includes also lands dominated by woody vegetation less than two meter tall and with shrub canopy cover greater than 10%. The shrub foliage can be either evergreen or deciduous. This category also includes savannahs and grasslands with herbaceous and other understory systems. These lands may have a tree or shrub cover of less than 60% (University of Maryland, 2002). The term savannah also applies to areas where forest and grassland biomes respective ecotones integrate: the climatic conditions and community features are intermediate between grassland and forest. Australian savannah plant communities are very common and widely distributed throughout Australia. The total savannah coverage is estimated at 19% of Australia's land mass (Groombridge, 1992). This broad view of savannah may help to understand its high overall biodiversity. In the past, savannah biodiversity has often been underestimated (Medina & Huber, 1992). There are many different ecosystems within the savannah biome ranging from temperate savannah in mountainous areas in the Ash Mountains to wet tropical savannah in the Kimberleys.

Biodiversity

Also savannah plant communities usually have a simple physical structure; they are often rich in species numbers. Australian savannah contains endemism in several taxa. A rich reptile fauna as well as extensive marsupial, rodent, and bat fauna in some of the tropical savannah of Australia exist. The savannahs are particularly rich in annual grasses. Most of the 950 Australian Acacias species (*Mimosaceae*) and 800 eucalypts species (*Myrtaceae*) are found in the savannah. Australia has a great diversity of *Proteaceae* with 860 species. There are many ephemeral herbs, which appear above ground for a brief time, usually in the wet season or early dry season. On a half square kilometer of savannah (including a section of creek line), Braithwaite (unpublished) obtained 70 species of woody plants, 55 species of grasses and sedges, and over 150 species of herbs. Relative to other vegetation types in the area, the savannahs are rich in mammals, lizards and insects (Braithwaite, 1990; Braithwaite et al., 1990). As an adaptation to extreme climate conditions, herbivores and burrowing animals are commonly most active in the rainy season and many are nocturnal. During the dry season, many small animals are dormant or survive on seeds and dead plant parts.

Potential Risks due to Climate Change Effects

Climate change may effect savannahs by an increase of temperature, change of fire events, decrease of rainfall and change in saisonality. CSIRO (2001) simulations suggest 20% less rainfall and an increase in temperature of 3°C for central Australia.

Some adaptations and ecological features of savannah species are due to extrem climate conditions and can be regarded as typical of the Australian environment. These include sclerophylly and adaptations to frequent fire, aridity, an often unpredictable climate, high levels of salinity, low and patchy levels of soil nutrients, and variable hydrology (Barlow, 1981). Frequent fires inhibit invasion by trees, maintaining the grasses (wind pollinated) and forbs (often insect pollinated). Those caracteristics are assumed to be good requirements to face the predicted climate change effects. In fact vegetation thickening over the last 50 -100 years has been recorded in Australia in a number of environments such as semiarid woodlands (Henry *et al.*, 2002), and eucalypt savannahs (Bowman *et al.*, 2001). This does not necessarily come with an increase of species and complexity or stability of such woodlands. But can in fact be an indication that some semiarid woodland communities maybe advanced under climate change.

Many Australian plants are adapted to fire and some require fire for regeneration. Sclerophyllous characteristics are strongly represented in Australian *Myrtaceae* (including tea-trees and eucalypts), *Proteaceae* (grevilleas, hakeas, banksias, waratahs and relatives), *Epacridaceae* (heaths), and Mimosaceae (mainly acacias) (Barlow, 1981).

Also this shows that savannah vegetation is more adapted to fire and certainly to drier conditions, this does not prevent it from negative climate change effects as recent investigations have shown. Levy *et al.*, (2004) used a global vegetation model to simulate the effects of changes in climate, CO_2 concentration and land use on natural ecosystems. The regions predicted to be at greatest risk, with spatial pattern in vegetation losses (similar in all scenarios) are consistently being seen in Amazonian, the Sahel, South Central USA and Central Australia.

A number of Australian savannah species are restricted to certain conditions. Hughes *et al.* (1996) state that 53% of 819 eucalypt species have current ranges spanning less than 3°C of mean annual temperature and 23% of species have ranges of mean annual rainfall that span less than 20% variation, making them vulnerable to predicted climate change. Some plant species rely primarily on fire to assist development of offspring (i.e. recruitment) such as *Eucalyptus regnans* (Gill, 1981). In many cases fire can crack resistant seed coats, open fruit held on the parent plant and provide a rich medium for seedling growth. For some species, alteration of such fire regimes can threaten their viability. The change of alteration of fire has already contributed to two species being considered endangered: *Rutidosis leptorhynchoides* and *Swainsona recta* (Leigh & Briggs, 1992).

Drier conditions will be especially critical for grasslands and rangelands where approximately 90% of the variance in primary production can be accounted for by annual precipitation (Campbell *et al.*, 1997). Sensitivity studies by Hall *et al.* (1998) indicated that climate change scenarios for Australia's arid and semiarid regions have assumed that both variability and unpredictability will increase (Stafford *et al.*, 1994; Graetz *et al.*, 1988; Pickup, 1998). Individual rainfall events may be larger and more frequent with a threefold reduction in the return period of 100-year events and longer dry spells between rainfall events. Any enhanced runoff redistribution will intensify vegetation patterning and erosion cell mosaic structure in degraded areas and there may also be an increase in dryland salinity (Stafford & Pickup, 1990).

Major changes in vegetation composition will be the result of shifts in rainfall pattern and increased runoff distribution, and will favour the establishment of simple woody vegetation communities or shrubs. Changes in rainfall variability and quantity will also have important impacts on fire frequency, which greatly increases after wet periods (Griffin & Friedel, 1985). In native forests and woodlands, warmer and drier conditions could threaten many eucalypt species. A recent study of climate change impacts in woodland ecosystems in south-western Australia found that the habitats for all frog and mammal species, 28% of *Dryandra* species (a native shrub) and one *Acacia* species in the region could be significantly reduced by a 0.5°C warming. Other results of research at Murdoch University suggest that climate change may severely impact on many *Dryandra* species, which are found only in Western Australia (Pouliquen-Young & Newman, 2000).

The above outlined assumptions indicate that some areas of savannah might be particular vulnerable to climate change such as mountain areas and dry areas whereas some savannah plant communities might expand under projected climate change conditions. Future research should target on species composition in climate change advanced savannah ecosystems.

Rainforest

Rainforest is still supporting unknown numbers of animal species, which directly depend on the rainforest plants. It provides the highest level of biodiversity for Australia (Rainforest CRC, 2002). Rainforest can be defined as closed forests characterised by dense foliage in the upper layers (>70% cover). Adapted to regenerating in low light conditions and not dependent on fire for successional regeneration. Vines, epiphytes and mosses form a conspicuous and important element of the structure in the tropical and subtropical rainforests. They cover a diverse range of vegetation types-from deciduous, cool temperate, southern beech forests in Tasmania dominated by only one or two canopy species, to the species-rich tropical complex mesophyll vine forests in the Wet Tropics of Queensland where no one species dominates the canopy and hundreds of species may be found. Between these two extreme types lies a series of warm temperate and subtropical forests and vine thicket communities, stretching northwards from Victoria to Cape York Peninsula. Isolated patches also occur in the Kimberley region of Western Australia. Its present extent within Australia is approximately 30,231km^2 of which 11,244km^2 are in protected areas. Over the last 150 years 13,000km^2 of rainforest has been lost due to human exploitation (Floyd, 1987; Young & McDonald, 1987; Specht & Specht, 1999).

Biodiversity

Although rainforests cover only about 0.3% of Australia, they contain about half of all Australian plant families and about a third of Australia's mammal and bird species. The Central Eastern Rainforest Reserves have an extremely high conservation value and provide habitat for more than 200 rare or threatened plant and animal species. The distributional limits of several species and many centres of species diversity occur in this area. The Central Eastern Rainforest Reserves are a particularly rich area with the highest concentration of frog, snake, bird and marsupial species in Australia (Adam, 1992).

The Wet Tropics inhabit Australian highest number of plant species both in number of families as well as at the genus level. Scientists assume that more then 4,500 different plant species exist in the Wet Tropics, from those are 40% endemic (Werren, 2001 pers. comment). Among these species, are over 3,500 species of higher taxonomy such as *Proteaceae, Myrtaceae, Rutaceae, Elaeocarpaceae, Lauraceae, Meliaceae, Fabaceae, Moraceae, Araliaceae* (Frith & Frith, 1995). The Wet Tropics inhabit 65% of the Australian fern species, 37% of the conifers, 21% the *Cyatheaceae* and 30% of the orchids (Trott & Goosem, 1996). Some of the rainforest in Australia evolved from endemic Cretaceus rainforests and numerous original taxa (*Zamiaceae; Indiospermum australiense*). It is therefore one of the oldest centres of floral evolution on earth. The number of taxa with primitive characteristics has high scientific value.

Potential Risks due to Climate Change Effects

As indicated by current research, climate change may affect rainforest by reduced rainfall, increase in seasonality, and increase in temperature and in fire events (Hilbert *et al.*, 2002). Beer and Williams (1995) used the Macarthur Forest Fire Danger Index and CSIRO (1992) climate scenarios to predict changes in future fire incidence. The Macarthur Index incorporates climatic parameters such as air temperature, relative humidity and days since rain and fuel load, to predict fire danger. The models indicate an increase in fire danger over much of Australia. More quantitative modelling by Williams *et al.* (2001) confirmed this general result, indicating an increase in the number of days of very high and extreme fire danger.

Rainforest species adopt to climate change over the past major climate shifts but are limited in their adaptation potential. Important stress factors are water, light, soil and temperature as well as the destruction by fire events (Bowman, 2000; Nix & Switzer, 1991). If fire occurs in regular intervals, rainforest can not re-establish. Due to the adaptation of many species to the dry season, there is a minor correlation between rainfall and rainforest compared to other rainforest sites on earth. Many rainforest species such as *Calltris intratropica* can resist long and dry periods. However, it is obviously that rainforest vegetation is supported by fog and a higher humidity in the mountains. Rainforest is particularly limited, where dry winds occur regularly, for example at exposed mountain-slopes where a lack of water functions as a stress factor (Webb & Tracey, 1981).

Recognised as particularly threatened, are tropical mountain wet forests and evergreen rainforests and the epiphytes they contain. Major risks are shifts of precipitation, seasonality as well as changes in the biological community and an increase in fragmentation (Markham *et al.*, 1998). Past climate effects had significant effects on the formation of rainforest communities and with it for a number of species. An overview of the vegetation in the past ten million years can be given by pollen analyses from terrestrial and marine drill cores (Kershaw & Nix, 1988). *Nothofagus* and *Araucaria* as well as the absence of *Eucalyptus*, *Poaceae* and charcoal, function as indicators for the reconstruction of fossil rainforest on the basis of pollen analytic research (Martin, 1978).

An increased warming of the sea surface in the last 500,000 years (Ishern *et al.*, 1996) supported the distribution of open vegetation of *Myrtaceae* and *Casuarinaceae*. Large shifts of rainforest vegetation took place during the last glacial-interglacial cycles in the passed 120,000 years. It was followed by a period of moderate cooling and reduced precipitation, which lead to a formation of conifer forests (*Araucaria*, *Podocarpus*, *Agathis*). The family

Araucariaceae with the subfamilies *Araucria* and *Agathis* were able to occupy large areas of dry rainforest (Webb & Tracey, 1981). 27,000 to 7,600 years B.P. the rainforest was replaced by sclerophyll vegetation and savannah. Fire events increased, which limited the rainforests to wet areas (Winter, 1997). Reconstruction of the last glacial climate (18,000 years ago) showed that the rainforest had withdrawn to a substantially small area compared to its current distribution. The cooler and drier climate achieved its peak during this time. Pollen analytic investigations at craters and sediment at swamps in the Atherton Tableland predominantly at Lynchs Crater (Kershaw & Nix, 1988) could show that the last interglacial period 126,000 to 115,000 years ago, the vegetation and in conclusion the climate has been very similar to the last 1,000 years. It is known by geological investigations that the temperatures at the sea surface varied from the Mesozoic to the Cainozoic between +3°C and +5°C in average (Barron, 1995). According to studies of Schlesinger and Mitchell (1987) a doubling of carbon dioxide concentrations leads to an increase of the tropical sea surface temperature of 2 °C to 4°C. Thus the temperatures in the MYA period were around 3°C to 4°C higher with a four times higher CO_2 concentration than today.

The present distribution structure of a few species such as amphibians has been strongly influenced by past climate changes and has led to fragmentation and speciation in a variety of species, particularly for immobile species such as amphibians (Winter *et al.*, 1984; Winter, 1988, 1991; House & Moritz, 1991; Nix & Switzer, 1991; Hopkins *et al.*, 1993). Initial work in north Queensland suggests that the upland tropical rainforests of the world heritage listed Wet Tropics of Queensland could be significantly reduced in extent, possibly by 50%, with a 1°C increase in temperature. Such a reduction could present a threat to the rainforest vertebrates, as almost all of the regionally endemic species are cool-adapted upland species, and it is estimated that the range of such endemic species could decrease to a mean of 63% of their current range size (Hilbert *et al.*, 2002; Williams *et al.*, 2003; Meynecke, 2004). It is clear that less rainfall, an increase in seasonality and an increase in fire events will further isolate the rainforest patches throughout Australia and set species at risk of extinction. Further research should target on the southern limits of rainforest distribution and effects on common rainforest species.

Where to Start a Management Strategy?

The last section assessed different types of climate change risks for three types of ecosystems and indicated that climate change already affects these ecosystems. Consolidated management strategies are required. Due to the complexity and wide range of climate change effects a management strategy should focus on potential sensitive species or communities within the ecosystems in the first place. For its identification biological and ecological data is essential to allow a meaningful ranking of vulnerability to climate change and possible risk of extinction. So far there is no general classification system established (Ferrier, 2002). Incorporation of any mapping data and identification of priorities for conservation and rehabilitation is integral for protecting the values of an ecosystem. Monitoring and archiving data for example from remote sensing provide important opportunities for conservation planning, more particularly for coarse-filter conservation (Davis, 1995; Burke, 2000; McLean & Tsyban, 2001).

Diverse communities are more likely to adapt to climate change and climate variability than ones with low diversity. In addition, high genetic diversity within species appears to increase their long-term persistence. A stable ecosystem can be defined by its range of biodiversity. Ideally, as much biodiversity as possible should be guaranteed. A management strategy has to incorporate this as a prior target. However, they are difficulties measuring and defining biodiversity (Gray, 2000; Faith *et al.*, 2003). It must be stressed that the effect of genetic and species diversity within ecosystem processes is still poorly known. The ability of ecosystems to either resist or return to their former state following disturbance may also depend on given levels of functional diversity. This can have important implications on the design of activities aimed at mitigating and adapting to climate change. Therefore, conservation of genotypes, species and functional types, along with the reduction of habitat loss, fragmentation and degradation, may promote the long-term persistence of ecosystems and the provision of ecosystem goods and services (Secretariat of the Convention on Biological Diversity, 2003).

Fragmentation – A Major Risk

In combination with factors such as anthropogenic land use, habitat fragmentation can set a number of species at risk. Habitat fragmentation has confined many species to relatively small areas within their previous ranges, with reduced genetic variability. Between 1985 and 1995 approximately 5 million ha of natural vegetation has been cleared in Australia as a whole (Glanznig, 1995). The annual rate of around 500,000 ha per annum gives Australia the distinction of having the highest rate of vegetation clearance of any developed country (Australian Greenhouse Office, 2000; Australian Conservation Foundation, 2001).

Many authors agreed that global climate change will cause an increase in habitat fragmentation (House & Moritz, 1991; Murcia, 1995). The fragmentation can change environmental factors such as micro climate regarding humidity and temperature or variation in forest structures or the under storey. The effects of fragmentation on the reproduction for rare species is significantly higher than for widespread species (Hubbell & Foster, 1983) and danger of species extinction is clearly smaller, if an exchange between subpopulation exists, thus a metapopulation exists, because a larger genetic pool and further resources are available. After an extinction of a subpopulation the free habitat can be resettled. Species in small habitats, disbursed by air, can drift into new areas (Johnson *et al.*, 1981). According to House and Moritz (1991) genetic adverse effects are expected under a fragmentation of forests. The fragmentation reduces the gene flow and the genetic variation and heterozogism of individuals, which leads to a decrease of the vitality and a higher mortality rate of new-born, as a consequence genetic differences between subpopulation increases. The consequences of fragmentation depend on the size of the population respective the habitat fragment and on their distance to each other (House & Moritz, 1991). Therefore, we suggest to simulate the most likely distribution of a number of sensitive species or communities and allow protection of refuge areas. Protecting vulnerable ecosystems to external stresses can enhance their resilience in view of climate change. Establishing the connection of protected systems rather than protection fragmented areas is often useful for current species movements, but could also facilitate future redistribution or migration in the event of climate shifts (Swart *et al.*, 1998, 2002). Any impacts such as road building, land clearing, housing and groundwater reduction in refuge areas and corridors should be reduced as much as possible. However, some species will not be able to find their preferred "environmental envelope" and may be placed at risk of extinction (Pouliquen-Young & Newman, 2000).

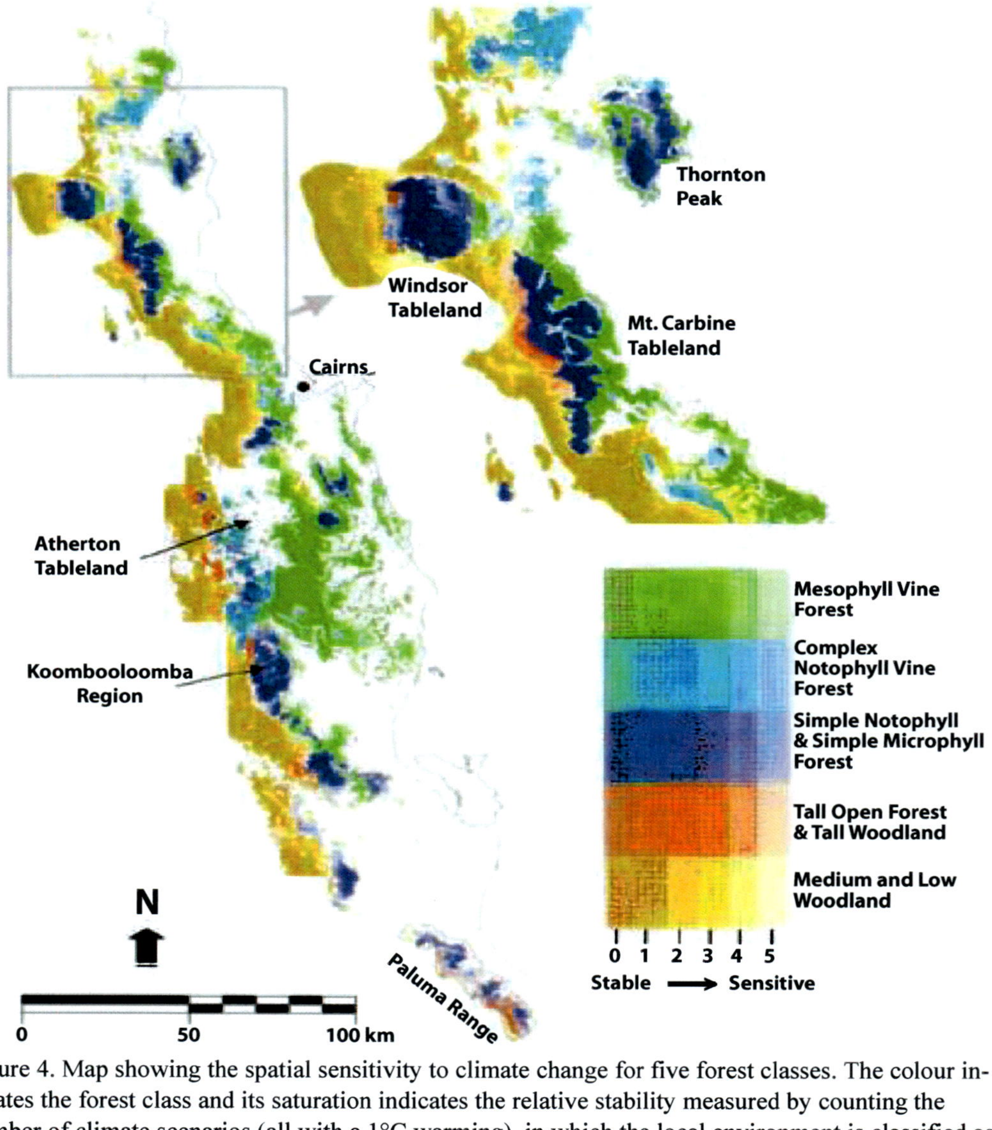

Figure 4. Map showing the spatial sensitivity to climate change for five forest classes. The colour indicates the forest class and its saturation indicates the relative stability measured by counting the number of climate scenarios (all with a 1°C warming), in which the local environment is classified as being most appropriate to the same forest class that is present today. White indicates forest classes not considered in the analysis and areas of the five mapped classes that were excluded because of extrapolation of the model. Source: Hilbert *et al.*, 2002

Assuming that habitat fragmentation is likely to be a major risk for biodiversity under climate change, models should focus on habitat shifts to identify future fragmentation. Model scenarios for different species have already shown serious reduction and shift of their distribution areas. On average species would require a migration rate of over 1 km/year (the post-glacial rate of movement) to reach new suitable areas. Boreal trees from the Genus *Picea* would require 1,000 years rather than 100 years of migration to keep up with the shifting boreal biome (Green *et al.*, 2003). Many species that are already vulnerable are likely to become extinct. The most vulnerable species are typically those with limited climatic ranges and/or with limited geographical regions (e.g. mountain top species), species with restricted habitat requirements and/or small populations (Secretariat of the Convention on Biological Diversity, 2003). As demonstrated for mountain rainforest, Hilbert *et al.* (2002) came to similar results investigating possible vegetation shifts due to climate change in the Wet Tropics bioregion located in North-East Queensland. The Wet Tropics represent a mosaic of different environmental conditions for varying forest classes (Tracey, 1975). Climate change will have direct influence on this mosaic and in the long term the distribution of the forest classes (Figure 4).

Although ecosystems react in different ways to climate change as certain species being more sensitive than others, the same method can be applied to identify future species distribution and display their refuge areas. An optimum of species composition is difficult to estimate even so a selection is based on various quantitative and qualitative information. Investigations, based on past distribution of ecosystems and simulations where most of their species will survive under climate change can help to develop and support management plans for different regions. A strategy consisting of modelling and field work to show future distribution of sensitive species is the first step.

Case Study

A case study undertaken in the Wet Tropics bioregion in Queensland, Australia, shows how modelling tools and field work can be used to develop meaningful scenarios for climate change effects. From the past sections we learned about possible effects of climate change on rainforest and about its past distribution. Such information is required when interpreting modelling results in a further step. Similar approaches should be undertaken for savannah and mangrove ecosystems.

Climate Model

For climate change predictions an improved regional climate model for Queensland was used. CSIRO developed a climate model for Queensland with a resolution of 60 km (Division of Atmospheric Research Limited Area Model - DARLAM-60) using temperature and precipitation data from the period 1961 to 1991 (Jones & Trewin, 2000; Walsh *et al.*, 2000; Jeffrey *et al.*, 2001). On this basis the regional climate data for the study was generated with the programme OZCLIM from CSIRO. The programme supplied different results for the region depending on the global climate model used. The smallest expected temperature change over the next 100 years was +1°C and the highest +3,5°C. Shifts of rainfall distribution were difficult to predict and limited for areas such as the Wet Tropics. Although all models predicted a decrease in rainfall, accrued values on monthly shifts were not possible to derive. For further model calculations in this study a 10% precipitation reduction was used, which was a more conservative prognoses and considered the general difficulties in the prediction of rainfall. According to this background four models based on today's climate were created (Table 1): (1) a conservative procedure with a climate warming of 1°C and no change in rainfall (Cl1). (2) a climate warming with an annual average of 1°C and 10% less rainfall per annum (Cl2), (3) a less conservative procedure with a climate warming of 3,5°C per annum (Cl3) and (4) a warming of 3,5°C and 10% less rainfall per annum (Cl4).

Table 1. Scenarios used for modelling

Scenario	Temperature change (^{0}C)	Rainfall change %
Conservative C11	+1	-
Conservative C12	+1	-10
Extreme C13	+3,5	-
Extreme C14	+3,5	-10

Field Work

Row data for the modelling was derived from a long term project carried out at the James Cook University in Townsville, Australia. A hierarchical sampling method to investigate patterns of distribution and biodiversity of vertebrates was used. The sampling was arranged to cover the entire width of relevant space levels. On the regional level one kilometre was used as the ultimate distance. This length had worked successfully in previous work (Williams & Marsh, 1998; Williams, 1998) and corresponded to the assumed genetic neighbourhood (Endler, 1982). Six points of sampling with a 200m distance were determined along the one kilometre section. At each of the six points reptiles, mammals and birds were determined. Frogs were sampled at creeks closed to the sites (Figure 5).

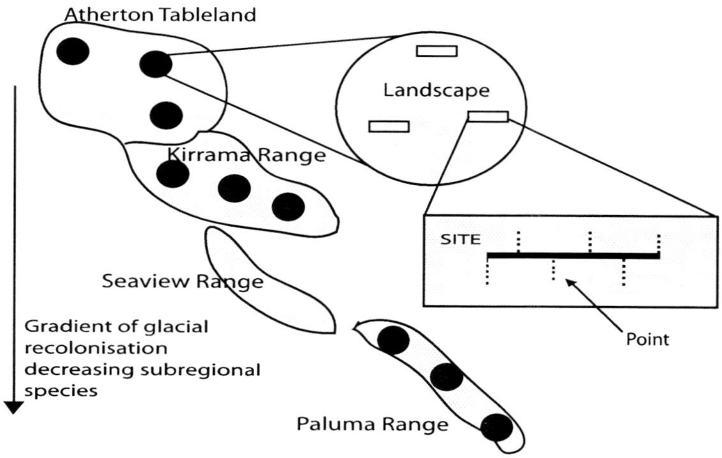

Figure 5. Schematic diagram of sampling over nested spatial scale. The arrow indicates the recolonisation gradient since the Pleistocene contractions in rainforest. Point sample transects each 150m long (dotted lines) are shown at 200m intervals along one kilometre of track at each landscape unit and three landscape units in each region of the Wet Tropics. Source: Williams & Marsh, 1998; Williams, 1998)

Species Selection

The species for modelling were selected under the criteria of availability and quality of current distribution data, their sensitivity to climate change and their wide range of characteristics. A database describing georeferenced specification for each species record and environmental factors such as temperature and humidity provided sufficient distribution information. One reason for the distribution structure of the vertebrates, is the influence of past climate change leading to a fragmentation of habitats and species in particular of immobile species such as amphibians, causing evolution of various species (Winter *et al.*, 1984; Winter, 1988, 1991; House & Moritz, 1991; Nix & Switzer, 1991; Hopkins *et al.*, 1993). Therefore many species and in particular endemic species concentrate in the highlands often in isolated population (Winter 1984; Winter & Atherton, 1991; Winter, 1997). The number of endemic species increases with altitude. Thus 56 of the endemic species were found in altitudes from 400m to 600m (Nix & Switzer, 1991). Peters and Darling (1985) determined the following characteristics of species, which would make them vulnerable under climate change:

(1) Species with a small and localised distribution
(2) Habitat specialists
(3) Alpine species
(4) Species with reduced possibilities to expand
(5) Species with genetic potential
(6) Species with edge population as well as separate population

Species with the last characteristics are particularly endangered, because of their limited ability for migration and survival in new areas. The consequences of global climate change for the biodiversity should become more understandable by the comparison of species with different characteristics. At least one of the selected target species from each group should show such a characteristic.

On the basis of these assumptions twelve terrestrial vertebrate species whose distributions covered a wide range of annual rainfall (300 - 6400mm), elevation (300 – 1500m) and annual temperature (18 - 26°C) were selected on the basis of data presented by Nix and Switzer (1991) (Figure 6) These species were Grey-headed Robin (*Heteromyias albispecularis*), Green Ringtail Possum (*Pseudocheirops archeri*), Common Nursery Frog (*Cophixalus ornatus*), Prickly Forest Skink (*Tropidophorus queenslandiae*); Northern Leaf-tailed Gecko (*Saltuarius cornutus*), Windsor Nursery Frog (*C. bombiens*), Fernwren (*Oreoscopus gutteralis*), Antechinus (*Antechinus adustus*); Lemuroid Ringtail Possum (*Hemibelideus lemuroides*), Mountain Thornbill (*Acanthiza katherina*), Chamelon Gecko (*Carphodactylus laevis*) and Tangerine Nursery Frog (*C. neglectus*) (Meynecke, 2004).

A quantitative methodical framework for the simulation of the distribution for the twelve terrestrial, endemic Vertebrates was created. In particular endemic species with their relatively small distribution areas, their high diversity in habitats and due to their high value for the biodiversity as well as their protection status were of high interest. Scientists assumed that mountain species could be particularly endangered such as *Cophixalus negelectus* with very limited distribution and that due to immobility of this species and landscape fragmentation, a total loss of the current population could be possible.

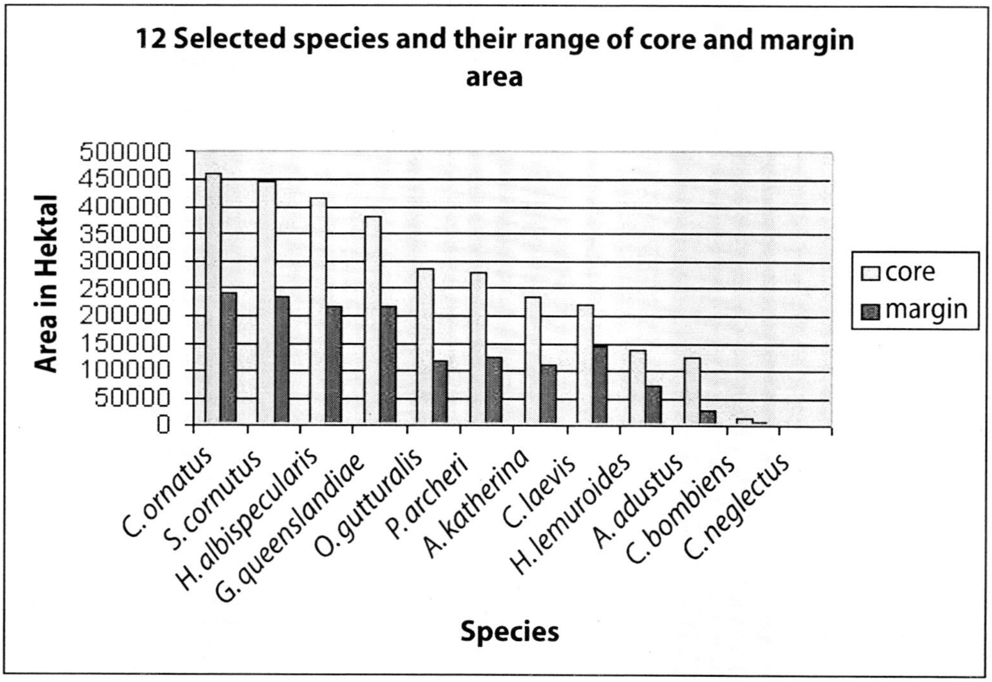

Figure 6. The range of distribution area for twelve investigated species. Source: Nix & Switzer, 1991.

Modelling Tool

Basis for modelling the distribution of the twelve species was the computer program ANUCLIM version 5.1 with the subroutines BIOCLIM and BIOMAP, developed by H.A. Nix, J.R. Rusby, J.P. McMahon and M.F. Hutchison. Bioclimatic modelling programs such as BIOCLIM are important tools for modelling the effects of climate change on selected terrestrial species. Such bioclimatic models do not produce an exact prediction of future distributions, but they offer evidences of potential effects of climate change on the distribution of species (Hill *et al.*, 1999), and they are at present the only method to create distribution scenarios for a number of species in a short period of time. Being aware that effects of a global climate change are not simple linear, as it could be concluded from bioclimatic models. BIOCLIM required a DEM (in our case study a 1:100,000 DEM with a resolution of 80m) to summarise the climatic parameters from each cell of the DEM and to identify all cells, which correspond to the climatic profile of each species (for a complete description of BIOCLIM see Nix, 1986 and Houlder *et al.*, 1999).

Creation of Distribution Models

Maps created with BIOMAP were displayed in (GIS) Arc/View 3.1 showing the potential climatic distribution of the twelve species with core and margin area. The final maps of the current distribution were compared with the results from Nix and Switzer (1991). These distribution maps were the base for distribution models under changed climate conditions. Temperature and precipitation in BIOCLIM were changed and a new climatic profile for each type created. The actual area size was calculated in Arc/View to show loss and increase in relation to current distribution areas.

Substantial shifts of the potential climate distribution area were obvious for all twelve species under the four scenarios with +1°C (Cl1), +1°C and -10% of the annual precipitation (Cl2), +3.5°C (Cl3) and +3.5°C and -10% of the precipitation (Cl4). A simulation of a temperature increase of around 1°C led to a reduction of the distribution area of almost 40% for all species. Under a simulation of +3.5°C, only 5% of the total core area remained and seven species experienced a complete reduction (Cl3).

However, the results for a decrease in rainfall in the annual average of 10% were less dramatic. Only slight reductions in the area sizes occurred. As expected, a decrease of the precipitation of 10% had only slight effects, since the precipitation in the entire investigation area was high in general and therefore the species developed a larger tolerance to precipitation fluctuations than to temperature variations. Some species could increase their distribution area, because areas in higher altitudes provided wetter conditions and offered now better climatic conditions than before. For this reason, the margin areas of some species increased. A clear shift of the distribution areas for all created models under the four climate scenarios was shown towards the North into wetter and higher regions. Regions with altitudes between 900m and 1,300m and high precipitation appeared as refuge areas for nearly all species. In particular two regions in the North of the Wet Tropics formed the last refuge under simulated warmer and drier conditions for example for the two species *Saltuarius cornutus* and *Pseudocheirops archeri* (Figure 7, 8). Similar results from paleoclimatic investigations were presented by Hilbert *et al.*, 2002 and Kershaw & Nix, 1988. Already isolated subregions were not suitable for species even with a small rise in temperature in simulation, conforming to Williams (1997) results for the distribution of species in the past. After assumed extinction during the last ice age, these regions remained comparatively poor in diversity.

Overall, further investigations done by Williams *et al.* (2003) including all endemic species came to similar conclusions. According to the results it is obvious that certain areas require protection and allow access for migrating animals. Further work is needed to determine the climatic distribution constraints and the climate change impacts on ecosystems such as mangroves and savannah. Model results suggest that species whose current environmental envelope is very small are predicted to disappear with small increases in global temperatures (+0.5°C) as demonstrated in this case study. Species with larger environmental envelopes are more resistant, but with global warming of +2°C we could expect widespread loss of native plant species (Pouilquen-Young & Newman, 2002)

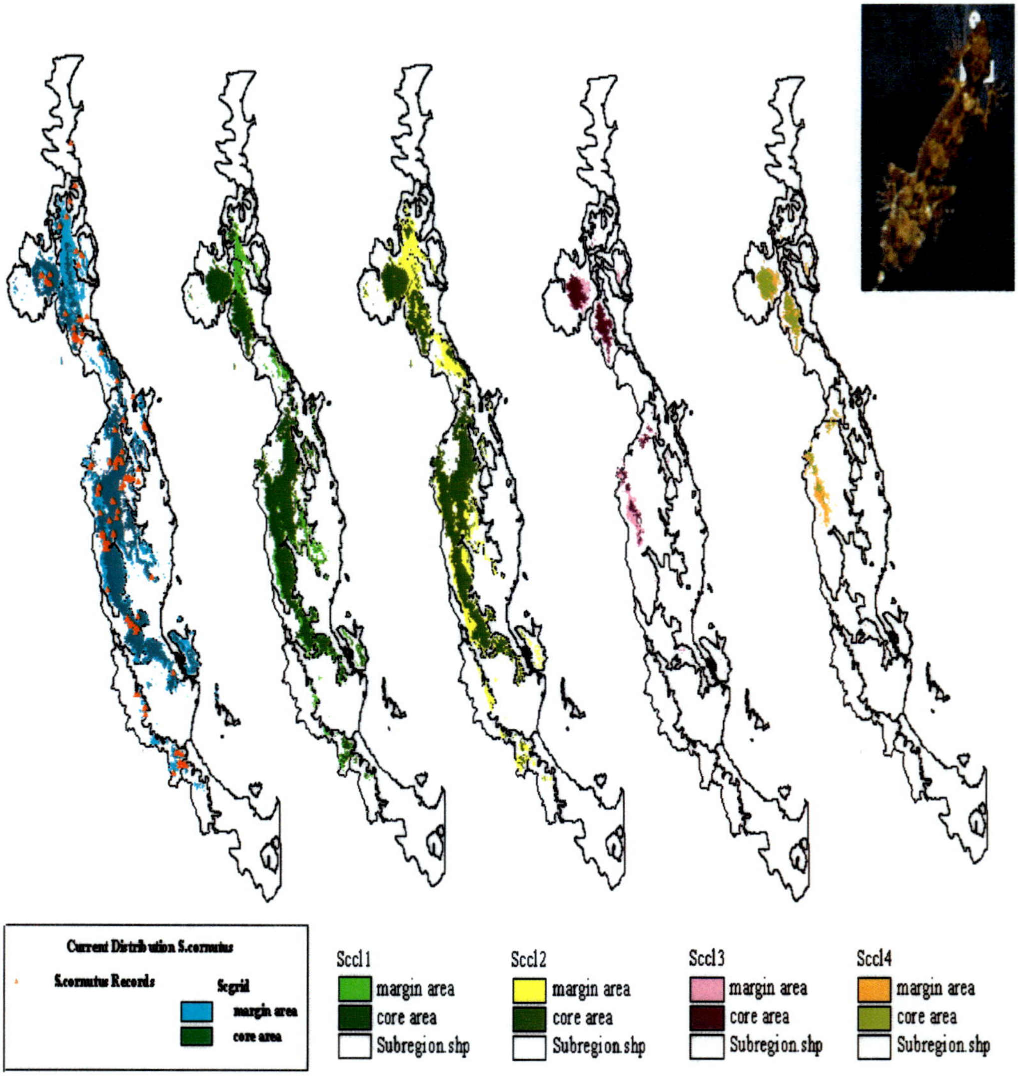

Figure 7. Distribution of *Saltuarius cornutus* under different scenarios with BIOCLIM (Photo: Meynecke)
Legend for the scenarios: Sccl1 = +1°C; Sccl2 = +1°C / -10% Rainfall; Sccl3 = +3,5°C; Sccl4 = +3,5°C / -10% Rainfall

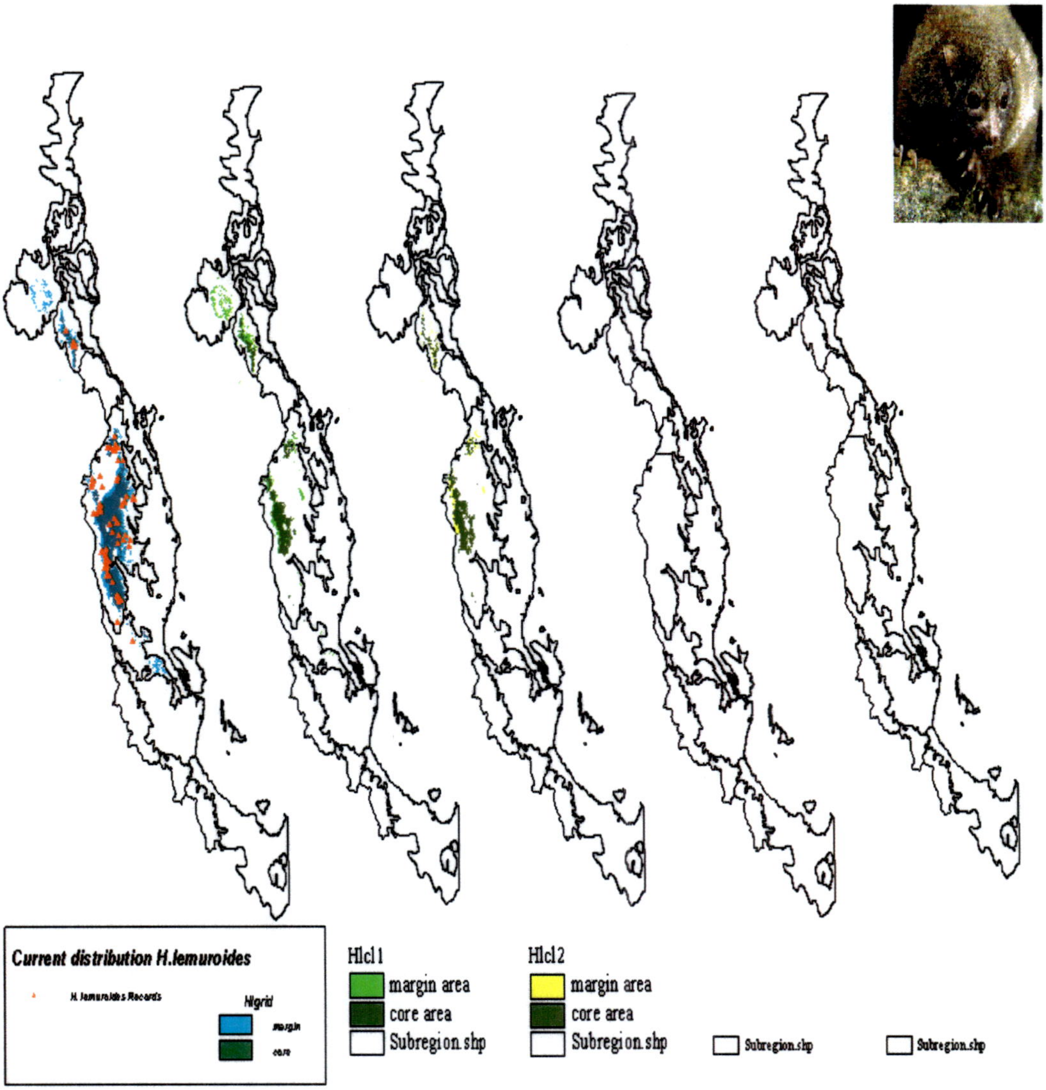

Figure 8. Distribution of *Pseudocheirops archeri* under different scenarios with BIOCLIM (Photo: C & D Frith Australia's Wet Tropics Rainforest Life).
Legend for the scenarios: HLCl1 = +1°C; HlCl2 = +1°C / -10% Rainfall ; HlCl3 = +3,5°C; HlCl4 = +3,5°C / -10% Rainfall.

DISCUSSION

A wide range of ecosystems ranging from mangroves, rainforest to savannah, will be threatened by climate change. Mangroves are likely to be affected by sea level rise and change in rainfall patterns. Some mangrove stands will extend as shown in recent investigations by Howarth (2002). We do not know how fast mangrove assemblages will change or the consequences for the estuarine ecology. In contrast savannah might be advanced where wet regions receive less rainfall. On the other side large areas of savannah can vanish in sensitive areas such as drylands or highlands. Most threatened to this ecosystem are changes of rainfall frequency, increasing temperature and with it a change of fire frequency. Rainforest appears highly sensitive to higher temperatures and a change of seasonality. I introduced a method to determine consequences of climate change and identify potential refuge areas. The results come with a clear message that climate variability poses enormous threats.

Scientist, social and governmental bodies need to develop and implement appropriate strategies to reduce the risks associated with a changing climate. Management and policies rely on the validation of results given by the scientific community. It often comes down to the terms of good and bad. Unfortunately there is no good nor bad in nature. Models of predicted species and/or communities' distribution under climate change have not yet been widely used as a decision support tool for policy makers and conservation management. Also our case study demonstrated the power of such tools, giving clear direction for biodiversity management. The uncertainties coming with all model approaches in general seem to be a hurdle. Therefore all modelling should be verified clearly by historical data and field work to avoid false prediction. I suggest using broad scale data to illustrate refuge areas in a wider context and give policy makers a clear direction. Detailed analyses should follow for uncertain areas or species, helping to implement policies. If a region is of high interest e.g. habitat for vulnerable species as an outcome to prior classification of broad scale data, the abundance of the target species needs to be assessed by field work. When an area is too large or inaccessible, satellite images and aerial photographs might be used to define the distribution. A quality and as far as possible a quantitative comparison with past distribution of the target species and closely related species is recommended. Climate data of the region should be obtained carefully and its error size considered in the assumptions. Different programmes can be used to simulate distribution of species such as BIOCLIM. Good results for smaller groups of species can be simulated with the program GARP (Genetic Algorithm for Rule set Production) to receive automated modelling of plant and animal distribution (for further description see Stockwell, 1995). GARP is rather logically oriented than mathematical and includes a high complexity. An alternative to BIOCLIM is the program MIGRATE used by Hill *et al.* (2002) to simulate distribution rates of species. MIGRATE can represent and determine insular expansion of species in heterogeneous habitats, in which species can follow or remain under a climate shift. However, MIGRATE failed to simulate high levels of occupancy (Hill *et al.*, 2001). Another option to map potential distribution of plants and animals is DOMAIN model (Carpenter *et al.*, 1993) or CLIMEX (Sutherst *et al.*, 1998). Similar to BIOCLIM an environmental 'habitat envelope' is constructed. The range standardisation for DOMAIN model is based on the Gower metric algorithm (Gower, 1971). Overall BIOCLIM is more flexible and is most consistent with the known ecology of the species I was modelling with some minor deviation in the range areas. So far BIOCLIM has been used in a number of climate change studies (Brereton *et al.*, 1995; Hughes *et al.*, 1996; Chapman & Milne, 1998; Pouliquen-Young & Newman, 2000; Beaumont & Hughes, 2002). Nevertheless, the power of BIOCLIM is questioned by some authors (see Walker & Cocks, 1991; Carpenter *et al.*, 1993; Baker *et al.*, 2000; Kriticos & Randal, 2001), primarily because each size of the suitable climate variable is described as a straight-line in the Euclidean distance. Consequently, BIOCLIM may not circumscribe a habitat envelope accurately. It is also criticised that BIOCLIM assumes that climate is the only driver affecting a species distribution and is sensitive to the accuracy of the distributional data used (Hughes, 2003). Despite this criticism, BIOCLIM remains a useful tool if major climate shifts are subject of research and the data sets are well assessed.

Mainly single species or certain groups of species have been investigated so far. The effect on whole ecosystems has not been studied in detail yet in view of the complexity of ecosystem response this remains an important task for the scientific community – especially with the perspective to support policy makers and the management. Some authors argue that further modelling will not bring the results required to understand global climate change (for example Christy, 2000; Hansen *et al.*, 2000; Jacobson *et al.*, 2001; Lindzen *et al.*, 2001). The complexity of a functional system can not be represented by inflexible variables and statistically calculated drivers. In fact a system never works without the influence of surrounding systems. In order to make true predictions all earth systems would need to be combined into one model. Even the fastest computer would not be able to run such a model in the near future. Therefore a "true" simulation is not an objective so far.

Difficulties of Strategy Implication

It was shown that core areas of high biodiversity under possible climate change conditions can be identified by modelling tools. I have argued that areas offer a limited defence against problems posed by rapid environmental change and that protected areas will themselves need to be changed and adapted if they are to meet the challenges posed by global warming. Recent research suggests that the types of environmental changes predicted in climatic models are already taking place (Post *et al.*, 1997; Parmesan *et al.* 1999; Sparks, *et al.,* 1999; Wilkinson, 2000; Hughes, 2000; McCarty, 2001; Walther *et al.*, 2001; Thomas *et al.*, 2004a). The impacts of climate change may necessitate a fundamental rethinking in the approach to protection.

Protected area agencies have rightly resisted attempts to move protected area boundaries or de-designate protected areas for periods of time. But under climate change, species for which a particular protected area was established may no longer survive there. Some protected areas - for instance in coastal, arctic and mountain regions - may disappear altogether in their current form. The current extinction crisis is likely to become more intense as environmental conditions change and fluctuate at an accelerated rate.

Protected area agencies could be faced with the massive task of having to shift protected areas to keep up with moving habitats and ecosystems. The agencies need advice - and political support -for planning protected area networks to withstand or adapt to change as much as possible (WWF Manual, 2004). Practical difficulties will arise as "Moving" protected areas would have enormous implications for their infrastructure, surrounding human communities and the many businesses associated with parks (Wunder, 2000). Shifting reserves would have cultural implications; societies build emotional bonds to national parks and nature reserves, they cannot be swapped and replaced, however, arguments for shifting protection areas may also come with a new approach done by Faith *et al.* (2003). They used biodiversity surrogate information for "biodiversity viability analysis" (BVA) focusing on the important role of biodiversity complementarity, to estimate the gain in biodiversity representation and persistence, when an area is added to an existing set of protected-areas (Faith *et al.*, 1996). Flexible protection areas should also be part of the implementation of appropriate reserve design principles such as incorporation of buffer zones into land-use management and conservation planning. A national system of corridors linking refugia and reserves to assist migration and dispersal is required as well as developing and promoting incentives for landholders adjacent to parks and reserves to manage parts of their land for the provision of buffer zones and corridors to increase connectivity between reserves (Department of the Environment and Heritage, 2004).

Resource management is not just a question of maintaining mortality within sustainable limits for a series of target species, but recognising the interconnectivity of ecosystems and the problem of management of complex systems. These issues have been widely discussed in recent years (Rosenberg *et al.*, 1993; Ludwig *et al.*, 1993; Walters *et al.*, 1996; Garcia *et al.*, 1996; Hilborn, 1997; Caddy, 1999). Cochrane (2000) concluded that the primary reasons for the failure of management can be summarised as: high biological and ecological uncertainty as to resource dynamics, the conflict between social and economic priorities, and the lack of definition or observance of constraints imposed by the limits to production of the resources. Protection of certain areas to prevent severe climate change effects on biodiversity and resources should also be combined with several other strategies.

International and National Strategies

International approaches aim mainly on the reduction of the greenhouse gases. The optimum way to reduce the impacts of climate change on protected areas is to dramatically reduce the heat-trapping gases that cause climate change such as CO_2 (Green *et al.*, 2003). If these emissions are not controlled, there is little chance of saving many protected areas (WWF Manual, 2004). At the 2002 World Summit on Sustainable Development (WSSD), world leader's reaffirmed the central importance of the Convention on Biological Diversity and the United Nations Framework Convention on Climate Change (UNFCCC). Climate change is one of the threats to biodiversity, and the need for its rate to be reduced to allow ecosystems to adjust to climate change is recognised as an objective of the UNFCCC (Secretariat of the Convention on Biological Diversity, 2003).

International negotiations under the UN Framework Convention on Climate Change could take several different approaches to advance future mitigation commitments. A key will be to intensify and broaden participation in emission reduction so as to bring absolute global emissions trends down and allow stabilisation of concentrations of greenhouse gases to occur in a timely manner. The Kyoto Protocol calls for starting new negotiations on next steps by 2005.

A stabilisation of greenhouse gas concentrations in the atmosphere should be achieved within a time-frame sufficient to allow ecosystems to adapt naturally to climate change (UNFCCC, 1992). This includes ecosystem stability and resilience (Root *et al.*, 2003; Leemans & Eickhout, 2003; Parmesan & Yohe, 2003), and the ability for natural resource systems to continue to provide the necessary resource base for future economic development (OECD, 2001a, b). Thus, long-term climate policy requires integration of scientific information, socio-economic assessments and ethical judgements to determine just how risk-averse today's society chooses to be on behalf of future generations.

The international approaches are to be combined with national strategies. First steps in the right direction are the recognition of climate change as a key threatening process by the

Australian Environment Protection and Biodiversity Conservation Act 1999 and the developing of a "National Biodiversity and Climate Change Action Plan" by the Australian Dep. of Environment and Heritage.

I showed an appropriate strategy to identify priority actions for addressing the impacts of climate change on biodiversity (see also Morton *et al.*, 2002), including the identification of key native ecosystems. This should be one element in a chain of action to handle the effects of climate change on a national level. Further steps are necessary such as:

- Developing guidelines on the collection and use of data for input into predictive modelling;
- Establishing of early warning systems for detecting new incursions of alien species;
- Undertaking integrated risk assessment on the response of terrestrial and aquatic weeds and pest species to a range of climate change scenarios;
- Incorporate planning for multiple climate change scenarios into planning and management processes at a range of levels (e.g. national, state, regional and local) (Secretariat of the Convention on Biological Diversity, 2003)

Such improvements only succeed when management plans, as well as protected areas themselves, are linked on the basis of ecological requirements. Future land and fishery management should include improved collection, sharing of information and modified fishing industry and agricultural practices to harvests within sustainable production levels (McLean *et al.*, 2001; Swart, 2002).

Outlook

Prognoses of future climate development indicate considerable uncertainties. However, there are different scenarios and their possible consequences are public. Despite uncertain forecasts, politics and economics must take decisions to stay in action. Although Australian people can probably do little to reverse the trend and have only a secondary influence on the creation of this environment in view of the complexity. But the impact of a suggested 4°C temperature increase in sea surface temperatures several hundred thousand years ago appears to have been environmentally disastrous (Kershaw *et al.*, 2003). Moss and Schneider (1999) already claimed that climate change is to be measured on its potential consequences and not on the likelihood of risk. Some scientists say that a global climate warming is unlikely; others do see a repetition of the past. We cannot determine what the future brings. Even models are only auxiliary constructions, to work against the uncertainties of the present. We have enough evidence of climate warming. Considering all global environmental risks, it is only a further missing link in a chain of threats. Thomas *et al.* (2004b) calls the current extinction of species the sixth mass extinction after the five major mass extinctions on earth in its four billion year old history. The last one, which wiped out the dinosaurs, happened 65 million years ago at the end of the Cretaceous period and was possibly caused by a giant meteor collision. The current extinction is being precipitated by the widespread loss of habitats because of human activity. The remaining habitats are small and fragmented. Also biodiversity is dynamic and can not be conserved; giving ecosystems their required space and drivers is our future task. The enormous risk of climate change needs to be managed as long as the resources are available. Once a certain stage has been reached, stabilisation of threatened ecosystems appears unlikely.

REFERENCES

ACF (Australian Conservation Foundation, 2001). *Australian Land Clearing, A Global Perspective: Latest Facts & Figures.* Melbourne, Australia: Australian Conservation Foundation (ACF).

Adam, P. (1992). Australian rainforest. Oxford, UK: Clarendon Press

Allen, C.D. & Breshears, D.D. (1998). Drought-induced shift of a forest-woodland ecotone: rapid landscape response to climate variation. *Proc. Natl. Acad. Sci. U.S.A 95*, 14839 – 14842.

Anklin, M., Barnola, J.M., Beer, J., Blunier, T., Chappellaz, J., Clausen, H.B., Dahlen-Jensen, B., Daansgard, W. & De Angelis, M. (1993). Climate instability during the last interglacial period recorded in the GRIP ice core. *Nature, 364*, 203-207.

Arnell, N.W. (1999). Climate change and global water resources. *Global Environ. Change, 9*, 31–46.

Australian Greenhouse Office (2000). *Land clearing: a social history*. Canberra, Australia: Australian Greenhouse Office.

Baker R.H.A., Sansford C.E., Jarvis C.H., Cannon R.J.C., MacLeod A. & Walters K.F.A. (2000). The role of climatic mapping in predicting the potential geographical distribution on non-indigenous pests under current and future climates. *Agric. Ecosyst. Environ.,* ***8***, 57–71.

Ball, M.C., Cochrane, M.J. & Rawson, H.M. (1997). Growth and water use of the mangroves Rizophora apiculata and R. stylosa in response to salinity and humidity under ambient and elevated concentrations of atmospheric CO_2. *Plant, Cell and Environment, 20* 1158-1166.

Barlow, B.A. (1981). The Australian flora: Its origin and evolution. In George A.S., (Ed.) *Flora of Australia.* Vol 1, Canberra, Australia: AGPS.

Barron, E.J. (1995). Tropical Climate Stability and Implications for the Distribution of Life. In National Research Council (U.S.A.). *Effects of past global change on life* (pp.108-115). Washington D.C., U.S.A.: National Academy Press.

Bayliss, B., Brennan, K., Eliot, I. *et al.* (1997). *Vulnerability Assessment of Predicted Climate Change and Sea Level Rise in the Alligator Rivers Region, Northern Territory Australia.* Supervising Scientist Report 123. Canberra, Australia: Supervising Scientist.

Beadle, N.C.W. (1981). *The Vegetation of Australia.* Cambridge, U.S.A.: Cambridge University Press.

Beaumont L. & Hughes L. (2002). Potential changes in the distributions of latitudinally restricted Australian butterflies in response to climate change. *Global Change Biol,. 8*, 954–71.

Beattie, A.J. (1995). Biodiversity and Bioresources. *Australasian Biotechnology 5*, 212-213.

Beer, T. & Williams, A. (1995). Estimating Australian forest fire danger under conditions of doubled carbon-dioxide concentrations. *Climatic Change, 29*, 169-88.

Berger, A., Imbrie, J., Hays, J., Kukla, G., & Saltzman, B. (Eds.) (1984). *Milankovitch and Climate.* Dordrecht, Holland: Reidel.

Bijlsma, L. (1997). Climate Change and the management of coastal resources. *Journal of Climate Research 9*, 47-56.

Blasco, M. F., & Field, C. (Eds.) (1997). *World Mangrove Atlas*. Okinawa, Japan: ISME.

Bowman, D.M.J.S., Walsh, A. & Milne, D.J. (2001). Forest expansion and grassland contraction within a *Eucalytpus* savanna matrix between 1941 and 1994 at Litchfield National Park in the Australian monsoon tropics. *Global Ecol. Biogeog., 10*, 535–548.

Bowman, D.M.J.S. (2000). *Australian Rainforests. Islands of green in a land of fire.* Cambridge, U.S.A.: Cambridge University Press.

Braithwaite, R.W. (1990). The implications of Australia's unique biota for ecological processes. *Journal of Biogeography 17*, 347-354.

Braithwaite, R.W., Friend, G.R. & Wombey, J.C. (1990). Reptiles and amphibians. In Ridpath, M.G., Haynes, C., Williams, M.A.J. (Eds.). *Monsoonal Australia: Landscape, Ecology and Man* (pp. 109-124). Rotterdam, Netherlands: AA Balkema.

Brereton R., Bennett S. & Mansergh I. (1995). Enhanced greenhouse climate change and its potential effect on selected fauna of south-eastern Australia: A trend analysis. *Biol. Conserv. 72*, 339–54.

Bulger, A.J., Hayden, B.P., Monaco, M.E., Nelson, D.M. & McCormack-Ray, M.G. (1993). Biologically-based estuarine salinity zones derived from a multivariate analysis. *Estuaries 16* (2), 311-322.

Burbidge, S. & Wallace, D. (1995). Practical methods for conserving biodiversity. In Bradstock (Ed.). *Conserving Biodiversity: Threats and Solutions* (p. 24). Surrey, Australia: Beatty & Sons.

Burke, V.J. (2000). Landscape ecology and species conservation. *Landscape Ecology 15*, 1–3.

Bureau of Meteorology (2004). Australian Annual Mean Temperature Anomalies. Assessed 19 July 2004 at http://www.bom.gov.au/climate/change/amtemp.shtml

Caddy, J.F. (1999). Fisheries management in the twenty-first century: will new paradigms apply? Reviews in *Fish Biology and Fisheries 9*, 1–43.

Campbell, B.D., Stafford Smith, D.M. & McKeon, G.M. (1997). Elevated CO_2 and water supply interactions in grasslands: A pastures and rangelands management perspective. *Global Change Biol., 3*, 177–87.

Carpenter, G.A., Gopal, S., Macomber, S., Martens, S., Woodcock, C.E. & Franklin, J. (1999). A neural network method for efficient vegetation mapping. *Remote Sens. Environ., 70*, 326–38.

Chapman A.D. & Milne D.J. (1998). *The Impact of Global Warming on the Distribution of Selected Australian Plant and Animal Species in Relation to Soils and Vegetation.* Canberra, Australia: Environmental Resources Information Network Unit, Environment Australia.

Christopher, H. & Cheng, D. (2003). Ecological assessment and strategies for the management of mangroves in Brisbane Water - Gosford, New South Wales, Australia. *Landscape and Urban Planning, 62*, 219–240.

Christy, J.R. (2000). Global Climate Change: Scientific and Social Impacts. A Personal View. *Bridges, 7*, 39-57.

Church, J.A., Gregory J.M., Huybrechts P., Kuhn M., Lambeck C., Nhuan M.T., Qin D. & Woodworth P.L.(2001). Changes in sea level. In Houghton, J.T., Ding, Y., Griggs, D.J.,

Noguer, M., Van der Linden, P.J., Dai, X., Maskell, K., & Johnson, C.A. (Eds.). *Climate Change 2001: The Scientific Basis: Contribution of Working Group I to the Third Assessment Report of the Intergovernmental Panel on Climate Change* (pp. 639-694). Cambridge, New York, USA: Cambridge University Press.

Claridge, D. & Burnett, J. (1993). Mangroves in Focus. *Wet Paper, 14,* 3.

Cochrane, K.L. (2000). Reconciling sustainability, economic efficiency and equity in fisheries: the one that got away? *Fish and Fisheries 1*, 3–21.

Commonwealth of Australia (2000). *Report of the National Taskforce on the Prevention and Management of Marine Pest Incursions*. For the Joint SCC/SCFA National Taskforce on the Prevention and Management of Marine Pest Incursions, Environment Australia/Agriculture, Fisheries and Forestry - Australia, 23 December 1999 (Revised edition October 2000).

Conservation International (1999). Megadiversity countries. Assessed 17 June at http://www.conservation.org/webfieldact/megadiv/megadic.htm

Crowley, T.J. (2000). Causes of climate change over the past 1000 years. *Science*, *289*, 270 - 277.

CSIRO (1992). *Climate Change Scenarios for the Australian Region.* Aspendale, Victoria, Australia: CSIRO Climate Impact Group.

CSIRO (2000). Atmospheric Research Greenhouse Information Paper. Assessed 15 June 2004 at http://www.dar.csiro.au/publications/greenhouse_2000f.htm

Cubasch, U., Danter, B.D., Hellbach, A., Hock, H., Maier-Reimer, R., Mickolajewicz, U., Stossel, A., & Voss R. (1994). Monte Carlo climate change forecast with a global coupled ocean-atmosphere model. *Clim. Dyn., 10*, 1-19.

Davis, S.D., Heywood, V.H., & Hamilton, A.C. (1995). *Centres of Plant Diversity: A Guide and Strategy for Their Conservation. Volume 2: Asia, Australasia and the Pacific.* Cambridge: IUCN.

Davis, F.W. (1995). Information systems for conservation research, policy and planning. *BioScience Supplement,* 36–42.

Department of Environment and Planning (1983). *Brisbane Water Estuarine Wetlands Study.* Sydney, Australia: Department of Environment and Planning.

Department of the Environment and Heritage (2004). *Australia's Biodiversity. An Overview of Selected Significant Components.* Biodiversity Series Paper No 2., Canberra, Australia: Commonwealth of Australia.

Duke N.C., Ball M.C. & Ellison J.C. (1998). Factors influencing biodiversity and distributional gradients in mangroves. *Global Ecology and Biogeography Letters* 7: 27–47.

Endler, J.A. (1982). Pleistocene forest refuges: fact or fancy? In Prance, G.T. (Ed.). *Biological Diversification in the tropics* (pp. 641-657). New York, USA: Columbia University Press.

Faith, D.P., Carter, G., Cassis, G., Ferrier, S. & Wilkie, L. (2003). Complementarity, biodiversity viability analysis, and policy-based algorithms for conservation. *Environmental Science & Policy 6*, 311–328.

Faith, D.P., Walker, P.A., Ive, J., Belbin, L. (1996). Integrating conservation and forestry production exploring trade-offs between biodiversity and production in regional land-use assessment. *For. Ecol. Manage. 85*, 251–260.

Ferrier, S. (2002). Mapping spatial pattern in biodiversity for regional conservation planning: where to from here? *Systematic Biology 51*, 331–363.

Floyd, A.G. (1987). The status of rainforests in northern New South Wales. In *The Rainforest Legacy, Australian National Rainforest Study* (vol. 1). Canberra, Australia: Australian Heritage Commission, AGPS.

Frith, D.W., Frith, C.B. (1995). *Cape York Peninsula: a natural history*. Chatswood, N.S.W., Australia: Reed Books.

Galloway, R.W. (1982). *Distribution and Physiographic Patterns of Australian Mangroves*. Canberra, Australia: Australian National University Press.

Garcia, S.M. & Grainger, R. (1996). Fisheries management and sustainability: a new perspective of an old problem? In Hancock, D.A., Smith, D.C., Grant, A., Beumers, J.P. (Eds.). *Developing and sustaining world fisheries resources. The state of science and management* (p. 631-654). Proceedings of the Second World Fishing Congress. Australia: CSIRO.

Gill, A.M. (1981). Adaptive responses of Australian vascular plant species to fire. In Gill, A.M., Groves, R.H. & Noble, I.R. (Eds.). *Fire and the Australian Biota*. Canberra, Australia: Aust. Acad. Sci.

Glanznig, A. (1995). *Native Vegetation Clearance, Habitat Loss and Biodiversity Decline* (Biodiversity Series Paper No. 6). Canberra, Australia: Department of Environment, Sport and Territories, Biodiversity Unit.

Goldammer, J.G. & Price, C. (1998). Potential Impacts of climate change on fire regimes in the tropics based on MAGICC and a GISS GCM-derived lightning model. In Markham, A. (Ed.). Potential Impacts of Climate Change on Tropical Forest Ecosystems. *Climate Change*, 39, Nos. 2-3, 274-296.

Graetz R.D., Walker B.H. & Walker P.A. (1988) The consequences of climate change for seventy percent of Australia. In Pearman, G. (Ed.). *Greenhouse: Planning for Climate Change* (pp. 399–420). Melbourne, Australia: CSIRO.

Graham, N.E. (1995). Simulation of recent global temperature. *Science, 267*, 666-671.

Gray, J.S. (2000). The measurement of marine species diversity, with an application to the benthic fauna of the Norwegian continental shelf. *Journal of Experimental Marine Biology and Ecology, 250*, 23-49.

Griffin, G.F. & Friedel, M.H. (1985). Discontinuous change in central Australia: Some implications of major ecological events for land management. *J. Arid Environ., 9*, 63–80.

Grindrod, J., Moss, P. & van der Kaars, S. (1999). Late Quaternary cycles of mangrove development and decline on the north Australian continental shelf. *Journal of Quaternary Science, 14*, 465–470.

Groombridge, B. & Jenkins, M. (1994). *Biodiversity data sourcebook* (WCMC Biodiversity Series 1). Cambridge, UK: World Conservation Press.

Groombridge, B. (Ed.) (1992). *Global Diversity - Status of the Earth's Living Resources. Compiled by the World Conservation Monitoring Centre*. London, U.K.: Chapman & Hall.

Gower, J.C. (1971). A General Coefficient of Similarity and Some of Its Properties. *Biometrics 27*, 857-872.

Hall, W.B., McKeon, G.M., Carter, J.O. *et al.* (1998). Climate change in Queensland's grazing lands. II. An assessment of the impact on animal production from native pastures. *Rangel. J., 20*, 177–205.

Hansen, J., Sato, M., Ruedy, R., Lacis, A., & Oinas, V. (2000). Global warming in the twenty-first century: An alternative scenario. *Proceedings of the National Academy of Sciences, 97*, 9875-9880.

Harty, C. & Cheng, D. (2003). Ecological assessment and strategies for the management of mangroves in Brisbane - Gosford, New South Wales. *Australia Water Landscape and Urban Planning 62*, 219–240.

Hassall & Associates (1998). *Climate Change and Managing the Scarce Water Resources of the Macquarie River*. Canberra, Australia: Australian Greenhouse Office.

Hengeveld, H. (1997). 1994-95 In Review: An Assessment of New Developments Relevant to the Science of Climate Change. CO2/Climate Report 97-1, Environment Canada, and Climate Change Newsletter Vol. 9 (1-2), 1-43, Bureau of Resource Sciences, Australia.

Henry, B.K., Danaher, T., McKeon, G.M. & Burrows, W.H. (2002) A review of the potential role of greenhouse gas abatement in native vegetation management in Queensland's rangelands. *Rangel. J., 24*, 112–32.

Herron, N., Davis, R. & Jones, R. (2002). The effects of large-scale afforestation and climate change on water allocation in the Macquarie River catchment, NSW, Australia. *J. Environ. Manage. 65*, 369–81.

Heywood, V.H. (Ed.) (1995). *Global Biodiversity Assessment*. Melbourne, Australia: Cambridge University Press.

Hilbert, D.W., Ostendorf, B., Hopkins, M. (2002). Sensitivity of tropical forests to climate change in the humid tropics of north Queensland. *Australian Ecology 26*, 590–603.

Hilborn, R. (1997). Uncertainty, risk and the precautionary principle. In Pikitch, E.K., Huppert, D.D. & Sissenwine, M.P. (Eds.). *Global trends: fisheries management* (pp. 100-106). American Fisheries Society Symposium, vol. 20, Bethseda, MD.

Hill, J.K., Collingham, Y.C., Thomas, C.D., Blakeley, D.S., Fox, R., Moss, D. & Huntley, B. (2001). Impacts of landscape structure on butterfly range expansion. *Ecological Letters 4*, 313-321.

Hill, J.K., Thomas C.D. & Huntley B. (1999). Climate and habitat availability determine 20th century changes in a butterfly's range margin. *Proceedings of the Royal Society of London B, 266*, 1197-1206.

Hill, K.D. & Johnson, L.A.S. (1995). Systematic studies in the eucalypts. 7. A revision of the bloodwoods, genus Corymbia (Myrtaceae). *Telopea, 6*,185.

Hilton-Taylor, C. (compiler) (2000). *2000 IUCN Red List of Threatened Species*. Gland, Switzerland and Cambridge, U.K.: IUCN.

Hogarth, P. J. (1999). *The Biology of Mangroves*. Oxford, U.K.: Oxford Univ. Press.

Hope, G.H., Kershaw, A.P., van der Kaars, S., Xiangjunc S., Liewd, P.-M., Heussere, L.E., Takaharaf, H., McGloneg, M., Miyoshih, N. & Moss, P.T. (2004). History of vegetation and habitat change in the Austral-Asian region. *Quaternary International 118–119*, 103–126.

Hopkins, M.S., Ash, J., Graham, A.W., Head, J. & Hewett, R.K. (1993). Charcoal evidence of the spatial extent of the Eucalyptus woodland expansions and rainforest contractions in north Queensland during late Pleistocene. *Journal of Biogeography, 20*, 357-372.

Houghton, J.T., Meira Filho, L.G., Callander, B.A., Harris, N., Kattenberg, A., Maskell, K. (1995). Climate Change 1995: The Science of Climate Change. Cambridge, U.S.A.: Cambridge University Press.

Houlder D., Hutchinson M., Nix H. & McMahon J. (1999). ANUCLIM Version 5.0 User Guide. Canberra, Australia: Centre for Resource and Environmental Studies, Australian National University.

House, S. & Moritz, C. (1991). The impact of rainforest fragmentation on flora and fauna. In N. Goudberg, M. Bonell & D. Benzarken. (Eds.). *Tropical Rainforest Research in Australia: Present Status and Future Directions for the Institute for Tropical Rainforest Studies* (pp. 115-125). Townsville, Australia: Institute for Tropical Rainforest Studies.

Howarth, R. (2002). Changes in mangrove/salt-marsh distribution in the Georges River estuary, southern sydney, 1930 - 1970. *Wetlands (Australia) 20*(2), 80-103.

Hubbell, S.P. & Foster, R.B. (1983). Diversity of canopy trees in a neotropical forest and implications for conservation. In Whitmore, S.L., Chadwick, T.C., Sutton, A.C. (Eds.), *Tropical Rain Forest: Ecology and Management* (pp. 25-41). Blackwell Scientific Publications.

Hughes, L. (2003). Climate change and Australia: Trends, projections and impacts. *Austral. Ecology 28*, 423–443.

Hughes, L. (2001). Climate Change and Biodiversity in Australia. Macquarie University Assessed 28 June 2004 at
http://www.nccnsw.org.au/member/cbn/projects/EducationCentre/Edu_CCBA.htm

Hughes, L. (2000). Biological consequences of global warming: is the signal already apparent? *Trends Ecol. Evol., 15*, 56-61.

Hughes, L., Westoby, M. & Cawsey, M. (1996). Climatic range sizes of Eucalyptus species in relation to future climate change. *Global Ecology and Biogeography Letters* 5, 23 – 29.

Hulme M. & Viner D. (1998). A climate change scenario for the tropics. *Climatic Change 39*, 145-176.

Hutchings, P. & Saenger, P. (1987). *Ecology of Mangroves*. (pp. 388). St. Lucia, Qld., Australia: University of Queensland Press.

IPCC (Intergovernmental Panel on Climate Change) (2001a). Climate Change 2001: The Scientific Basis WGI Third Assessment Report of the Intergovernmental Panel on Climate Change. Cambridge, U.S.A.: Cambridge University Press.

IPCC (Intergovernmental Panel on Climate Change) (2001b). Special Report on Emissions Scenarios (SRES). Special Report of the Intergovernmental Panel on Climate Change. Nakicenovic, N.& Swart, R. (Eds.). Cambridge, U.S.A.: Cambridge University Press.

IPCC (1996). *Climate Change 1995: The Science of Climate Change. Contribution of Working Group I to the Second Assessment Report of the Intergovernmental Panel on Climate Change* (pp. 572). Houghton, J.T., L.G. Meira Filho, B.A. Callander, N. Harris, A. Kattenberg, & K. Maskell (Eds.). Cambridge, U.S.A. and U.K.: Cambridge University Press.

Ishern, A.R., McKenzie, J.A & Feary, D.A. (1996). The role of sea surface-temperature as a control on carbonate platform development in the western coral sea. *Paleogeography, Paleoclimatology, Paleoecology, 124*, 247-272.

IUCN (1994). *Guidelines for protected area management categories*. Gland, Switzerland: IUCN Commission on National Parks and Protected Areas, with the assistance of the World Conservation Monitoring Centre.

Iverson, L.R., Prasad, A. & Schwartz, M.W. (1999). Modelling potential future individual tree species distributions in the eastern United States under a climate change scenario: a case study with *Pinus irginiana. Ecol. Mod., 115*, 77-93.

Jacobson, M.Z. (2001). Strong radiative heating due to the mixing state of black carbon in atmospheric aerosols. *Nature 409*, 695-7.

Jeffrey, S.J., Carter, J.O., Beswick, A.R. & Modie, K.M. (2001). Using spatial interpolation to construct a comprehensive archive of Australian climate data. *Environmental Modelling and Software, 16*, 309-330.

Johnson, B. (1998) Consequences for the Macquarie Marshes. In Hassall and Associates (Eds.). *Climate Change Scenarios and Managing the Scarce Water Resources of the Macquarie River* (pp. 61–68). Canberra, Australia: Australian Greenhouse Office.

Johnson, W.C., Sharpe, D.M., De Angelis, D.L., Fields, D.E. & Olson, R.J. (1981). Model seed dispersal and forest island dynamics. In Burgess, R.L., Sharpe, D.M. (Eds.). *Forest Island Dynamics in Man-Dominated Landscapes* (pp. 215-240. New York, U.S.A.: Springer Verlag.

Jones, R.N. & Trewin, B. (2000). The spatial structure of monthly temperature anomalies over Australia. *Aust. Met. Mag., 49*, 261-276.

Kaustuv, R., Jablonski, D. & Valentine, J.W. (2001). Climate change, species range limits and body size in marine bivalves. *Ecology Letters, 4*, 366-370.

Kershaw, A.P., Moss, P.T. & van der Kaars, S. (2003). Causes and consequences of long-term climatic variability on the Australian continent. *Freshwater Biology, 48*, 1274–1283.

Kershaw, A.P. & Nix, H.A. (1988). Quantitative paleoclimate estimates pollen data using bioclimatic profiles of extant taxa. *Journal of Biogeography, 15*, 589-602.

Kershaw, A.P. (1986). Climate change and Aboriginal burning through the last two glacial-interglacial cycles from northeastern Queensland. *Nature 322*, 47–49.

Kothavala Z. (1999). The duration and severity of drought over eastern Australia simulated by a coupled ocean-atmosphere GCM with a transient increase in CO_2. *Environ. Modelling Software 14*, 243–52.

Kriticos, D.J., Randal, R.P. (2001). A comparison of systems to analyse potential weed distributions. In Groves, R.H., Panetta, F.D. & Virtue, J.G. (Eds). *Weed Risk Assessment* (pp. 61-79). Collingwood, Australia: CSIRO Publishing.

Lavery, B., Joung, G. & Nicholls, N. (1997). An extended high quality historical rainfall data set for Australia. *Australian Meteorological Magazine, 46*, 27-38.

Leemans, R. & Eickout, B. (2003). Analysing Changes in Ecosystems for Different Levels of Climate Change. OECD, Paris (ENV/EPOC/ GSP(2003)5/FINAL).

Leigh, J.H. & Briggs, J.D. (1992). *Threatened Australian Plants: Overview and Case Studies.* Canberra, Australia: ANPWS.

Levy, P.E., Cannell, M.G.R., Friend, A.D. (2004). Modelling the impact of future changes in climate, CO_2 concentration and land use on natural ecosystems and the terrestrial carbon sink. *Global Environmental Change 14*, 21–30.

Ley, J.A., Halliday, I.A., Tobin, A.J., Garrett, R.N. & Gribble, N.A. (2002). Ecosystem effects of fishing closures in mangrove estuaries of tropical Australia. *MEPS 245*, 223-238.

Lindgren, E. (1998). Climate change, tick-borne encephalitis and vaccination needs in Sweden - a prediction model. *Ecol. Mod., 110*, 55–63.

Lindzen, R.S., Chou, M.D. & Hou, A.Y. (2001). Does the Earth Have an Adaptive Infrared Iris? *Bull. Am. Meteorological Soc., 82* (3), 417-432.

Lindzen, R.S. (1994). On the Scientific Basis for Global Warming Scenarios. *Environmental Pollution 83*, 125–34.

Loehle, C., & LeBlanc, D. (1996). Model-based assessments of climate change effects on forests: a critical review. *Ecol. Mod., 90*, 1–31.

Ludwig, D.E., Hilborn, R. & Walters, C. (1993). Uncertainty, resource exploitation and conservation lessons from history. *Science 260*,17–36.

Markham, A. (ed.) (1998). Potential Impacts of Climate Change on Tropical Forest Ecosystems. *Climate Change, 39*, 2-3.

Martin, H.A. (1978). Evolution of the Australian flora and vegetation through the Tertiary: evedince from pollen. *Alcheringa, 2*, 181-202.

McCarty, J.P. (2001). Ecological consequences of recent climate change. *Conserv. Biol., 15*(2), 320-331.

McInnes, K.L., Walsh, K.J.E., Hubbert, G.D. & T. Beer, T. (2003). Impact of sea-level rise and storm surges on a coastal community. *Natural Hazards, 30*, 187-207.

McLean, R.F., & Tsyban, A. (2001). Coastal zones and marine ecosystems. In McCarthy, J.J., Canziani, O.F., Leary, N.A., Dokken, D.J., & White, K.S. (Eds.). *Climate Change 2001: Impacts, Adaptation, and Vulnerability* (Chapter 6, pp. 343-379). Cambridge, U.K.: Cambridge University Press.

Medina, E. & Huber, O. (1992). The role of biodiversity in the functioning of savanna ecosystems. In Solbrig, O.T., van Emden, H.M. & van Oordt, P.G.W.J. (Eds). *Biodiversity and Global Change* (Monograph. No. 8, pp.139 158). Paris, France: International Union of Biological Sciences.

Meynecke, J.-O. (2004). Effects of global climate change on geographic distributions of vertebrates in North Queensland. *Ecol. Mod., 174*, 347–35.

Morton, S., Bourne, G., Cristofani, P., Cullen, P., Possingham, H. & Young, M. (2002). *Sustaining our Natural Resources and Biodiversity*, an independent report to the Prime Minister's Science, Engineering and Innovation Council. Canberra, Australia: CSIRO and Environment Australia.

Morton, R.M. (1990). Community structure, density and standing crop of fishes in a subtropical Australian mangrove area. *Mar. Biol., 103*, 385–394.

Moss, P.T. & Kershaw, A.P. (2000). The last glacial cycle from the humid tropics of northeastern Australia: comparison of a terrestrial and a marine record. *Palaeogeography Palaeoclimatology Palaeoecology, 155*, 155–176.

Moss, R.H. & Schneider, S.H. (1999). Towards consistent assessment and reporting of uncertainties in the IPCC TAR: Initial recommendations for discussion by authors. Draft Version 2, Intergovernmental Panel on Climate Change.

Murcia, C. (1995). Edge effects in fragmented forests: implications for conservation. *Tree, 10* (2). 58-62. J.

Myers, N., Mittermeier, R.A., Mittermeier, C.G., da Fonseca, G.A.B. & Kent, J. (2000). Biodiversity hotspots for conservation priorities. *Nature, 403*, 853-858.

National Task Group on the Management of Climate Change Impacts on Biodiversity (2003). *National Biodiversity and Climate Change Action Plan*. Consultation Paper. Canberra, Australia: NRM Ministerial Council's Land, Water and Biodiversity Committee, Department of the Environment and Heritage.

Nix, H.A. & Switzer, M.A. (Eds.) (1991). *Rainforest animals: atlas of vertebrates endemic to Australia's wet tropics*. Canberra, Australia: A.N.P.W.S.

Nix, H.A. (1986). A Biogeographic analysis of Australian Elapid snakes. In Longmore, R. (Eds.), *Australian flora and fauna series No.7*. Canberra, Australia: Bureau of Flora and Fauna.

OECD (2001a). OECD Environmental Strategy for the First Decade of the 21st Century. OECD, Paris, France. Available at http://www.oecd.org/env.

OECD (2001b). OECD Environmental Outlook. Paris, France: OECD.

Orchard, A.E. (Ed.) (1999). *Flora of Australia Vol. 1 Ed. 2*. Melbourne, Australia: CSIRO.

Palmer, T. N. (1993). Extended-range atmospheric prediction and the Lorenz model. *Bull. Amer. Meteo. Soc.*, *74*(1), 49.

Parmesan, C. & Yohe, G. (2003). A globally coherent fingerprint of climate change impacts across natural systems. *Nature 421*, 37–41.

Parmesan, C., Ryrholm, N. Stefanescu, C. Hill, J.K. Thomas, C.D. Descimon, H. Huntley, B., Kaila, L., Kullberg, J., Tammaru, T., Tennent, W.J., Thomas, J.A. & Warren, M. (1999). Poleward shifts in geographical ranges of butterfly species associated with regional warming. *Nature 399*, 579-583.

Parmesan, C. (1996). Evolution & ecology: climate and species' range. *Nature*, *382*, 765–766.

Peters, R.L. & Darling, J.D.S (1985). The greenhouse effect and nature reserves. *Bioscience*, *35*, 707-717.

Pickup, G. (1998). Desertification and climate change: The Australian perspective. *Climate Res.*, *11*, 51–63.

Plummer, N., Lin, Z. & Torok, S. (1995). Trends in the diurnal temperature range over Australia since 1951. *Atmospheric Research*, 37, 79-86.

Post, E., Stenseth, N.C., Langvatn, R. & Fromentin, J.-M. (1997). Global climate change and phenotypic variation among red deer cohorts. *Proc. R. Soc. Lond. B 264*, 1317-1324.

Pouliquen-Young, O. & Newman, P. (2000). *The Implications of Climate Change for Land-Based Nature Conservation Strategies*. Final Report 96/1306. Perth and Canberra, Australia: Institute for Sustainability and Technology Policy, Murdoch University and Australian Greenhouse Office, Environment Australia.

Pounds, J.A., Fogden, M.P.L., Savage, J.M. & Gorman, G.C. (1997). Tests of null models for amphibian declines on a tropical mountain. *Conserv. Biol.*, *11*, 1307–1322.

Green, R.E., Harley, M., Miles, L., Scharlemann, J., Watkinson, A. & Watts, O. (2003). Global Climate Change and Biodiversity. Norwich, U.K.: University of East Anglia.

Rainforest CRC (2002). *Wet Tropics Region Natural Resource Management Plan:Statement of Planning Intent*. Cairns, Australia: Rainforest CRC.

Root, T.L., Price, J.T., Hall, K.R., Schneider, S., Rosenzweig, C. & Pounds, A. (2003). Fingerprints of global warming on wild animals and plants. *Nature 421*, 57–60.

Rosenberg, A.A., Fogarty, M.J., Sissenwine, M.P., Beddington, J.R., Shepherd, J.G. (1993) Achieving sustainable use of renewable resources. *Science 262*, 828–829.

Rosenzweig, M.L. (1995). *Species Diversity in Space and Time*. New York, U.S.A.: Cambridge University Press.

Saintilan, N. & Williams, R.J. (1999). Mangrove transgression into saltmarsh environments. *Global Ecology and Biogeography* 8: 117-124.

Schlesinger, M.E. & Mitchell, J.F.B. (1987). Climate model simulations of the equilibrium climatic response to increased carbon dioxide. *Reviews of Geophysics*, *25*(4), 760-798.

Schreider S.Y., Jakeman A.J., Whetton P.H. & Pittock A.B. (1997). Estimation of climate impact on water availability and extreme events for snow-free and snow-affected catchments of the Murray–Darling Basin. *Aust. J. Water Res., 2*, 35–45.

Secretariat of the Convention on Biological Diversity (SCBD) (2003). *Interlinkages between biological diversity and climate change. Advice on the integration of biodiversity considerations into the implementation of the United Nations Framework Convention on Climate Change and its Kyoto protocol* (p. 154). Montreal, Canada: SCBD Technical Series no. 10.

Semeniuk, V. (1994). Predicting the effect of sea-level rise on mangroves in northwestern Australia. *Journal of Coastal Research, 10*, 1050-1076.

Singh, G. & Geissler, E.A. (1985). Late Cainozoic vegetation history of vegetation, fire, lake levels and climate, at Lake George, New South Wales, Australia. *Philosophical Transactions of the Royal Society of London Series B, 311*, 379–447.

Spalding, M., Blasco, F., & Field, C. (Eds.) (1997). *World Mangrove Atlas. International Society for Mangrove Ecosystems*. Otley, U.K.: Smith Settle.

Sparks, T., Heyen, H., Braslavska, O. & Lehikoinen, E. (1999). Are European birds migrating earlier? *BTO News 223*, 8-9.

Specht, R.L. & Specht, A. (1999). *Australian Plant Communities. Dynamics of Structure, Growth and Biodiversity*. Oxford, U.K.: Oxford University Press.

Stafford, S.D.M., Campbell, B.D., Steffen, W. & Archer, S. (1994). *State-of-the-science Assessment of the Likely Impacts of Global Change on the Australian Rangelands*. Global Change and Terrestrial Ecosystems Working Document 14. Canberra, Australia: CSIRO Division of Wildlife and Ecology and GCTE Core Project Office.

Stafford, S. D. M. & Pickup G. (1990). Patterns and production in arid lands. *Proc. Ecol. Soc. Aust., 16*, 195–200.

Still, C.J., Foster, P.N. & Schneider, S.H. (1999). Simulating the effects of climate change on tropical mountain cloud forests. *Nature, 398*, 608-610.

Stockwell, R.B. (1995). *Evaluation and Training in the Use and Interpretation of GARP Genetic Algorithms for Prediction of Species and Species Assemblages*. Consultancy report. Hobart, Australia: Environmental Resources Information Network by the Tasmanian Parks and Wildlife Service, GIS Section.

Available at http://biodi.sdsc.edu/Symbiotik/Doc/Validate/validate.html

Suppiah, R., Hennessy, K., Hirst, T., Jones, R., Katzfey, J., Pittock, B., Walsh, K., Whetton, P. & Wilson, S. (1998). *Climate change under enhanced greenhouse conditions in northern Australia. Third Annual Report, 1996-1997*. Canberra, Australia: CSIRO Division of Atmospheric Research.

Sutherst R.W., Maywald G. F., Stevens P. M. & Yonow T. (1998). *CLIMEX for Windows Version 1.1. User's Guide*, Brisbane, Asutralia: CRC for Tropical Pest Management.

Swart, R., Mitchell, J., Morita, T. & Raper, S. (2002). Stabilisation scenarios for climate impact assessment. *Global Environmental Change, 12*(3), 155-165.

Swart, R., Berk, M., Janssen, M., Kreileman, E., & Leemans, R. (1998). The Safe Landing Approach: Risks and Trade-offs in Climate Change'. In Alcamo, J., Leemans, R., & Kreileman, E. (Eds.). *Global Change Scenarios of the 21st Century – Results from the IMAGE 2.1. Model* (pp. 193–218). Oxford, U.K.: Pergamon.

Thomas, A., Telfer, M.G., Roy, D.B., Preston, C.D., Greenwood, J.J.D., Asher J., Fox R., Clarke R.T., & Lawton, J.H. (2004b). Comparative Losses of British Butterflies, Birds, and Plants and the Global Extinction Crisis. *Science 303*, 1879-1881.

Thomas, C.D. Cameron, A,. Green, R.E, Bakkenes, M., Beaumont, L.J., Collingham, Y.C., Erasmus, B.F.N., de Siqueira, M.F., Grainger, A., Hannah, L., Hughes, L., Huntley, B., van Jaarsveld, A.S., Midgley, G.F., Miles, L., Ortega-Huerta, M.A., Townsend Peterson A., Phillips, O.L.& Williams, S.E. (2004a). Extinction risk from climate change. *Nature, 427* (8), 145-148.

Tomlinson, P.B. (1986). *The Botany of Mangroves.* Cambridge, New York, U.S.A.: Cambridge University Press.

Torok, S.J. & Nicholls, N. (1996). An historical annual temperature data set for Australia. *Australian Meteorological Magazine*, *45*, 251-260.

Tracey, J.G. (1975).Vegetation of the Humide Tropical Region of North Queensland. Fifteen Maps at a Scale of 1:100000 plus Key and Notes. Indooroopilly, Queensland, Australia: CSIRO.

Trott, L. & Goosem, S.P. (1996). *Wet tropics in profile: a reference guide to the wet tropics of Queensland World Heritage Area.* Wet tropics Management Authority, Cairns, Australia.

Underwood, A.J. & Chapman, M.G. (Eds.) (1995). *Coastal Marine Ecology of Temperate Australia.* Sydney, Australia: UNSW Press.

UNFCCC (1992). United Nations framework convention on climate change. *International Legal Materials 31*, 849.

University of Maryland (UMd) & Global Land Cover Facility (GLCF) (2002). *MODIS 500m Vegetation Continuous Fields Percent Tree Cover.* Assessed 13 July 2004 at http://glcf.umiacs.umd.edu/data/.

Visser, M.E., van Noodwijk, A.J., Tinbergen, J.M. & Lessells, C.M. (1998). Warmer springs lead to mistimed reproduction in great tits *(Parus majo*r). *Proc. R. Soc. Lond.* B *265*, 1867–1870.

Walker, P.A, Cocks K.D. (1991). Habitat: a procedure for modelling a disjoint environmental envelope for a plant or animal species. *Global Ecology and Biogeography Letters*, *1*, 108-118.

Walsh, K., Hennessy, K., Jones, R., Pittcock, A.B., Rotstayn, L., Suppiah, R. & Whetton, P. (2000). *Climate Change in Queensland under enhanced greenhouse conditions: Second Annual Report, 1999-2000* (129 pp.). Canberra, Australia: CSIRO Atmospheric Research.

Walters, C. & Maguire, J.J. (1996). Lessons for stock assessment from the northern cod collapse. Reviews in *Fish Biology and Fisheries 6*, 125–37.

Walther, G.-R., Burga, C. A. & Edwards, P. J. (Eds.) (2001). *"Fingerprints" of Climate Change -Adapted Behaviour and Shifting Species Ranges.* New York, U.S.A.: Kluwer Academic/Plenum.

WCMC (1992). *Global Biodiversity: Status of the Earth's Living Resources.* London, U.K.: Chapman & Hall London.

Webb, L. & Tracey, J.G. (1981). Australian rainforest patterns and change. In Keast, A. (Ed.). *Ecology biogeography of Australia* (pp. 607-694). The Hague, Netherlands: W. Junk.

Werren, G. (2002). In talk 7.02.02.

Weston, N. & Goosem, S. (2004). *Sustaining the Wet Tropics: A Regional Plan for Natural Resource Management, Volume 2A Condition Report: Biodiversity Conservation* (pp. 211). Cairns, Australia: Rainforest CRC and FNQ NRM Ltd,.

White, M.E. (1994). *The greening of Gondwana.* Chatswood, N.S.W., Australia: Reed Books.

Whittaker, R.H. (1965). Dominance and diversity in land plant communities. *Science 147*, 250–260.

Whittaker, R.H. (1960). Vegetation of the Siskiyou mountains, Oregon and California. *Ecological Monographs 30*, 279-338.

Wilkinson, C.R. (Ed.) (2000). *Status of Coral Reefs of the World: 2000.* Townsville, Australia: Global Coral Reef Monitoring Network, Australian Institute of Marine Science.

Williams, A.A.J., Karoly, D.J. & Tapper, N. (2001). The sensitivity of Australian fire danger to climate change. *Climatic Change 49*, 171-91.

Williams, J., Read C, Norton T., Dovers S., Burgman M., Proctor, W. & Anderson, H. (2001). *Australia State of the Environment Report 2001 (Theme Report).* Department of the Environment and Heritage, Canberra, Australia: CSIRO Publishing.

Williams, S.E., Bolitho, E.E. & Fox, S. (2003). Climate change in Australian tropical rainforests: an impending environmental catastrophe. *Proc. R. Soc. Lond. B 270*, 1887–1892.

Williams, S.E. (1998). Spatial patterns of vertebrate biodiversity and assemblage structure in the rainforests of the Australian wet tropics. *Australian Journal of Ecology 23*. 185-186. (Phd thesis abstract).

Williams, S.E. & Marsh, H. (1998). Changes in small mammal assemblage structure across a rainforest/open forest ecotone. *Journal of Tropical Ecology 14*, 187-198.

Williams, S.E. (1997). Patterns of mammalian species richness in the Australian tropical rainforests: are extinctions during historical contractions of the rainforest the primary determinant of current patterns in biodiversity? *Wildlife Research 24*, 513-530.

Winter, J.W. (1991). Northeastern Queensland: some conservation issues highlighted by forest mammals. In D. Lunney. (Ed.). *Conservation of Australia's Forest Fauna* (pp. 113-118). Sydney, Australia: Royal Zoological Society of New South Wales.

Winter, J.W. & Atherton, R.G. (1991). Distributions of selected north-eastern Australian rainforest mammals. In Werren, G. & Kershaw, P. (Eds.). *The Rainforest Legacy, Vol.2.* Canberra, Australia: Australian Government Publishing Service.

Winter, J.W. (1997). Responses of non-volant mammals to late quaternary climatic changes in the Wet Tropics region of north-eastern Australia. *Wildlife Res., 24*, 493–511.

Winter, J.W. (1988). Ecological specialization of mammals in Australian tropical and sub tropical rainforest: refugial or ecological determinism. *Proc. Ecol. Soc. Aust. 15*, 127-138.

Winter, J.W., Bell, F.C., Pahl, L.I. & Atherton, R.G. (1984). The specific habitats of selected northeastern Australian rainforest mammals. Report to World Wild Life Fund, Sydney (unpublished).

Witting, L. & Loeschke, V. (1995). The optimization of biodiversity conservation. *Biological Conservation 16*, 205-207.

Woodroffe, C.D., Chappell, J.M.A., Thom, B.G. & Wallensky, E. (1986). *Geomorphological Dynamics and Evolution of the South Alligator Tidal River and Plains, Northern Territory.* Darwin, Australia: North Australia Research Unit.

WRI (World Resources Institute), IUCN (The World Conservation Union), UNEP (United Nations Environment Programme), FAO (Food and Agriculture Organization) & UNESCO (the United Nations Education, Scientific and Cultural Organization) (1992). *Global Biodiversity Strategy: Guidelines for action to save, study and use Earth's biotic wealth sustainably and equitably*. Washington, DC, U.S.A.: World Resource Institute.

WRI (World Resources Institute) (1995). *Coastlines at risk: an index of potential development-related threats to coastal ecosystems*. World Resources Institute Indicator Brief. Washington, DC, U.S.A.: World Resource Institute.

Wunder, S. (2000). Ecotourism and economic incentives — an empirical approach. *Ecological Economics 32*, 465–479.

WWF Manual (2004). Assessed at 24 June 2004 at www.panda.org/climate/pa_manual

Young, P.A.R. & McDonald, W.J.F (1987). The distribution, composition and status of rainforests in southern Queensland. In *The Rainforest Legacy, Australian National Rainforest Study* (vol. 1). Canberra, Australia: Australian Heritage Commission, AGPS.

In: Trends in Biodiversity Research
Editor: A. R. Burk, pp. 81-101
ISBN 1-59454-385-2

Chapter 3

CONTAMINATED ZONE AROUND A NICKEL-COPPER SMELTER: A DEATH TRAP FOR BIRDS AND MAMMALS?

Mikhail V. Kozlov[1,*], Elena L. Zvereva[1], Alex S. Gilyazov[2] and Gennady D. Kataev[2]

[1]Section of Ecology, Department of Biology, University of Turku, Turku, Finland;
[2]Lapland Biosphere Reserve, Monchegorsk, Murmansk region, Russia

ABSTRACT

To test the hypothesis that the contaminated landscapes around a big polluter represent a sink habitat for birds and mammals, we quantified population densities and estimated biomass of birds and mammals at ten sites located within 65 km distance from the nickel-copper smelter at Monchegorsk, NW Russia, and used relative densities of burying beetles as an index reflecting mortality of vertebrates from factors other than predation. Biomass of birds (estimated from transect counts) and large mammals (estimated from snow-tracking) declined monotonously with increase in pollution, while biomass of small mammals (estimated from snap-trapping) peaked in moderately polluted areas. Population densities of vertebrates in industrial barrens were 10-50% of densities observed in unpolluted forests, depending on the group studied. Population density of burying beetle *Nicrophorus vespilloides*, measured by bait-trapping, peaked 15-30 km from the polluter, indicating increased mortality rate of vertebrates in moderately polluted forest habitats. The increase in mortality, in absence of compensatory increase in reproduction (as reported in earlier studies), suggests that populations in the polluted (low quality) habitats are supported by migration from the surrounding unpolluted territories, and that migrants are not able to assess habitat quality in terms of toxic contamination before breeding. Moderately polluted habitats may be attractive for the dispersing birds and mammals not only because of permanent vacation of territories due to high mortality, but also because some resources are more abundant there than in surrounding unpolluted

---

* Mikhail V. Kozlov, Section of Ecology, University of Turku, Turku FIN-20014, Finland. Phone: 358-2-3335716, fax: 358-2-3336550, e-mail: mikoz@utu.fi.

forests. We concluded that the contaminated area of about 1000 km^2 works like a death trap for dispersing birds and mammals, and the moderately contaminated forested part of this area can possibly be classified as an attractive sink habitat.

Key words. Attractive sink habitat. Biomass of birds and mammals. Burying beetle. Carrion resource. Environmental contamination. Kola Peninsula. Monchegorsk smelter.

INTRODUCTION

In a heterogeneous environment the habitats used by a species can be divided into sources and sinks, depending on whether or not local reproduction is sufficient to balance mortality [Pulliam 1988]. Reproduction in source populations exceeds mortality, and surplus individuals disperse to sink populations where deaths exceed births; in the absence of immigration a sink population would deterministically go extinct [Watkinson & Sutherland 1995]. Identification of sink populations requires profound understanding of population demography and is therefore rather laborious [Watkinson & Sutherland 1995; Solarz 1998]. As the result, many of the studies, cited as evidence for source-sink dynamics, cannot distinguish a sink habitat from a habitat with a low carrying capacity [Diffendorfer 1998].

Impact zones of big polluters represent an extremely harsh environment for nearly all kind of organisms, primarily due to toxicity of pollutants and associated habitat disturbance. They can be classified as 'low quality habitats' for birds and small mammals, because both population densities and individual fitness characteristics (including success of reproduction) in contaminated sites are lower than in surrounding unpolluted habitats [Bezel 1987; Gilyazov 1993b; Kataev 1995; Dmowski *et al.* 1995; Eeva & Lehikoinen 1998; Lebedeva 1999; Eeva *et al.* 2000]. Although the tissue concentrations of heavy metals may reach toxic levels [Gilyazov 1993a; Panichev *et al.* 1993; Gilyazov & Panichev 1994; Spurgeon & Hopkins 1996; Lebedeva 1999], the evidence of increased mortality of birds and animals in the impact zones of polluters is scarce [Eeva & Lehikoinen 1998]. Therefore the question arises, whether the local populations in the contaminated habitats are self-supporting, or their long-term persistence is due to immigration from the surrounding populations.

While direct evaluation of total vertebrate mortality along a pollution gradient is rather laborious, an indirect estimate can be obtained by monitoring population densities of burying beetles (Coleoptera, Silphidae) that use carrion resource. Density of these beetles was found to correlate with available food resources calculated, in particular, as biomass of mammals plus birds [Holloway & Schnell 1997]. However, when mortality varies among study sites, resource should be estimated by multiplying biomass and mortality rate. If low population density of both birds and mammals around big polluters [Gilyazov 1993b; Kataev 1995; Dmowski *et al.* 1995] is the consequence of low carrying capacity of the contaminated habitats, and mortality pattern in vertebrates remains unchanged, then density of burying beetles should decline monotonously with an increase in contamination. In contrast, if the impact zone represents a sink (or pseudosink) habitat, mortality of birds and mammals will increase with increase in environmental contamination, and populations in the contaminated habitats (supported by immigration) will produce relatively more carrion resources than populations in unpolluted landscapes.

The present study was designed to test the hypothesis that the contaminated landscapes around a big nickel-copper smelter represent a sink habitat for birds and mammals. To test this hypothesis, we quantified population densities and estimated biomass of birds and mammals along the strong pollution gradient, and used relative densities of burying beetles as an index reflecting mortality of vertebrates from factors other than predation.

MATERIALS AND METHODS

Study Area

The study was conducted in the lowland forest zone of the Kola Peninsula, north-western Russia, north of the Polar Circle. The study sites were located within 65 km of the Severonikel nickel-copper smelter at Monchegorsk (67° 55' N, 32° 48' E). This smelter is one of the largest European sources of aerial pollution, predominantly of sulphur dioxide and heavy metals [Anonymous 1994]. In 1990, it emitted 2.33 x 10^8 kg SO_2, 2.71 x 10^6 kg Ni and 1.81 x 10^6 kg Cu; since that time, emissions have steadily declined, reaching 0.44 x 10^8 kg SO_2, 1.21 x 10^6 kg Ni and 0.83 x 10^6 kg Cu in 2001 [Barcan 2002].

Before the smelter started to operate, the dominant type of lowland vegetation in the areas south of Monchegorsk was spruce forest [Bobrova & Kachurin 1936]. Vast quantities of sulphur and heavy metals emitted during the last 60 years have caused widespread destruction of soils and vegetation around the smelter [Kozlov & Haukioja 1995; Rigina & Kozlov 1999]. The total area influenced by aerial pollution in early 1990ies exceeded 10,000 km², with industrial barrens covering tens of square kilometres [Kryuchkov 1993; Tikkanen & Niemelä 1995]. For vegetation characteristics and levels of environmental disturbances in study area, see Barkan [1993], Koroleva [1993], Kryuchkov [1993], Kozlov & Haukioja [1995], Rigina & Kozlov [1999], Kozlov & Barcan [2000] and Zvereva & Kozlov [2001, 2004].

Pollution Loads at the Study Sites

Emissions of any smelter consist of dozens of substances, many of which may cause toxic effects. The main pollutants (in terms of total weight) in the study area are sulphur dioxide and heavy metals, predominantly nickel and copper. Concentrations of all pollutants in all media (ambient air, soils, plants, animals) strongly correlate to each other, decreasing exponentially with increase of distance from the smelter [Barcan 1993; Barcan *et al.* 1993; Kozlov *et al.* 1995; Ruohomäki *et al.* 1996; Valkama & Kozlov 2001]. Since it is impossible to attribute the effects observed in the course of field studies to any of the individual pollutants, we have chosen to use both ambient SO_2 concentrations and content of nickel in foliage of mountain birch, *Betula pubescens* subsp. *czerepanovii* (Orlova) Hämet-Ahti, as two indices of pollution load in our study sites (Table 1). Ambient SO_2 concentrations were measured in summer of 1994 by using the lead-dioxide absorbers (the method described by Barcan [1993]), whereas foliar concentrations of heavy metals were estimated by X-ray fluorescence and ICP spectrophotometry [Kozlov *et al.* 1995; Kozlov 2005].

Table 1. Characteristics of study sites

Plot position[1]	Plot coordinates		Foliar nickel[2] mg kg^{-1}	Ambient SO_2[3] mkg m^{-3}	Habitat type[4]	Stand basal area, m^2 ha^{-1}
	Latitude	Longitude				
14.6NE	68°02'20"	33°01'06"	40	9	WF	5.3
11.1NE	68°00'59"	32°57'17"	68	24	DF	3.0
5.0N	67°58'07"	32°53'41"	138	176	BC	0.3
1.6NW	67° 56'13"	32°50'07"	254	151	IB	0.3
6.6S	67°52'05"	32°48'16"	166	186	IB	<0.3
13.8S	67°47'55"	32°47'13"	82	76	BC	2.0
18.3S	67°45'31"	32°48'39"	62	39	DF	11.3
27.4S	67°40'39"	32°49'31"	33	36	WF	12.0
36.2S	67°36'25"	32°39'25"	20	24	HF	11.0
63.0SE	67°32'16"	33°57'52"	12	2	HF	18.7

[1] Position: distance and direction from the polluter (note that the same sites in several earlier publications were labelled as 15NE, 11NE, 5N, 1N, 7S, 14S, 20S, 29S, 41S and 65SE, respectively; present estimate of the distances is more accurate as based on the GPS data).

[2] Determined by X-ray fluorescence in leaves of mountain birch; multiyear (1991-2000) mean value (after Kozlov *et al.* 1995, and Kozlov 2005).

[3] Measured by lead-dioxide absorbers during the summer of 1994 (method described by Barcan 1993).

[4] IB, industrial barren; BC, birch transitional community; DF, severely damaged and declining forest; WF, weakened and slightly damaged forest; HF, healthy (nearly undamaged) forest.

Design of Study Sites

Ten sites (Fig. 1), designed to estimate the densities of the study organisms within a plot of 1000 x 500 m size (0.5 km^2), were coded with the distance (km) and direction from the emission source, e. g. 13.8S for the site at 13.8 km distance South of the smelter. Nine sites were selected along the road from St.Petersburg to Murmansk, and one site – along the road from Kirovsk to Koashva (Fig. 1). The road divided all plots into two equal parts, and the transect lines used to monitor densities of birds and mammals (200 m apart) were perpendicular to the road (Fig. 1).

Counts of Birds

Birds were counted by A. Gilyasov on June 9-11, 2001, in three parallel transects, 1000 m each, situated 200 m apart (method described by Stchegolev [1977]). Both visual observations and song records were combined, which in the investigated habitats (from sparse subarctic forests to industrial barrens) allowed to count birds within 50 m distance from the observational line. It was assumed that the pair demonstrating anxiety has a brood. Biomass estimation is based on mean values of live bird weight and brood size (after Semenov-Tjan-Shanskij & Gilyazov [1991]).

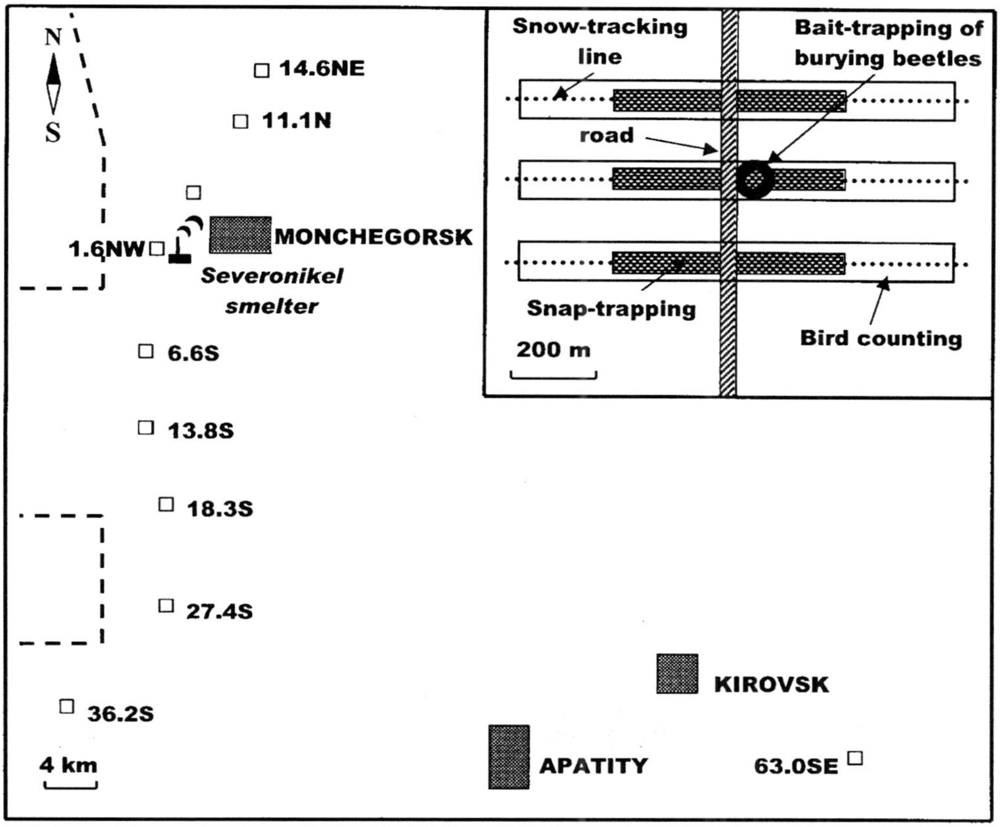

Figure 1. Study area, position of study sites (small squares), and external border of the Lapland reserve (dash line). Inserted: design of study site. Note that caption should appear on the same page as the figure

Counts of Small Mammals

Density indices of shrews and voles (exx $trap^{-1}$ $night^{-1}$), thereafter referred to as 'small mammals', were obtained by G. Kataev on September 11-13, 2001, by using mouse snap traps. This kind of sampling is widely used in both Scandinavia and Russia to monitor populations of voles and mices [Myllymäki *et al.* 1971; Kataev *et al.* 1994; Norrdahl & Korpimäki 1995]. Total of 33 traps (11 traps per line) operated during three nights at each site, giving the sampling effort of 99 trap nights per site. Traps were checked once a day; trapped animals were determined and weighed. Controlled trapping experiments, conducted as described by Smirnov [1964], allowed to conclude that in our study region 11 traps situated 50 m apart (one sampling line of 500 m length) during three nights gives an unbiased estimate of the number of shrews and voles inhabiting an area of 0.29 ha (G. D. Kataev, unpublished data). Biomass estimation is based on actual live weight of trapped animals.

Counts of Large Mammals

Density indices of 'large' mammalian species [weasels (*Mustela nivalis* L.) and larger] (tracks km^{-1} day^{-1}) were obtained by G. Kataev by snow-tracking on April 2-5, 2002, following the methodology widely used in monitoring of game animals in Finland and Russia [Priklonsky 1965, 1973; Lindén *et al.* 1996; Lomanov 2000]. Each route was visited twice, with 24-h interval. During the precheck, all old tracks were marked; therefore the new tracks counted during the second visit reflect the activity of animals during the 24-h period. Only those tracks were included which actually crossed the passageway. All the crossings were counted, even if the observer was sure that all tracks were left by the same individual [Lindén *et al.* 1996]. Track density was converted to absolute population density assuming that movement by individuals is random and the mean daily cruising distance of individuals is more or less constant [Formosov 1932; Priklonsky 1965; 1973]. We applied conversion coefficients routinely used in the neighbouring Kandalaksha reserve (N. S. Boiko, pers. comm.); mean live weight of animals is according to Siivonen [1977].

Counts of Burying Beetles

Densities of burying beetles were estimated by M. Kozlov in summer of 2000. Funnel bait traps were made from 2 litre plastic bottles. The bottom of bottle was removed and replaced by screen cone made from plastic net (cell size 1.5 x 1 mm). The traps were established on June 10, which corresponds to the late spring in the study region: in some sites the ground was still covered by snow. Traps (three per site) were hang on tree branches, some 1-1.5 m above the ground, 15-20 m apart. The small (5-10 g) piece of meat in a plastic vial was attached inside the bottle. New baits were added on July 5 and 30, e.g. with 25 d intervals; the old one remained in the trap until the nearest sampling date. Beetles were killed by insecticide (a piece of DDVP strip attached to the inner surface of the bottle). Traps were emptied with 10 d intervals from June 20 until August 30, 2000 (eight sampling dates); burying beetles were determined and counted.

Data Analysis

Among-site variation in biomass of birds and mammals was investigated by ANOVA; relationships between site-specific biomass and pollution load were evaluated by calculating Pearson correlation coefficients. Sources of variation in catches of burying beetles were explored by SAS GLM procedure, followed by Tukey's HSD test [SAS Institute 1990]. Note the change of font size in the paragraph above!

The number of burying beetles divided by the estimated site-specific biomass of birds plus mammals was considered an index of mortality: higher relative number of burying beetles per unit of potential carrion resource indicates higher mortality rate. Relationship between this index and pollution load (calculated as log-transformed concentrations of ambient sulphur dioxide and foliar nickel) was investigated by both linear and quadratic regressions [SAS Institute 1990].

Table 2. Density indices of birds (records km^{-1}; mean ± S. E., based on three lines 1000 m each, censused June 9-11, 2001)

Species	Study sites									
	14.6NE	11.1NE	5.0N	1.6NW	6.6S	13.8S	18.3S	27.4S	36.2S	63.0SE
Tringa glareola	0.67±0.33	0	0	0	0.33±0.33	0	0	0	0.33±0.33	0
Tringa nebularia		0	0	0	0	0	0	0	0.33±0.33	0
Actitis hypoleucos	0.67±0.33	0	0	0	0	0	0	0	0	0
Sterna paradisaea	0.33±0.33	0	0	0	0	0	0	0	0	0
Anthus tivialis	0	0	0	0	0	0	0	0	0	1.00±0.00
Anthus pratensis	1.00±1.00	1.33 ±0.67	0	0.67±0.33	0	0	0.33±0.33	0	0.33±0.33	0
Motacilla flava	0	0.67±0.67	0	0	0	2.00±0.58	0	0	2.00±1.00	0
Motacilla alba	0	0	0.67±0.33	0	0	0.67±0.33	0	0	0	0
Bombycilla garrulus	0.33±0.33	0	0	0	0	0	0	0.67±0.33	0	0.33±0.33
Phylloscopus trochilus	3.67±1.28	0	0.67±0.33	0	0	0	3.67±0.67	7.33±0.67	5.67±1.45	4.67±0.67
Muscicapa striata	0	0	0	0	0	0	0.67±0.33	0.33±0.33	0.33±0.33	1.67±0.33
Saxicola rubetra	0	0	0	0	0	0	0	0	0.33±0.33	0
Oenanthe oenanthe	0	0.67±0.67	0	0.67±0.67	1.33 ±0.67	0	0	0	0	0
Phoenicurus phoenicurus	2.00±1.00	0	0	0	0	1.67±0.33	1.33±0.33	2.33±0.33	1.67±0.88	2.33±0.88
Luscinia svecica	0	0	0	0	1.00±0.00	0	0	0.33±0.33	0	1.33±0.33
Turdus iliacus	2.00±0.00	0	0	0	0	0	0	2.00±0.00	2.00±0.00	2.00±0.00
Turdus philomelos	0	0	0	0	0	0	0	0	0.33±0.33	0
Parus cinctus	0	0	0	0	0	0	0	1.33 ±0.67	0.67±0.67	0
Fringilla montifringilla	0	0	0	0	0	1.67±0.33	1.00±0.00	3.00±0.58	0.33±0.33	2.33±0.88
Acanthis flammea	0.67±0.33	0.33±0.33	0.67±0.33	0.67±0.33	2.0 ± 0.6	1.00±0.58	1.67±0.33	1.67±0.33	1.33±1.33	2.00±0.00
Pinicola enucleator	0	0	0	0	0	0	0	0.67±0.33	0	0
Loxia curvirostra	0	0	0	0	0	0	0	0	1.00±1.00	0
Loxia leucoptera	0	0	0	0	0	0	0	1.00±0.58	0	0.67±0.33
Pyrrhula pyrrhula	0	0	0	0	0	0	0.33±0.33	0.33±0.33	0	0
Emberiza rustica	0	0	0	0	0	0.33±0.33	0	0	0.33±0.33	0.33±0.33

Table 3. Density indices of small mammals
(specimens per 100 $trap^{-1}$ $night^{-1}$; mean ± S. E., based on three lines, 11 traps per line, operated September 11-13, 2001)

Species	Study sites									
	14.6NE	11.1NE	5.0N	1.6NW	6.6S	13.8S	18.3S	27.4S	36.2S	63.0SE
Sorex araneus	4.00±2.65	2.00±1.00	0	0	0	3.00±1.75	10.0±1.00	8.00±1.00	3.00±0.00	2.00±0.67
Sorex caecutiens	1.00±1.00	0	0	0	0	1.00±1.00	2.00±1.00	3.00±1.75	1.00±1.00	1.00±1.00
Neomys fodiens	1.00±1.00	0	0	0	0	0	0	0	0	0
Clethrionomys rufocanus	2.00±2.00	1.00±1.00	0	1.00±1.00	0	2.00±1.00	6.00±1.75	5.00±1.00	3.00±1.75	1.00±1.00
Microtus oeconomus	0	0	0	1.00±1.00	1.00±1.00	1.00±1.00	0	0	0	0
Microtus agrestis	0	0	0	0	0	0	0	1.00±1.00	0	0

Table 4. Density indices of large mammals
(tracks km^{-1} day^{-1}; Mean ± S. E., based on three lines of 1100 m each; censused April 3-5, 2002)

Species	Study sites									
	14.6NE	11.1NE	5.0N	1.6NW	6.6S	13.8S	18.3S	27.4S	36.2S	63.0SE
Lepus timidus	0.6 ± 0.3	1.2 ± 0.3	0.6 ± 0.3	0.3 ± 0.3	0	0.6 ± 0.3	0.9 ± 0.5	2.4 ± 0.3	0.3 ± 0.3	3.3 ± 1.1
Sciurus vulgaris	0	0	0	0	0	0	0	0.6 ± 0.3	0	1.5 ± 0.6
Canis familiaris[1]	0	0	0.3 ± 0.3	0	0	0	0	0	0	0
Vulpes vulpes	0	0.6 ± 0.6	0	0	0.3 ± 0.3	0.3 ± 0.3	0.6 ± 0.3	0.6 ± 0.3	0.6 ± 0.3	0.6 ± 0.3
Mustela nivalis	0	0	0	0	0	0	0	0	0	0.3 ± 0.3
Mustela erminea	0.3 ± 0.3	0	0	0	0	0	0.3 ± 0.3	0	0	0
Mustela vison	0	0	0	0	0	0	0	0.3 ± 0.3	0.3 ± 0.3	0
Martes martes	0	0.3 ± 0.3	0	0	0	0	0	0	0.3 ± 0.3	0

[1] Stray dogs are common in surrounding of Monchegorsk (pers. obs.) Note adjusted position of the footnote!

RESULTS

Species Composition and Densities of Birds and Mammals

Twenty-five bird species were recorded at our study sites (Table 2); willow-wren (*Phylloscopus trochilus* L.), common redstart (*Phoenicurus phoenicurus* L.), brambling (*Fringilla montifringilla* L.) and lesser redpoll (*Acanthis flammea* L.) were most common. The number of recorded species decreased from 11-15 per site in unpolluted forests to 3-4 per site in industrial barrens (Table 2).

Total of 66 specimens of six species of small mammals were collected by snap traps (Table 3), which gives an average density index 0.067 ex trap^{-1} night^{-1}. The common shrew (*Sorex araneus* L.) and large-toothed redback vole (*Clethrionomys rufocanus* Sund.) were most common (32 and 20 specimens, respectively); only large-toothed redback vole and root vole (*Microtus oeconomus* Pall.) were captured in industrial barrens (one and two specimens, respectively).

During the winter counts of large mammals, 61 track of eight species was recorded (Table 4), which gives an average density index 1.85 tracks km^{-1} day^{-1}. Mountain hare (*Lepus timidus* L.) and red fox (*Vulpes vulpes* L.) were most common (34 and 12 tracks, respectively), and only these two species were recorded in industrial barrens.

Biomass of Birds and Mammals

All investigated groups of vertebrates demonstrated among-site variation in biomass (Tables 5, 6), which was most pronounced in birds. Biomass in industrial barrens relative to unpolluted forests was reduced to 12.7% in birds, 51.8% in small mammals, and 10.4% do not separate percent sign from the value! in large mammals (Table 5). Decline in biomass of birds and large animals was monotonous (Table 5), showing significant negative correlation with pollution load (Table 6). Density of small mammals peaked at slightly damaged and moderately damaged forests (Table 5); as the result, changes in total biomass were also non-linear, with peaks associated with slightly and moderately damaged forests (Fig. 2a).

Table 5. Biomass (Mean ± S. E., g km^{-2}) of birds and mammals

Site	Birds	Small mammals	Large mammals
14.6NE	3042 ± 140	11798 ± 4864	1821 ± 916
11.1NE	459 ± 37	3794 ± 1380	4424 ± 940
5.0N	279 ± 36	0	1981 ± 1018
1.6NW	327 ± 62	4945 ± 2704	854 ± 854
6.6S	692 ± 118	2645 ± 2645	445 ± 445
13.8S	1608 ± 97	10766 ± 4676	2153 ± 1144
18.3S	1256 ± 65	22663 ± 1608	3566 ± 1516
27.4S	4587 ± 386	21327 ± 3203	7903 ± 1336
36.2S	4090 ± 193	9866 ± 4383	1964 ± 1155
63.0SE	3949 ± 270	4791 ± 2641	10555 ± 3417

Table 6. Among-site variation in biomass of birds and mammals and correlation of site-specific means with two indices of pollution load

Character	Among-site variation		Correlation with pollution load (n = 10 sites)			
			Ambient SO_2		Foliar Ni	
	$F_{9, 20}$	P	r	P	r	P
Bird biomass	94.0	<0.0001	-0.68	0.03	-0.87	0.0009
Biomass of small mammals	5.87	0.0005	-0.18	0.61	-0.33	0.34
Biomass of large mammals	4.81	0.0017	-0.72	0.02	-0.72	0.02
Total biomass	9.85	<0.0001	-0.48	0.16	-0.63	0.05

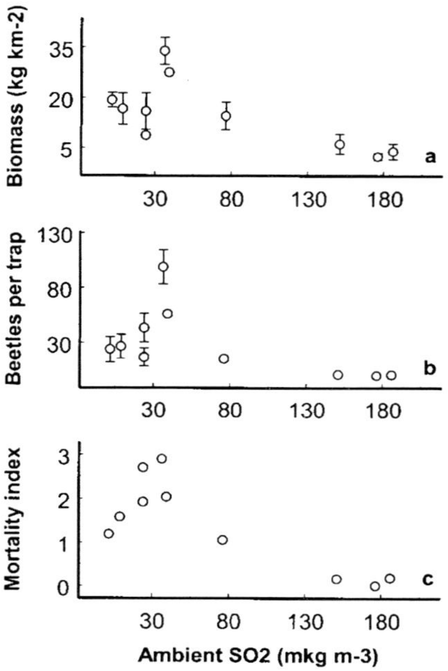

Figure 2. (a) Total biomass of birds and mammals (kg km^{-2}, means of three transect estimates ± SE) in relation to the ambient SO_2 concentration. (b) Total catches of *Nicrophorus vespilloides* (specimens per trap, means of three traps per site ± S.E.) in relation to the ambient SO_2 concentration. (c) Mortality index (number of burying beetles per unit of biomass of birds plus mammals) in relation to the ambient SO_2 concentration.

Densities of Burying Beetles

Four species of burying beetles have been trapped: 845 specimens of *Nicrophorus vespilloides* Hbst., three specimens of *Thanatophilus rugosus* L., one specimen of *Oiceoptoma thoracica* L., and one specimen of *T. lapponicus* F. The catches peaked in the last decade of June, when 78.3% of specimens were collected; nearly all (99.1%) individuals were trapped between June 21 and July 20, 2000.

Catches of *N. vespilloides* demonstrated pronounced among-site variation (Table 7), peaking at the site 27.4S (Fig. 2b). The latter site differed from all the remaining sites, including the most distant (unpolluted) localities (Tukey's test, $P < 0.05$). An interactive effect of study site and sampling date on beetle catches indicates phenological differences between the investigated beetle populations.

Table 7. Sources of variation in catches of the burying beetle *Nicrophorus vespilloides* (SAS GLM procedure, type III Sum of Squares)

Source	DF	Mean Square	F	P
Site	9	572.2	13.54	<.0001
Date	4	2609.8	61.77	<.0001
Site*Date	36	293.6	6.95	<.0001
Error	100	42.2	-	-

Mortality of Vertebrates

Although the mean catch of burying beetles strongly correlated with total biomass of birds and mammals ($r = 0.93$, $n = 10$ sites, $P < 0.0001$), mortality index (relative number of burying beetles per unit of biomass of birds plus mammals) varied with pollution (Fig. 2c), peaking at moderately to slightly polluted forests (second-order regression: $F_{2,9} = 16.2$, $P = 0.0024$, $R^2_{adj} = 0.77$; for regression coefficients, see Table 8). The number of beetles per unit of vertebrate biomass in these sites (2.39 ± 0.24) is 73% higher than in unpolluted forests (1.38 ± 0.20).

Table 8. Regression of the mortality index (number of burying beetles per unit of biomass of birds plus mammals) on the logarithmized concentration of sulphur dioxide (POL)

Variable	DF	Parameter estimate	Standard error	t	$P > \|t\|$
Intercept	1	-1.18	0.74	-0.25	0.81
POL	1	1.92	0.49	3.94	0.0056
POL^2	1	-0.36	0.08	-4.81	0.0020

DISCUSSION

Densities of Birds and Mammals

The densities of breeding birds in moderately and severely polluted habitats along the Monchegorsk pollution gradient, estimated in 1980ies, were 60 and 13% of the density at the unpolluted forests, respectively [Gilyazov & Kataev 1990; Gilyazov 1993b]. Results of our counts are in good agreement with these earlier data, as well as with other reports demonstrating decline of bird populations with increase in pollution [Eeva & Lehikoinen 1998; Lebedeva 1999; Eeva *et al.* 2000].

A long-term study by Kataev [1995] revealed monotonous population decline of small mammals when approaching the Monchegorsk smelter: the biomass decreased from 87 kg km^{-2} at the unpolluted forest site to 69 kg km^{-2} at the moderately polluted site and to 15 kg km^{-2} at the most polluted site. This biomass reduction (to 17.2% of the background level) is very close to the values obtained for birds and large mammals in the present study (12.7 and 16%, respectively). Similarly, density of bank vole (*Clethrionomys glareolus*) decreased monotonously when approaching the copper smelter at Revda in Southern Ural, reaching 15-21% of the background density in the most polluted areas [Mukhacheva 1994]. However, the pattern discovered in the course of the present study differs from earlier results by Kataev [1995]: the density decline in the most polluted sites was much smaller (51.8% of the background value) and, most important, the highest densities of small mammals were associated with slightly to moderately polluted forests (Table 3) like in another study of bank vole conducted at Revda [Mukhacheva & Lukianov 1997].

Quite expectedly, densities of large mammals also declined when approaching the polluter. Although this pattern seems trivial, to the best of our knowledge no data on the effect of pollution on abundance of large mammals had ever been published.

Since small mammals give the largest contribution to an estimate of the biomass of vertebrates, the detected changes in total biomass were non-linear, with peak associated with slightly damaged forests (Fig. 2a). However, the data by Kataev [1995] indicate that during the periods of higher densities of vole populations we may expect monotonous decline in the total biomass along the investigated pollution gradient, with the biomass reduced in industrial barrens by a factor of five to ten relative to the background level.

Both the main advantage and the main disadvantage of our data on vertebrate densities is that each of three data sets was obtained during a short period by the same observer. This assures that among-site variation is not due to different methodology or different skills of the observers; but on the other hand the data reflect the situation during very short time periods. However, compareson with published information demonstrated that our results are in agreement with the general pattern, and can therefore be used for estimation of total vertebrate biomass in our study sites.

Densities of Burying Beetles

Although two- to four-fold increase in catches of *N. vespilloides* in moderately polluted sites relative to unpolluted forests (Fig. 2b) corresponds to an increase in population densities of birds and small mammals (Fig. 2a), still the number of beetles per unit of vertebrate biomass (Fig. 2c) in these sites was higher than in both unpolluted and heavily polluted sites. Since we did not expect that the mortality index in the most polluted habitats will be much lower than in unpolluted sites, we were forced to check whether our estimates of burying beetle densities may have been biased due to pollution-induced habitat deterioration. Although it is easy to ascribe population decline of burying beetles to direct toxic effects of pollutants, this explanation seems unlikely. Insects can usually tolerate much higher concentrations of pollutants than vertebrates [Kozlov 1990; Heliovaara & Väisänen 1993], and they easily manage even with the highest concentrations of pollutants occurring neat the Monchegorsk [Kozlov *et al.* 2000, and references therein]. In contrast, secondary (climatic) effects of pollution-induced forest decline may appear very important. In particular, in dry open habitats carrion frequently dries out very fast, giving no chance to necrophagous insects to utilize it [Lyabzina & Lesonen 2002].

Density estimates obtained by bait-trapping may be biased due to different environmental conditions affecting odour distribution from traps. Since declining forests are more 'transparent', it was possible to suggest that the peak catches at early stages of forest decline are caused by an increase in the trapped area (from which beetles were attracted) due to an increase in wind velocity. However, wind speed measurements [Kozlov 2002] did not support this hypothesis: mean wind speed at the site with peak catches (27.4S) was lower (0.58 ± 0.13 m sec^{-1}) than at the most distant (65SE) site (1.22 ± 0.54 m sec^{-1}). Significant increase in wind speed was detected only in the most polluted sites (1.6NW, 6.6S), with the peak value (4.59 ± 0.87 m sec^{-1}) recorded at the barren site with a nearly zero catch (6.6S): this increase in wind speed may have contributed (by suppressing the flight activity) to the decline in beetle catches within the most polluted area.

Habitat preferences of the trapped species can also introduce a sampling bias. Koch [1989] classified *N. vespilloides* as eurytopic forest species. In Canada *N. vespilloides* was found to reproduce on *Sphagnum* bogs [Beninger & Peck 1992], but a later study demonstrated that both forest and bog habitats can be used [Beninger 1994]. The *Sphagnum* bogs are most extensive at the trapping sites 11.1N, 36.2S and 63.0SE, present (although not extensive) in moderately contaminated forests, but completely absent at three barren or semi-barren sites (5.0N, 1.6NW and 6.6S). Forest density and vitality declined gradually when approaching the smelter [Rigina and Kozlov 1999]. Thus, habitat association may have contributed to the absence of *N. vespilloides* in the most polluted area, but hardly explains the peak in catches at the moderately polluted sites.

Finally, the catches of organisms with low mobility may reflect local processes rather than the general pattern, being representative for small patches only. Although short-term migrations of *N. vespilloides* have not been investigated, another species of this genus, *N. americanus*, was found to move in an average 1.23 km $night^{-1}$ in the search for carrion, with a maximum of 10.0 km over six nights [Creighton & Schnell 1998]. Thus, the peak catch of *N. vespilloides* most likely reflects the changes observed on a relatively large territories (at least of several square kilometers), rather than in the immediate vicinities of trapping sites.

We concluded that environmental factors not related to resource (carrion) availability may have caused low densities of burying beetles in the industrial barrens. However, there is no reason to suspect that higher catches of burying beetles in moderately contaminated forests relative to unpolluted forests are due to sampling bias.

Mortality of Birds and Mammals

In absence of a sampling bias an increase in density of burying beetles may indicate an increase in resource availability [Holloway & Schnell 1997]. Thus, higher relative densities of *N. vespilloides* in moderately polluted sites can be considered a proof of an increase in mortality rates, more exactly in mortality from reasons other than predation. This result agrees with the data on high tissue concentrations of heavy metals, discovered in birds and mammals near the Monchegorsk smelter [Gilyazov 1993a; Panichev *et al.* 1993; Gilyazov & Panichev 1994], which sometimes exceed the toxicity levels established in experiments with white mice [Panichev *et al.* 1993] and therefore are likely to cause toxic effects. Even if pollutants do not kill the birds and animals, mortality may increase due to reduced ability to sustain environmental stresses such as diseases, low winter temperatures, shortage of food and others [Heinz 1989]. We suspect that winter mortality (examples in Novikov [1981]) may be especially high in the contaminated habitats.

Some earlier observations on birds and small mammals in the impact zones of big polluters support our conclusion on higher mortality in metal-contaminated areas. Nestling mortality of two passerine birds near the copper-nickel smelter at Harjavalta (SE Finland) was twice as high as in the unpolluted sites [Eeva & Lehikoinen 1996]. Moreover, when the population densities were accounted for, the absolute number of nestlings, which died during the last week before leaving the nest (the resource which can be used by *Nicrophorus* beetles), peaked in the moderately polluted zone (T. Eeva, personal communication). Also the proportion of adult voles in catches from the moderately polluted sites around the Severonikel smelter was higher than in clean sites [Kataev *et al.* 1994], suggesting that mortality of juvenile voles in moderately polluted sites is higher than in clean sites.

Impact Zone: An Attractive Sink?

All earlier studies consistently demonstrated decrease in reproduction of birds and mammals with increase in pollution [Bezel 1987; Gilyazov 1993b; Kataev 1995; Dmowski *et al.* 1995; Eeva & Lehikoinen 1998; Lebedeva 1999; Eeva *et al.* 2000]. An increase in mortality, in absence of compensatory increase in reproduction, suggests that populations in the polluted (low quality) habitats are supported by migration from the surrounding unpolluted territories.

Several data sets independently demonstrated frequent immigration of birds and mammals into heavily polluted areas. In particular, populations of bank voles around the copper smelter at Revda differ in proportion of migrants, which increased from 3.1% in an unpolluted forest to 100% in heavily contaminated forest at 1 km distance from the smelter [Mukhacheva & Lukjanov 1997]. Also the capture-recapture study conducted near Harjavalta smelter [Eeva & Lehikoinen 1998] detected immigration of two passerine birds to heavily polluted habitats. Similarly, counts of 16 bird species around the Severonikel smelter demonstrated that in spring birds migrate to heavily polluted areas, possibly because of the earlier disappearance of the continuous snow cover (which is reduced to one-third of the background depth: Kozlov [2001]), but later in the season they return to the surrounding (moderately contaminated) forest habitats [Gilyazov 1993b]. As the result, during the spring migration the density of birds in heavily polluted habitats was in an average 1.3 times as high as in moderately polluted sites. In contrast, during the nesting period the bird density in heavily polluted sites was 2.5 times lower, and during the post-nesting period 15-20 times lower than in moderately polluted sites [Gilyazov 1993b], an estimate similar to the obtained in the present study. These results in particular suggest that migrants are not able to assess habitat quality in terms of toxic contamination before breeding, the condition under which source-sink dynamics is more probable than the balanced dispersal [Diffendorfer 1998]. However, birds seem to assess the habitat quality in terms of landscape deterioration, and escape from barren sites before breeding.

Habitats contaminated by sulphur dioxide and heavy metals, except for the devastated industrial barrens, may be quite attractive for some birds and animals, because some resources are more abundant there than in the surrounding unpolluted forests. In particular, transitional communities at the external border of the declining coniferous forests (some 5-15 km from the smelter) are dominated by densely growing, low-stature willows and shrubby birches [Kozlov & Haukioja 1995; Rigina & Kozlov 1999], which can provide surplus food and attractive shelter for some mammalian herbivores (mountain hare, moose) and bud-feeding birds. Furthermore, densities of some insects, like birch-feeding leafrollers and leaf miners, as well as willow-feeding leaf beetles, peak in moderately and heavily polluted habitats [Kozlov 1985, 1997, 2003; Zvereva *et al.* 1995]; some of these insects (contaminated by heavy metals!) are intensively consumed by birds (M. Kozlov, pers. obs.). Fruit production by dwarf shrubs increases with increase in pollution, and berries of bilberry and lingonberry in contaminated habitats are often larger than in unpolluted forests, presumably due to larger light availability [Zvereva & Kozlov

2004, and unpublished]. Thus, contaminated habitats can be classified as attractive sinks (according to Delibes *et al.* [2001]), e. g. habitats where resources are abundant and reproduction could be high, but the harmful factors can not be detected by individual animals. Earlier examples of attractive sinks included habitats exposed to high hunting activities and marshes with high content of lead pellets [Delibes *et al.* 2001].

The external border of the area with an increased vertebrate mortality (as derived from counts of burying beetles) corresponds approximately to the soil concentrations of nickel 200 mg kg^{-1} and of copper 100 mg kg^{-1} (data after Barcan *et al.* [1993]). Plants within this zone are also contaminated by heavy metals; in particular metal concentrations in wild berries and edible mushrooms exceeded the permissible limits by the factor of two or more [Barcan *et al.* 1998]. At least the forested part of this area (a moderately contaminated zone) seems to represent an attractive habitat for dispersing birds and mammals, which regularly forage even in the most contaminated landscapes. Our data indicate that the contaminated territory, which exceeds 1000 km^2 [Barcan *et al.* 1998], works like a death trap for birds and small mammals.

Habitat sinks that attract dispersing animals are only rarely considered in the source-sink theory (but see Delibes *et al.* [2001]), although these sinks may have much larger impact on the surrounding source populations than 'typical' (non-attractive) sinks. Analysis of a deterministic model demonstrated, that even minor changes in proportion of attractive sink habitats, or a small decrease in survival, may have disproportionate effects on the population persistence [Delibes *et al.* 2001]. In our specific case the source populations are to a larger extent associated with the Lapland Biosphere Reserve; detection of an attractive sink on the border of the protected territory should be accounted for by conservation and management strategies.

Our conclusions (which of course should be viewed as tentative) point out the urgent need in the detailed investigation of the contaminated habitats under the perspective of the source-sink theory. More generally, our particular result demonstrates that 'unintentional pollution experiments' [Lee 1998] can provide an excellent opportunity for testing ecological theories and models in an evolutionarily novel environment [Ormerod *et al.* 1999; Zvereva & Kozlov 2001, 2004].

References

Anonymous. (1994). Europe's top 100 polluters. *New Scientist*, *143*, 9.

Barcan, V. S. (1993). Measurement of atmospheric concentrations of sulphur dioxide by passive lead dioxide absorbers. In M. V. Kozlov, E. Haukioja, & V. T. Yarmishko (Eds), *Aerial pollution in Kola Peninsula: Proceedings of the international workshop, 14-16 April 1992, St. Petersburg* (pp. 90-98). Apatity, Russia: Kola Science Centre.

Barcan, V. S. (2002). Nature and origin of multicomponent aerial emissions of the copper-nickel smelter complex. *Environment International*, *28*, 451-456.

Barcan, V. S., Pankratova, R. P., & Silina, A. V. (1993). Soil contamination by nickel and copper in area polluted by "Severonikel" smelter complex. In M. V. Kozlov, E. Haukioja, & V. T. Yarmishko (Eds), *Aerial pollution in Kola Peninsula: Proceedings of the international workshop, 14-16 April 1992, St. Petersburg* (pp. 119-147). Apatity, Russia: Kola Science Centre.

Barcan, V. S., Kovnatsky, E. F., & Smetannikova, M. S. (1998). Absorption of heavy metals in wild berries and edible mushrooms in an area affected by smelter emissions. *Water, Air and Soil Pollution, 103*, 173-195.

Beninger, C. W. (1994). Phenology, reproductive biology, and habitat association of *Nicrophorus* Fab. (Coleoptera, Silphidae) of the Mer Bleue bog area (Ottawa, Canada). *Memoirs of the Entomological Society of Canada, 169*, 135-143.

Beninger, C. W., & Peck, S. B. (1992). Temporal and spatial patterns of resource use among *Nicrophorus* Fab. carrion beetles (Coleoptera: Silphidae) in a Sphagnum bog and adjacent forest near Ottawa, Canada. *Canadian Entomologist, 124*, 79-86.

Bezel, V. S. (1987). *Population ecotoxicology of mammals.* Moscow, Russia: Nauka (in Russian).

Bobrova, L. I., & Kachurin, M. N. (1936). Vegetation of Monchetundra. In Y. D. Zinzerling (Ed.), *Materials on Vegetation of Northern and Western Parts of the Kola Peninsula* (pp. 95-121). Moscow and Leningrad, USSR: Academy of Sciences of the USSR (in Russian).

Creighton, J. C., & Schnell, G. D. (1998). Short-term movement patterns of the endangered American burying beetle *Nicrophorus americanus*. *Biological Conservation, 86*, 281-287.

Delibes, M., Gaona, P., & Ferreras, P. (2001). Effects of an attractive sink leading into maladaptive habitat selection. *American Naturalist, 158*, 277-285.

Diffendorfer, J. (1998). Testing models of source-sink dynamics and balanced dispersal. *Oikos, 81*, 417-433.

Dmowski, K., Kozakiewicz, M., & Kozakiewicz, A. (1995). Ecological effects of heavy metal pollution (Pb, Cd, Zn) on small mammal populations and communities. *Bulletin de l'Académie Polonaise des Sciences, Sciences Biologiques, 43*, 1-10.

Eeva, T., & Lehikoinen, E. (1996). Growth and mortality of nestling great tits (*Parus major*) and pied flycatchers (*Ficedula hypoleuca*) in a heavy metal pollution gradient. *Oecologia, 108*, 631-639.

Eeva, T., & Lehikoinen, E. (1998). Local survival rates of the pied flycatchers (*Ficedula hypoleuca*) and the great tits (*Parus major*) in an air pollution gradient. *Écoscience, 5*, 46-50.

Eeva, T., Tanhuanpää, S., Rabergh, C., Airaksinen, S., Nikinmaa, M., & Lehikoinen, E. (2000). Biomarkers and fluctuating asymmetry as indicators of pollution-induced stress in two hole-nesting passerines. *Functional Ecology, 14*, 235-243.

Formosov, A. N. (1932). Equation for quantitative censusing of mammals on the basis of their tracks. *Zoologicheskij Zhurnal, 11(2)*, 66-69 (in Russian).

Gilyazov, A. S. (1993a) Contents of metals in some birds of the Lapland reserve. In M. V. Kozlov, E. Haukioja, & V. T. Yarmishko (Eds), *Aerial pollution in Kola Peninsula: Proceedings of the international workshop, 14-16 April 1992, St. Petersburg* (pp. 206-209). Apatity, Russia: Kola Science Centre.

Gilyazov, A. S. (1993b) Air pollution impact on the bird communities of the Lapland biosphere reserve. In M. V. Kozlov, E. Haukioja, & V. T. Yarmishko (Eds), *Aerial pollution in Kola Peninsula: Proceedings of the international workshop, 14-16 April 1992, St. Petersburg* (pp. 383-390). Apatity, Russia: Kola Science Centre.

Gilyazov, A. S., & Kataev, G. D. (1990). An experience of zooindication of industrial pollution in the Kola Peninsula. In Y. D. Nukhimovskaja, & L. A. Bibikova (Eds.), *Anthropogenicic impacts on the nature of reserves* (pp. 5-24). Moscow, Russia: Central Research Laboratory of Game and Reserves (in Russian).

Gilyazov, A. S., & Panichev, N. A. (1994). Metal concentrations in tissues of willow ptarmigan (*Lagopus lagopus* L.) from industrially contaminated areas of the Kola Peninsula. In S. V. Degteva (Ed.), *Development of the North and recultivation problems: Reports on 2nd International conference, Syktyvkar, April 25-28 1994* (pp. 254-260). Syktyvkar, Russia: Institute of Biology (in Russian).

Heinz, G.H. (1989) How lethal are sublethal effects. *Environmental Toxicology and Chemistry*, 8, 463-464.

Heliövaara, K., & Väisänen, R. (1993). *Insects and pollution.* Boca Raton, Florida: CRC Press.

Holloway, A. K., & Schnell, G. D. (1997). Relationship between numbers of the endangered American burying beetle *Nicrophorus americanus* Oliver (Coleoptera: Silphidae) and available food resources. *Biological Conservation, 81*, 145-152.

Kataev, G. D. (1995). Small mammals. In V. V. Sytchev (Ed.) *Forest ecosystems of Kola Peninsula under atmospheric pollution influence of smelters* (pp. 102-110). St. Petersburg, Russia: Russian Academy of Sciences (in Russian).

Kataev, G. D., Suomela, J., & Palokangas, P. (1994). Densities of microtine rodents along a pollution gradient from a copper-nickel smelter. *Oecologia, 97*, 491-498.

Koch, K. (1989). *Die Käfer Mitteleuropas. Ökologie, Bd 1. (Beetles of Central Europe. Ecology, Vol. 1).* Krefeld, Germany: Goecke and Evers (in German).

Koroleva, N. (1993). Pollution-induced changes in forest vegetation structure as revealed by the ordination test. In M. V. Kozlov, E. Haukioja, & V. T. Yarmishko (Eds), *Aerial pollution in Kola Peninsula: Proceedings of the international workshop, 14-16 April 1992, St. Petersburg* (pp. 339-345). Apatity, Russia: Kola Science Centre.

Kozlov, M. V. (1985). Changes in communities of insect herbivores affected by airborne pollutants near the non-ferrous smelter. *Problems of Biosphere (Information Bulletin), 11*, 76-90 (in Russian).

Kozlov, M. V. (1990). *Impact of anthropogenic factors on the populations of terrestrial insects. (Itogi Nauki i Techniki, Entomologija, vol. 13).* Moscow, Russia: All-Union Institute of Scientific and Technical Information (in Russian).

Kozlov, M. V. (1997). Pollution impact on insect biodiversity in boreal forests: evaluation of effects and perspectives of recovery. In R. M. M. Crawford (Ed.), *Disturbance and recovery in Arctic lands: An ecological perspective: Proceedings of the NATO advanced research workshop on disturbance and recovery of arctic terrestrial ecosystems, Rovaniemi, Finland, 24-30 September 1995. (NATO ASI series. Partnership subseries 2. Environment, vol. 25)* (pp. 213-250). Dordrecht, The Netherlands: Kluwer Academic Publishers.

Kozlov, M. V. (2001). Snowpack changes around a nickel-copper smelter at Monchegorsk, northwestern Russia. *Canadian Journal of Forest Research, 31*, 1684-1690.

Kozlov, M. V. (2002). Changes in wind regime around a nickel-copper smelter at Monchegorsk, northwestern Russia. *International Journal of Biometeorology, 46*, 76-80.

Kozlov, M. V. (2003). Density fluctuations of the leafminer *Phyllonorycter strigulatella* (Lepidoptera: Gracillariidae) in the impact zone of a power plant. *Environmenal Pollution, 12,* 1-10.

Kozlov, M. V. (2005). Sources of variation in concentrations of nickel and copper in mountain birch foliage near a nickel-copper smelter at Monchegorsk, north-western Russia: results of long-term monitoring. *Environmental Pollution* 135: 91-99.

Kozlov, M. V., & Barcan, V. S. (2000). Environmental contamination in the central part of the Kola Peninsula: history, documentation, and perception. *AMBIO, 29*, 512-517.

Kozlov, M. V., & Haukioja, E. (1995). Pollution-related environmental gradients around the "Severonikel" smelter complex on Kola Peninsula, Northwestern Russia. In M. Munawar, & M. Luotola (Eds.), *The contaminants in the Nordic ecosystem: the dynamics, processes and fate. (Ecovision World Monograph Series)* (pp. 59-69). The Netherlands: S. P. B. Academic Publishing.

Kozlov, M. V., Haukioja, E., Bakhtiarov, A. V., & Stroganov, D. N. (1995). Heavy metals in birch leaves around a nickel-copper smelter at Monchegorsk, Northwestern Russia. *Environmental Pollution*, *90*, 291-299.

Kryuchkov, V. V. (1993). Extreme anthropogenic loads and the northern ecosystem condition. *Ecological Applications*, *3*, 622-630.

Lebedeva, N. V. (1999). *Ecotoxicology and biogeochemistry of bird's geographical populations*. Moscow, Russia: Nauka (in Russian).

Lee, J. A. (1998). Unintentional experiments with terrestrial ecosystems: ecological effects of sulphur and nitrogen pollutants. *Journal of Ecology*, *86*, 1-12.

Lindén, H., Helle, E., Helle, P., & Wikman, M. (1996). Wildlife triangle scheme in Finland: methods and aims for monitoring wildlife populations. *Finnish Game Research*, *49*, 4-11.

Lomanov, I. K. (2000). Winter transect counts of game animals on large territories: results and prospects. *Zoologicheskij Zhurnal*, *79*, 430-436.

Lyabzina, S. N., & Lesonen, A. A. (2002). On the problem of utilization of carrion of invertebrate animals under anthropogenic impact. In T. K. Golovko, S. V. Zagirova, V. G. Zainullin, E. M. Lapteva, M. Yu. Markarova, V. A. Martynenko, Yu. N. Mineev, & G. P. Sidorov (Eds.), *Relevant problems of biology and ecology: Materials of presentations at 8th young scientists' scientific conference of the Institute of Biology of Komi Science Centre of the Ural division of the Russian Academy of Sciences* (pp. 88-90). Syktyvkar, Russia: Institute of Biology (in Russian).

Mukhacheva, S. V. (1994). Impact of copper smelter emissions on populations of bank vole. In P. L. Gorchakovskij (Ed.), *Biota of Ural: Information Materials* (pp. 35-36). Ekaterinburg, Russia: Ural Branch, Russian Academy of Sciences (in Russian).

Mukhacheva, S. V., & Lukjanov, O. A. (1997). Migration activity of bank vole (*Cletrionomys glareolus*, Schreber 1780) populations in gradient of industrial impact. *Ekologia (Ecology,* Ekaterinburg*), 0(1)*, 34-39 (in Russian).

Myllymäki, A., Paasikallio, A., Pankakoski, E., & Kanervo, V. (1971). Removal experiments on small quadrats as a means of rapid assessment of the abundance of small mammals. *Annales Zoologici Fennici*, *8*, 177-185.

Norrdahl, K., & Korpimäki, E. (1995). Small carnivores and prey population dynamics in summer. *Annales Zoologici Fennici*, *32*, 163-169.

Novikov, G. A. (1981). *Life on and under snow: Life of our birds and animals, Issue 3.* Leningrad, Russia: Leningrad State University (in Russian).

Ormerod, S. J., Pienkowski, M. W., & Watkinson, A. R. (1999). Communicating the value of ecology. *Journal of Applied Ecology*, *36*, 847-855.

Panichev, N. A., Kataev, G. D., & Nosova, E. B. (1993). Contents of heavy metals in tissues of grey-sided voles (*Cletrionomus rufocanus*) in surroundings of Monchegorsk. In M. V. Kozlov, E. Haukioja, & V. T. Yarmishko (Eds), *Aerial pollution in Kola Peninsula: Proceedings of the international workshop, 14-16 April 1992, St. Petersburg* (p. 210). Apatity, Russia: Kola Science Centre.

Priklonsky, S. G. (1965). Coefficients for the analysis of data obtained during the winter censusing of game animals by tracks. *Bulletin of Moscow Society of Naturalists, Biological Series*, *70(6)*, 5-12 (in Russian).

Priklonsky, S. G. (1973). Route censusing of game animals in winter. In A. S. Rak (Ed.), *Methods of censusing of game animals in forest zone: Proceedings of Okskij State Reserve, vol. 11* (pp. 35-62). Ryazan, Russia: Moskovskij Rabochij (in Russian).

Pulliam, H. R. (1988). Sources, sinks, and population regulation. *American Naturalist, 132*, 652-661

Rigina, O., & Kozlov, M. (1999). Pollution impact on sub-Arctic northern taiga forests in the Kola peninsula, Russia. In J. L. Innes, & J. Oleksyn (Eds.), *Forest dynamics in heavily polluted regions: IUFRO Research Series, No 1* (pp. 37-65). Wallingford, UK: CAB International.

Ruohomäki, K., Kaitaniemi, P., Kozlov, M. V., Tammaru, T., & Haukioja, E. (1996). Density and performance of *Epirrita autumnata* (Lep., Geometridae) along three air pollution gradients in northern Europe. *Journal of Applied Ecology, 33*, 773-785.

SAS Institute. (1990). *SAS/STAT user's guide, Version 6.0.* Cary, NC: SAS Institute.

Semenov-Tjan-Shanskij, O. I., & Gilyazov, A. S. (1991). *Birds of Lapland.* Moscow, Russia: Nauka (in Russian).

Siivonen, L. (1977). *Pohjolan Nisäkkäät (Mammals of Northern Europe).* Helsinki, Finland: Otava (in Finnish).

Smirnov, V. S. (1964). Methods of density estimations of mammals: prerequisites for their perfection and evaluation of the accuracy of the results. *Proceedings of the Institute of Biology of the Ural Branch of the Academy of Science of USSR, Sverdlovsk, 39*, 3-54 (in Russian).

Solarz, W. (1998). On sources and sinks: what is new in population ecology. *Wiadomosci Ekologiczne, 44*, 181-194.

Spurgeon, D. J., & Hopkins, S. P. (1996). Risk assessment of the threat of secondary poisoning by metals to predators of earthworms in the vicinity of a primary smelting works. *The Science of the Total Environment, 187*, 167-183.

Stchegolev, V. I. (1977). Bird censusing in forest zone. In P. A. Zajantshkauskas, G. A. Noskov, A. M. Bolotnikov, G. I. Volskis, & N. A. Rashkevich (Eds.), *Methods of investigation of productivity and species structure of birds within their areals. Part 1* (pp. 95-102). Vilnus, Lithuania: Mokslas (in Russian).

Tikkanen, E., & Niemelä, I. (Eds.) (1995). *Kola Peninsula pollutants and forest ecosystems in Lapland: Final report of the Lapland Forest Damage Project.* Rovaniemi, Finland: Finnish Forest Research Institute.

Valkama, J. & Kozlov, M. V. (2001). Impact of climatic factors on developmental stability of mountain birches growing in a contaminated area. *Journal of Applied Ecology, 38*, 665-673.

Watkinson, A. R. & Sutherland, W. J. (1995). Sources, sinks and pseudo-sinks. *Journal of Animal Ecology, 64*, 126-130.

Zvereva, E. L., & Kozlov, M. V. (2001). Effects of pollution-induced habitat disturbance on the response of willow to simulated herbivory. *Journal of Ecology, 89*, 21-30.

Zvereva, E. L., & Kozlov, M. V. (2004). Facilitative effects of top-canopy plants on four dwarf shrub species in habitats severely disturbed by pollution. *Journal of Ecology, 92*, 288-296.

Zvereva, E. L., Kozlov, M. V., & Neuvonen, S. (1995). Population density and performance of *Melasoma lapponica* (Coleoptera: Chrysomelidae) in surroundings of smelter complex. *Environmental Entomology, 24*, 707-715.

In: Trends in Biodiversity Research
Editor: A. R. Burk, pp. 101-116

ISBN 1-59454-385-2

Chapter 4

DISPARATE STAKEHOLDER MANAGEMENT OF WILDLIFE ISSUES IN THE SOUTHERN GREATER YELLOWSTONE AREA

Lynne Koontz*
U.S. Geological Survey, Fort Collins, Colorado
Dana Hoag
Department of Agricultural and Resource Economics
Colorado State University, Fort Collins, Colorado

ABSTRACT

The authors combined concepts from decision analysis, political and institutional analysis, and public choice economics to develop an approach, called Disparate Stakeholder Management (DSM), that integrates these concepts to help decision makers better describe, measure, communicate and resolve management issues with disparate stakeholders. They then apply the DSM to an actual case study concerning elk and bison management in the Greater Yellowstone Area. Knowing stakeholders' preferences for management outcomes and the opportunities for developing a compromised solution allows for a more complete understanding of what influences the management decision.

INTRODUCTION

Natural resource management decisions are complicated by multiple property rights, management objectives, and stakeholders with varying degrees of influence over the decision making process. In order to make efficient decisions, managers must incorporate the opinions and values of the involved stakeholders as well as understand the complex institutional constraints and opportunities that influence the decision-making process. Involved federal, state, local, private and public stakeholder groups have diverse values and preferences about the use and management of public resources. Underlying institutional factors give certain

* lynne_koontz@usgs.gov 970-226-9384.

stakeholders a greater level of influence over the policy outcome. How stakeholders use their influence can greatly effect the time, effort and costs of the decision making process. The overall result of an individual stakeholder or stakeholder group's influence on a negotiation will depend both on their relative power and their level of conviction for a particular outcome.

Many tools have been developed to facilitate group negotiation and decision-making. Decision analysis models such as the Analytical Hierarchy Process (AHP) are commonly used to prioritize the goals and objectives of stakeholders' preferences for resource planning by formally structuring conflicts and assisting decision makers in developing a compromised solution (Forman, 1998). Institutional models such as the Legal Institutional Analysis Model (LIAM) have been used to describe the organizational rules of behavior and the institutional boundaries constraining the management decision (Lamb et al., 1998). While some stakeholders will not be able to effectively influence the outcome under the existing institutional constraints, public choice models have been used to predict the potential success of rent-seeking activity (spending additional time and money to exert political pressure) to change the political rules (Becker, 1983).

While these tools have been successful at addressing a certain piece of the natural resource decision making process, their use in isolation is not enough to fully depict the complexities of the physical and biological systems with the rules and constraints of the underlying economic and political systems. Often this type of information is not understood until after the decision has been made. We combined concepts from decision analysis, political and institutional analysis, and public choice economics to develop an approach, called Disparate Stakeholder Management (DSM), that integrates these concepts to help decision makers better describe, measure, communicate and resolve management issues with disparate stakeholders. Then we applied the DSM to an actual case study concerning elk and bison management in the Greater Yellowstone Area. Knowing stakeholders' preferences for management outcomes and the opportunities for developing a compromised solution allows for a more complete understanding of what influences the management decision.

Case Study

For more than the past ten years, the U.S. Fish & Wildlife Service (FWS) and the National Park Service (NPS) have been in the process of preparing a plan to manage the bison and elk inhabiting the National Elk Refuge (NER) and Grand Teton National Park (GTNP) near Jackson Hole, Wyoming. These animals are part of the bison and elk herds in Jackson, one of the largest concentrations of free-ranging bison and elk in the world. When deep snows cover the vegetation or the vegetation has been eaten by the elk, the FWS provides supplemental feed in the form alfalfa hay pellets on the NER. The Jackson bison herd population has been increasing rapidly over the past 20 years as the herd discovered the supplemental feed distributed for elk on the NER. The winter feed program at the NER artificially concentrates the elk and bison, thereby increasing the transmission and frequency of several diseases including brucellosis. A 1996 interagency management plan was approved that allowed public hunting of bison on NER lands to control the bison population. In 1998 an animal rights stakeholder group, Fund for Animals (FUND), sued the U.S. government for pending management actions (i.e. public hunting) of the Jackson bison herd. The FUND claimed that the 1996 interagency management plan had failed to adequately address the effects of winter-feeding of elk at the NER on the Jackson bison herd. The Washington DC district court judge agreed and halted fatal management actions of bison on the NER until an Environmental Impact Statement (EIS) is completed.

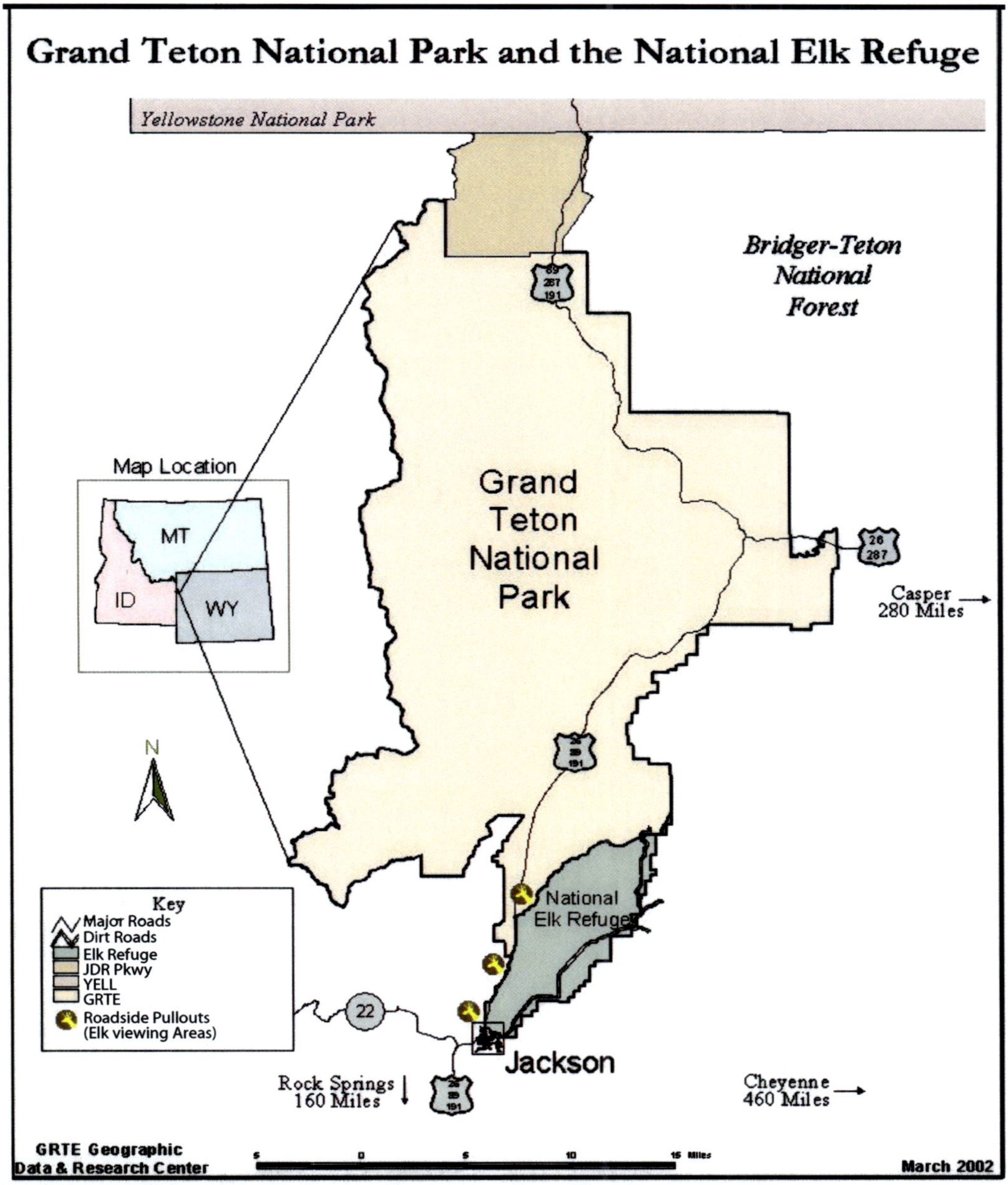

Figure 1. Map of the Jackson Elk and Bison Management Planning Area.

The EIS must develop a range of alternatives for managing the Jackson bison and elk herds which address the politically and socially sensitive issues of habitat management, disease management, winter feeding and hunting programs related to the NER and GTNP. Stakeholders have diverse and strong preferences for each of these management issues and have become polarized to the point where it is difficult to look at how important each issue is in the overall decision framework. Because the bison and elk herds migrate across several jurisdictional boundaries--the National Elk Refuge, Grand Teton and Yellowstone National Parks, the Bridger-Teton National Forest, and state and private lands—the FWS and NPS seek a cooperative effort among federal and state agencies and other stakeholders to develop a coordinated approach for managing the Jackson bison and elk herds. Given that a lawsuit from a stakeholder interest group created the need for this EIS, reaching a common ground solution could potentially avoid or greatly reduce the additional amount of time, money, and other resources that get expended by the federal government and stakeholder groups in the process leading to the actual implementation of a management plan alternative. Figure 1 provides a map of the Jackson Elk and Bison management study area.

PROCEDURES

To collect the information needed to construct the DSM framework, we interviewed 49 individuals representing 30 stakeholder organizations involved in the elk and bison management plan. The thirty stakeholder organizations interviewed included federal and state resource management agencies; tribal representatives; local government representatives; environmental organizations; agricultural/ranching representatives; hunting organizations; and outfitting organizations. At least one representative from each of the thirty organizations was interviewed. Whenever possible, more than one representative from an organization was interviewed, especially within the most actively involved agencies and organizations.

DEVELOPING THE DSM FRAMEWORK

Step 1: Structuring the Problem

The DSM starts with a hierarchy to describe the management problem in detail. The hierarchy reduces a problem into smaller decision points that are choice variables in the policy. We used the Analytical Hierarchy Process (AHP) to design the hierarchy and elicit stakeholder preferences. AHP is commonly used to prioritize the goals and objectives of stakeholders' preferences for resource planning by formally structuring conflicts and assisting decision makers in developing a compromised solution (Forman, 1998). The AHP approach organizes the management decision in a hierarchy framework that allows for the weighting of all factors influencing the decision.

During the early stages of the EIS process we worked extensively with the NPS and FWS managers (EIS team) to develop and define the management issues needed to form the AHP hierarchy. The hierarchy provided the EIS Team an effective way to visualize and conceptualize the large and detailed problem by breaking the problem down into all of its related parts. Consequently, the hierarchy was additionally able to assist the EIS Team in their process of structuring and developing the draft management alternatives.

The elk and bison management hierarchy is shown in Figure 2. The main management objectives identified through our discussions with stakeholders and policy makers deal with:

1) the transmission and prevalence of diseases; 2) managing forage by means of supplemental winter feeding and/or enhancing or increasing winter habitat; and 3) the use of hunting programs to control herd populations on the NER and GTNP. Management activities or strategies were identified for each of the main management objectives. For managing disease, strategies include one or more of the following: *vaccination*, *test & slaughter*, and *dispersal* (e.g., management that leads to increasing the distribution of animals over the landscape, thereby reducing the amount of concentration and disease risk). For managing forage, supplemental winter feeding strategies include the options of *annual feeding*, *emergency feeding* (feed only if there is not enough forage available), and *no feeding.* Forage management activities related to enhancing forage or increasing winter range include the options of *no active forage management, maintain current conditions, enhance forage/range in Jackson,* and *restore historic migrations outside of Jackson.* Management activities related to the use of hunting include *allow hunting on the GTNP and NER*, *only allow hunting on the NER*, and *no hunting allowed.* Because most stakeholders felt differently on how to manage elk or bison (i.e. wanted elk fed but not bison or wanted bison vaccinated but not elk) the management strategies were separated for bison and elk management options (Figure 2).

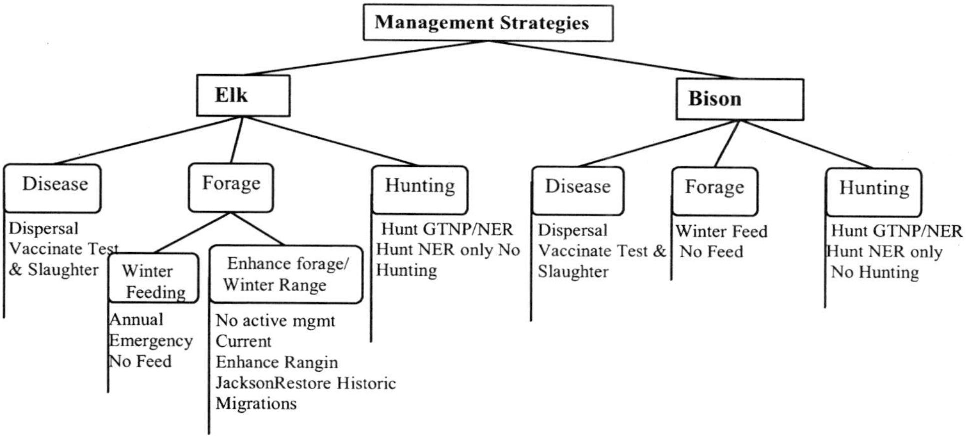

Figure 2. AHP Hierarchy for Elk and Bison Management Strategies.

Stakeholders were asked to fill out the AHP pairwise comparison survey to measure their weighted preferences for all of elk and bison management strategies and management objectives in Figure 1. Besides weighting of all factors influencing the decision, the AHP hierarchy framework provides traceability for every management issue in the overall decision context. The AHP weighting scores sum to one and can be analyzed at the localized or the overall decision context level. The localized scores focus on the preferences for a particular management option, where the overall decision scores include the weighting of the complete hierarchy. An example is shown in Figure 3 where at the localized level within the winter feeding for elk category, out of a total preference weight of 100% one conservation organization gave 16% to allowing annual feeding, 77% to allowing emergency feeding, and 7% to not allowing feeding. These scores seem to indicate this conservation organization has a very strong preference for a sufficient/emergency winter feed program for elk. Typically pubic meetings and discussions among stakeholder groups become polarized at this localized level making it difficult to look at how important one issue is as compared to other management issues.

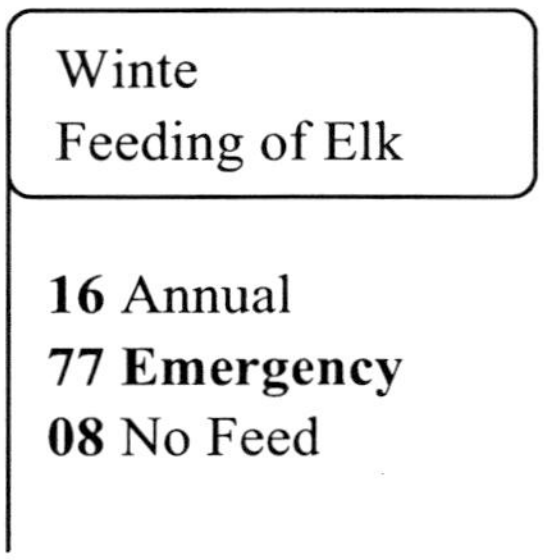

Figure 3. Example of a Conservation Group's Preference Weightings at the Localized Level.

Because the AHP weights each level of the hierarchy, we can analyze the importance of emergency elk winter feeding in terms of the overall management decision. As illustrated in Figure 4, at the top hierarchy level the conservation group gave 90% of their preference weight to elk management issues and only 10% to bison management issues. At the next level, elk forage issues were the most important accounting for 62% out of the 90% for elk management issues. Under elk forage issues, the majority of the preference weight went to enhancing the winter range, only 6% of the overall preference weight went to elk winter feeding issues. Even though it seemed like and important issue at the local level (Figure 3), emergency winter feeding of elk only gets 5% of this conservation organization's overall importance weight when all issues are considered (Figure 4).

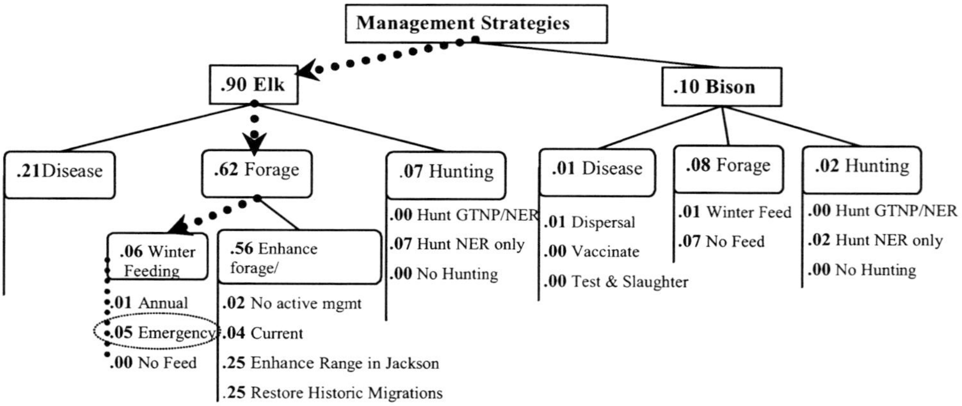

Figure 4. Tracing the Importance of Sufficient Winter Feeding of Elk a Conservation Group's Overall Preference Weighting.

Tracing out the importance of each issue in the overall context empowers the decision makers with the ability to: 1) go beyond the polarized public meeting discussions and see what issues are most and least important to every stakeholder group when all issues are considered; 2) develop compromised solutions that best maintain the interests of what was important to the most groups as possible; 3) to be able go back and meet with each stakeholder and show how their preferences were incorporated in the planning process.

Step 2: Building the Policy Possibilities Frontier

The second step in developing the DSM framework is to develop a display format that is easy for decision makers to understand and compare stakeholder preferences. Analogous to a production possibilities frontier in the economic literature (Bromley, 1989; Griffin, 1991; and Rhodes and Wilson,1995), a policy possibilities frontier (PPF), was developed to represent the technically efficient combinations of two types of land use management objectives with many alternative combinations of each objective possible along the curve. The PPF has two management objectives with many alternative policy combinations of each objective possible along the curve that can be produced using available resources.

Two management objective proxies, Land Use Management Practice 1 and Practice 2, represent the multiple objectives associated with each resource management objective (Figure 5). Current environmental laws and regulations as well as each land management agency's mandated mission, creates differing degrees of property rights (policy possibilities) over the management of the Jackson herds. The actual placement of the joint EIS team PPF curve is a combination of all land management agencies PPFs (PPF_{Joint} in Figure 5). The assumption of diminishing marginal returns creates a bowed PPF because every alternative offers some of each land use management practice objective. Amounts of land use services exterior the PPF_{Joint} boundary are not achievable without social reform and will not be considered.

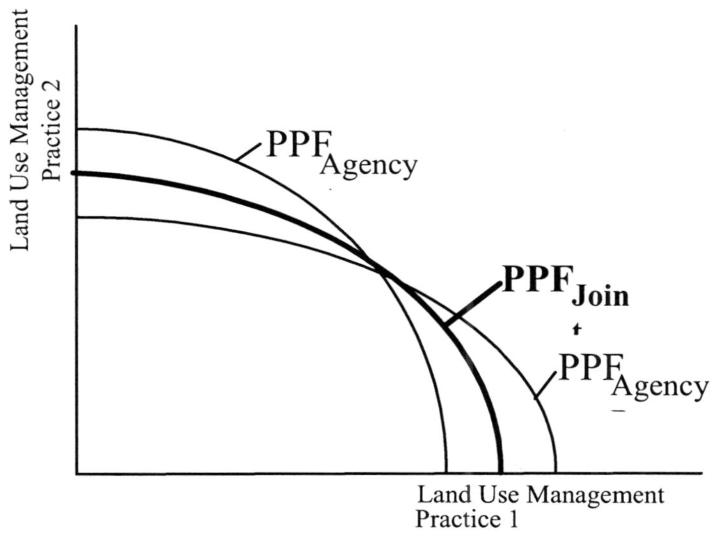

Figure 5. Policy Preference Frontier in a Natural Resource Management Planning Process.

Step 3: Policy Preference Mapping

Stakeholders that do not have property rights will not have leverage in determining the actual placement of the PPF_{Joint} curve. After the PPF_{Joint} curve boundaries have been legally established, it is assumed that the stakeholder groups involved in the public participation process can influence the position of the decision outcome along the PPF_{Joint} curve. Conceptually, the PPF_{Joint} curve will have a limited number of management alternatives that can be produced.

The management options stakeholders weighted in the AHP preference survey were placed within a spectrum of management practices ranging from a "natural" land use approach to a more "managed" land use approach. The most natural management approach allowed in the preference survey would use dispersal to manage disease and would not allow hunting or winter feeding. The most managed management approach allowed in the preference survey would use test and slaughter to manage disease, have an annual winter feeding program, and allow hunting on both the refuge and park. Indexes were developed in order to match stakeholders' AHP preference weightings with the placement of the management alternatives on the PPF_{Joint} curve. Because it was possible to combine management options that are considered natural with options that are considered managed, each management alternative has a natural and a managed index score to represent the amount of natural regulation and managed land use services included in each alternative (Table 1). The tangency slope of each stakeholder's preference index score provided the associated preference ratio between natural and managed management options. Each stakeholder's preference ratio tradeoff determines his or her placement on the PPF_{Joint} curve.

Table 1. Preference Index Percentages

Preference Index	Natural	Managed
Disease Management		
Dispersal	100%	0%
Vaccinate	25%	75%
Test & Slaughter	0%	100%
Winter Feeding		
Annual	0%	100%
Emergency	40%	60%
No Feeding	100%	0%
Hunting		
Both GTNP/NER	0%	100%
Only NER	25%	75%
No Hunting	100%	0%

In conjunction with the FWS and NPS, we matched the AHP preference weighting results to the potential policy alternatives. Using a PPF, both draft EIS management alternatives and stakeholder preferences were mapped in the same continuum. In this way, the degree that any particular policy (EIS management alternative) matched any particular stakeholder's preferences could be observed. As illustrated in Figure 6, the PPF conveniently displays the natural vs. managed spectrum of stakeholder preferences and draft EIS management alternatives and shows how stakeholder preferences align with the EIS management alternatives. Alternative A, contains the most hands off management approach with the highest possible amounts of dispersal, no winter-feeding, and no hunting. Alternative G has the most managed management options with allowing vaccination, annual winter feeding, and hunting on both the refuge and the park. No alternative is close to the managed border because no alternative included test and slaughter as a management option. Alternatives B, C, D, E, and F contain combinations of natural and managed management options. Since the AHP preference survey allowed stakeholders to choose any amount of each management option, some stakeholders fell between the alternatives.

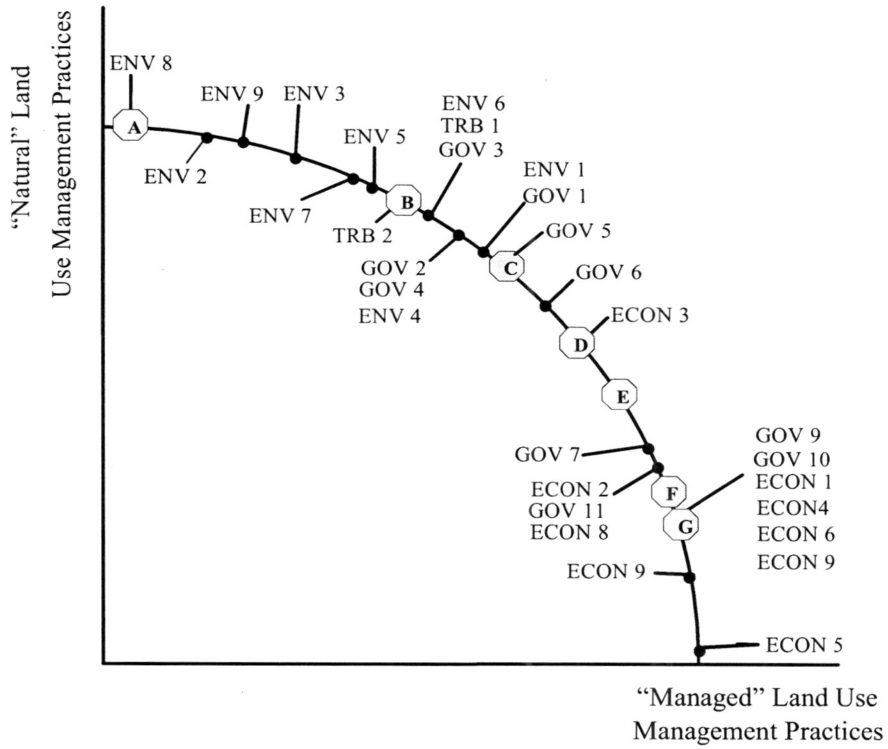

Figure 6. The Policy Possibilities Frontier for the EIS Elk Management Options.
Organizational Code Key:

GOV	= Government Interests (includes federal, state, and local)
ECON	= Economic Interests (includes agricultural, local business, hunting, and outfitting)
ENV	= Environmental Interests (includesconservation groups and animal rights)
TRB	= Tribal

Figure 6 illustrates the range of the current (July 2004) draft EIS management alternatives along the natural to managed land use practices spectrum. However, the initial set of alternatives developed by the EIS team excluded Alternatives B and C. By using the PPF, we were able to show the EIS team the potential gaps in preferred management alternatives along the curve. In fact, the initial set of alternatives did not include an alternative that came close to matching the preferences of the EIS Team agencies. As a result, the EIS Team added a new alternative and modified an existing alternative to more accurately reflect the range of stakeholder preferences identified by the PPF. The EIS Team intends on using our DSM work in efforts to work with stakeholders to identify areas of common ground after the draft EIS is released.

Step 4: Developing Compromised Solutions

Because the allocation of scarce resources necessarily excludes or limits some types of resource use, stakeholders have an incentive to compete for a larger share of the allocation through the political process. Rent seeking is the activity of influencing the political process by means of lobbying, media campaigns, public hearings, and litigation to obtain favorable results or avoid unfavorable ones. There will be certain issues in the decision (hunting, feeding, or vaccination) that some stakeholders might be less willing to agree on a compromise if the outcome looks unfavorable. After the planning team selects a Draft EIS preferred alternative, if the outcome is not close to the preferences of a given stakeholder, that stakeholder can increase its rent seeking activities to try to force a more favorable outcome. The difficulty in reaching a compromised solution has important welfare implications because the transactions costs associated with individual or group efforts to maximize their own utility can generate social waste rather than social surplus (Buchanan et al. 1980). Therefore, decision makers need to understand the level of importance or conviction each stakeholder holds for a particular management issue to determine where acceptable compromises are more likely to be reached.

The level of difficulty for reaching a compromised solution among stakeholders will depend on the degree of importance of each issue to a stakeholder (the policy benefit) and how different each draft alternative is to their preferred alternative (the policy cost), and the abilities stakeholders have to influence the outcome (political influence). Reaching a compromised solution could potentially avoid or greatly reduce the amount of time, money, and other resources that get expended by stakeholder groups in the process leading to the actual implementation of a management plan alternative. To determine which management alternatives are most likely to result in a compromised solution, results from the AHP survey were used to estimate the policy benefit and policy cost of the management alternatives and develop stakeholder compromise ratings for each management alternative. The compromise rating scores gives the decision maker a tool to evaluate stakeholder preferences, where the consequences of any policy choice are revealed. The decision maker will know explicitly how each stakeholder is impacted.

The policy cost was determined by the difference between a stakeholder's preferred management preference weighting scores and the weighting scores of each EIS management alternative. In Figure 6, this is represented by the distance between each stakeholder's placement on the PPF and the placement of each draft management alternative, these scores are at the localized AHP level. However, a stakeholder's position on the PPF does not account for how important the different issues are in the overall management decision context (i.e., how important issues related to disease management are to forage management and/or hunting issues). If all stakeholders did equally care about all management issues, the PPF would fully represent stakeholders' policy costs and benefits. As shown by the example in Figure 4, while some stakeholders may care equally about all management issues, others will care a great deal about one issue more than the others. The overall importance weights each stakeholder gave to the overall management strategies categories of disease management, forage management, and hunting were used to represent the policy benefit of each alternative.

Figures 7 and 8 show the aggregate preference weightings by stakeholder groups on the importance of elk and bison management issues, respectively. As shown in Figures 7 and 8, most stakeholder groups felt that one or two of the management issues were more important than the others issues for managing elk and/or bison (most did not weight all issues as having equal importance). As shown in Figure 7, most stakeholder groups thought forage management (winter range and/or winter feeding) was an important management issue for elk. Hunting was also an important management issue for elk, especially with representatives from the state and local government, tribal, agricultural interests, and hunting and outfitting organizations. Several groups rated disease management as an issue of low importance compared to forage and hunting issues indicating possible compromises on disease issues are more likely (Figure 7).

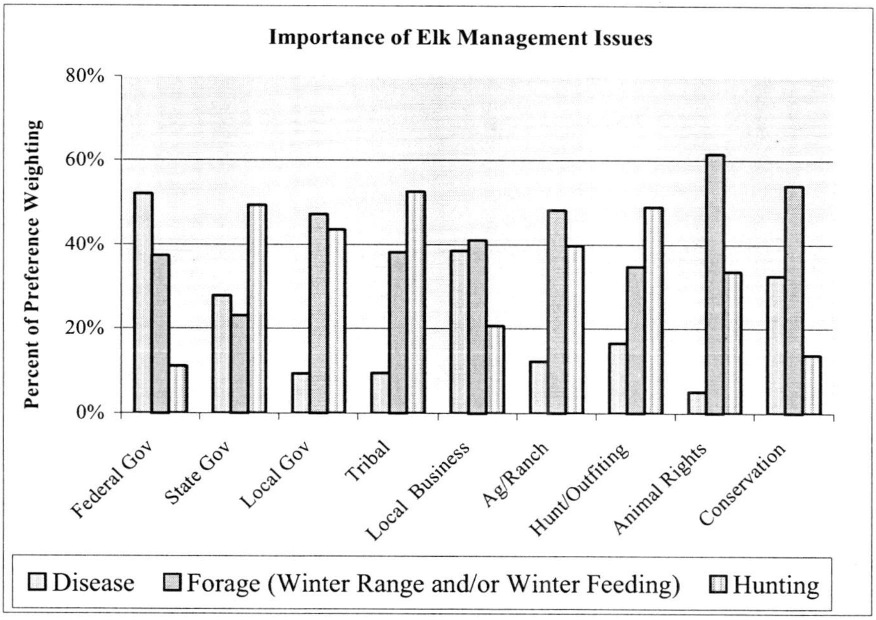

Figure 7. Stakeholder Preference Results for Elk Management Issues

As shown in Figure 8, for bison management the issue of hunting was strongly more important to local government and hunting and outfitting representatives, indicating possible compromises on bison hunting issues are not likely. The issue of winter range and feeding was strongly more important to tribal, animal rights, and conservation groups, indicating possible compromises on bison feeding issues are not likely.

A comparison of the main stakeholder group compromise ratings for each management alternative is presented in Table 2. These scores represent the combined ratings for all individuals within each stakeholder category. Table 2 reports the total compromise rating for each alternative as well as how much of the total rating is due to elk related or bison related management issues. A compromise rating of zero would indicate all individuals of the stakeholder group were completely satisfied will all elk and bison management aspects for the alternative. The farther a compromise score is away from zero suggests that individuals within the stakeholder group would be less satisfied with that particular alternative and therefore reaching an acceptable compromise would be more difficult. The closer a compromise rating score is to zero suggests that individuals within the stakeholder group are more satisfied with that alternative as compared to alternatives with higher compromised rating scores. Therefore, acceptable compromises with a particular stakeholder group will be more easily reached for alternatives with lower compromise rating scores (Table 2).

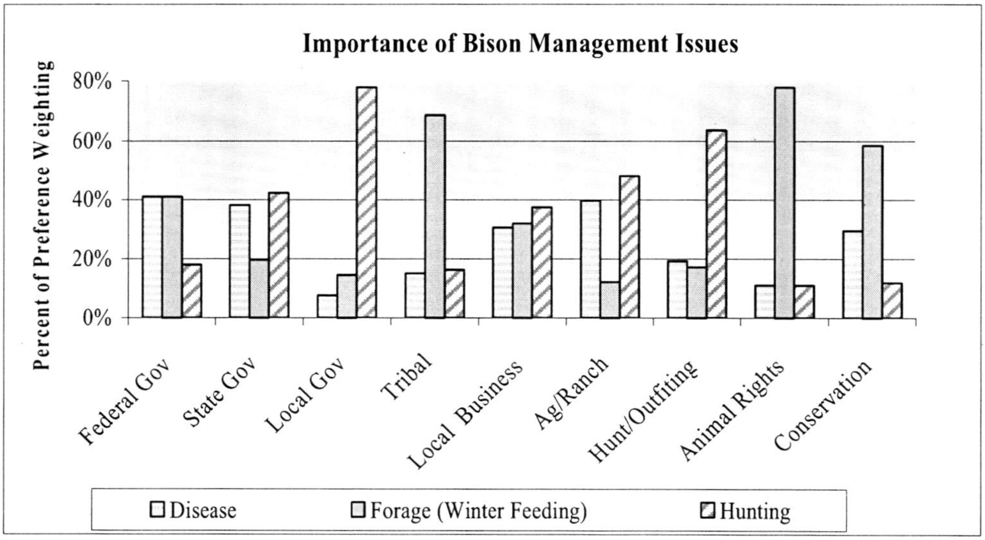

Figure 8. Stakeholder Preference Results for Bison Management Issues.

Because of similar scoring results, federal, state, and local government agencies were aggregated into the government agencies category and hunting, outfitting, agricultural, and local business interests were aggregated into an economic interests category. Conservation groups and animal rights organizations compromise scoring results were not similar and therefore could not be aggregated to represent a more general category of environmental interests.

As Shown in Table 2, compromise ratings indicate Alternatives C, F, and D are the most likely to reach an agreeable compromise by the most stakeholders. Alternatives G and B closely follow while Alternatives A and E stand out as alternatives that will not be agreeable to a majority of the stakeholders.

When examining the PPF in Figure 6, it would be expected that the alternatives falling in the middle of the natural vs. managed management spectrum would be easier to reach a compromised solution while the alternatives closest to the natural (Alternative A) and managed (Alternatives F and G) endpoints would be the hardest to reach a compromise. Alternative A is considered to be the animal rights groups preferred alternative that would not allow elk or bison to be fed or hunted. As expected, Alternative A would have the highest overall level of opposition. However, the only other alternative with a high compromise rating, Alternative E, is not at the other extreme end of the management spectrum. Alternative E is a continuance of the current management activities, which means bison hunting is not permitted. As shown in Figure 8, bison hunting is significantly more important than disease or forage issues to several stakeholder groups. The compromise scoring results in Table 2 indicate that how important the overall issues are matters more than the actual distance on the PPF in Figure 6. This gives the decision makers a tool work with stakeholders to identify areas of common ground.

Table 2. Group Aggregate Stakeholder Compromise Ratings for Each Management Alternative

	Government Agencies	Economic Interests	Conservati on Groups	Animal Rights Groups	Tribes	Average of All Groups
Alternative A						
Elk Issues	1.48	1.89	0.97	1.01	1.12	1.47
Bison Issues	2.43	2.82	1.65	0.41	1.99	2.2
Total	*3.91*	*4.71*	*2.63*	*1.43*	*3.11*	*3.67*
Alternative B						
Elk Issues	1.02	1.35	0.8	1.21	0.82	1.1
Bison Issues	0.77	0.84	0.46	0.45	0.26	0.67
Total	*1.78*	*2.19*	*1.26*	*1.66*	*1.08*	*1.77*
Alternative C						
Elk Issues	0.85	1.13	0.76	1.11	0.78	0.96
Bison Issues	0.68	0.74	0.37	0.46	0.26	0.59
Total	*1.53*	*1.87*	*1.13*	*1.56*	*1.04*	*1.55*
Alternative D						
Elk Issues	0.91	0.97	1.22	1.7	0.63	1.02
Bison Issues	0.58	0.63	0.63	0.94	0.7	0.66
Total	*1.49*	*1.61*	*1.85*	*2.65*	*1.32*	*1.68*
Alternative E						
Elk Issues	0.87	0.58	1.39	1.82	0.9	0.94
Bison Issues	2.22	2.50	2.51	1.73	3.15	2.39
Total	*3.09*	*3.08*	*3.90*	*3.55*	*4.05*	*3.33*
Alternative F						
Elk Issues	0.75	0.39	1.26	1.61	0.96	0.81
Bison Issues	0.50	0.43	1.36	1.67	1.37	0.8
Total	*1.26*	*0.82*	*2.61*	*3.28*	*2.33*	*1.61*
Alternative G						
Elk Issues	0.79	0.38	1.33	1.63	0.98	0.83
Bison Issues	0.56	0.45	1.53	1.85	1.54	0.88
Total	*1.35*	*0.83*	*2.86*	*3.48*	*2.52*	*1.71*

Note: The farther a compromise score is away from zero suggests that individuals within the stakeholder group would be less satisfied with that particular alternative and therefore reaching an acceptable compromise would be more difficult.

Step 5: Accounting for Political Influence

The final step in developing the DSM is accounting for how political influence can affect the compromised solutions. Decision-making activities for federal land management take place within established boundaries provided by statute, legal precedent and tradition. Institutional analysis provides an assessment of these boundaries by studying the legal, political, and administrative processes through which public policy decisions are made (Ingram et al. 1984). Interest in how institutions affect the decision-making process continues to increase as institutions become larger, more autonomous and more influential in political decision-making (March and Olsen 1984; Lamb et al. 1999). The Legal Institutional Analysis Model (LIAM) is a computerized model that examines the political aspects of a natural resource conflict (Lamb et al. 1998). The model enables the various stakeholders involved to understand the nature of the issue at hand as well as evaluate the roles, needs, and power of organizations involved in a natural resource conflict.

The LIAM uses a questionnaire to measure respondent knowledge about an organization's (stakeholder's) likely role and sources of power in the natural resource conflict (Taylor 1993). Organizational power is determined by the resources, expertise, and outside support that a stakeholder has as well as the degree to which it is willing to use these elements of power to force an outcome that is favorable to its own position (Wilds 1988). The three LIAM power measures (resource, information, and support) have several distinct attributes that are measured to characterize an organization's level of power. We had stakeholders complete the LIAM survey in order to assess the types of political power of their organization for the elk and bison planning process. Results from the LIAM survey were used to determine if the political influence of each stakeholder group affects the compromise ratings. Results indicate that no one or group of stakeholders has enough power characteristics to drastically change the outcome under the current property rights. In order to alter the outcome, a stakeholder would need an exceptionally high level of influence or would have to litigate to get the property rights changed.

CONCLUSIONS

Managers must consider all opinions when they develop management policies. By constructing the DSM framework, we were able to predict the level of support and conflict for all relevant policy decisions, and identify who would support or oppose each decision. The DSM approach has several advantages. First, it reduces polarity in stakeholder preferences by breaking problems down into smaller pieces where acceptable compromises are more likely. Second, it helps identify many dimensions of a problem, which gives policy makers more policy options. Third, it helps assure policy makers that policy options offered for consideration cover the gambit of stakeholder preferences. And fourth it promotes inclusion and equity for stakeholders by applying a consistent process to develop the PPM.

Even in early initial stages of developing the DSM, it has proved to be a useful decision tool to the federal land managers and planners. The DSM hierarchy assisted the EIS Team in their process of structuring and developing the draft management alternatives. Based on the DSM, the EIS team modified one alternative and added a new alternative to better reflect the preferences of different stakeholder groups (including the EIS team agencies). Additionally, the EIS team would like to use the DSM in efforts to work with stakeholders to identify areas of common ground after the draft EIS is released. The DSM can increase the overall efficiency of the natural resource decision-making process and reduce the risk of having the process sent into litigation.

REFERENCES

Becker, G.S., 1983. A theory of competition among pressure groups for political influence, *The Quarterly Journal of Economics*, XCV111 (3), 371-400.

Bromley, D.W., 1989. *Economic Interests and Institutions*, Oxford, Basil Blackwell.

Buchanan, J.M., R.D. Tollison, and G. Tullock., 1980. *Toward a Theory of the Rent-Seeking Society*. Texas A&M University Press, College Station.

Forman, E., 1998. *Decision By Objectives*. McLean VA: Expert Choice Inc.

Griffin, R.C., 1991. The welfare analytics of transaction costs, externalities, and institutional choice, *American Journal of Agricultural Economics*, 73, 601-614.

Ingram, H. M., Mann, D.E., Weatherford, G.D., and H.J. Cortner., 1984. Guidelines for improved institutional analysis in water resources planning, *Water Resources Research,* 20(3), 323-334.

Lamb, B. L., J. G. Taylor, N. Burkardt, P. D. Ponds., 1998. A policy model to initiate environmental negotiations: three hydropower workshops, *Human Dimensions of Wildlife*, 3(4), 1-17.

Lamb, B. L., J. G. Taylor, N. Burkardt, P. D. Ponds, and L. Caughlan., 1999. Report to Participants in the Workshops to Initiate a Collaborative Planning Process for the Wyoming State Grizzly Bear Management Plan. URL: http://www.mesc.usgs.gov/pubs/liam-biblio.html August 20, 2000.

March, J. G. and J. P. Olsen., 1984. "The New Institutionalism: Organizational Factors in Political Life." *American Political Science Review*. V 78. 734-749.

Rhodes, T.C., and P.N. Wilson., 1995. Sky islands, squirrels, and scopes: the political economy of an environmental conflict, *Land Economics*, 71(1), 106-121.

Taylor, J.G. and B.L. Lamb., 1993. Using Role Analysis for Instream Flow Negotiations. In: G.R. Baumli (ed.), *Legal, Institutional, Financial and Environmental Aspects of Water Issues. Proceeding of the Specialty Conference on the Irrigation and Drainage and Water Resource Planning and Management Division of the American Society of Civil Engineers*. Pages 131-140. New York, NY: ASCE.

Wilds, L. J., 1988. The Legal-Institutional Analysis Model (LIAM): A Validation Study. Instream Flow Information Paper No. 25. Biological Report 88(33). U.S. Fish and Wildlife Service, Washington, DC.

In: Trends in Biodiversity Research
Editor: A. R. Burk, pp. 117-145
ISBN 1-59454-385-2

Chapter 5

THE IMPORTANCE OF LOW-INTENSITY FARMING SYSTEMS FOR FAUNA, FLORA AND HABITATS PROTECTED UNDER THE EUROPEAN "BIRDS" AND "HABITATS" DIRECTIVES: IS AGRICULTURE ESSENTIAL FOR PRESERVING BIODIVERSITY IN THE MEDITERRANEAN REGION?

Francisco Moreira[1], Manuel João Pinto[2], Inês Henriques[1] and Teresa Marques[1]
[1]Centro de Ecologia Aplicada "Prof. Baeta Neves", Instituto Superior de Agronomia, Tapada da Ajuda, Lisboa, Portugal;
[2]Jardim Botânico da Universidade de Lisboa, Museu Nacional de História Natural, Rua da Escola Politécnica, Lisboa, Portugal.

ABSTRACT

Growing research highlights the importance of maintaining low-intensity farming systems for preserving European biodiversity, particularly in the Mediterranean region. The European Directives 79/409/EEC (Birds directive) and 92/43/EEC (Habitats directive) are the main political instruments for nature conservation in Europe. They identify and list the habitats, flora and fauna species of higher conservation concern in Europe, for which a network of protected areas, named Natura 2000, is being implemented. The objective of this paper is to quantify the importance of low-intensity agriculture to maintaining Natura 2000 values in Mediterranean countries, using Portugal as a case study. Each protected species of fauna and flora, as well as each protected habitat, occurring in the country were ranked according to the degree of dependence on low-intensity farming systems, using a set of criteria. For vertebrates, 46.8% of the 96 species listed in EU directives and occurring in Portugal depended on low-intensity agriculture. Most of these consist of bird species associated with low-intensity arable and pastoral systems, particularly pseudosteppes and "montados". For plants, 34.7% of the 72 species also depended on extensive farming systems, particularly grazed grasslands. Finally, 20.8% of the 91 habitats occurring in the country corresponded to early or intermediate phases of vegetation succession (e.g. hay meadows, scrublands) benefiting from disturbance originating from grazing, ploughing or burning associated with low-intensity arable and pastoral systems. We end up identifying the main farming systems holding relevant biodiversity values occurring in Portugal and discussing the importance of low-intensity farming for the whole Mediterranean region.

INTRODUCTION

The Importance of Low-Intensity Farming Systems to Biodiversity

Vast regions of Europe, particularly in the Mediterranean region, have been shaped by humans for millennia, first through fire, then pastoral and agricultural activities. The use of burning, clearing, cutting, coppicing, terracing, cultivating, animal breeding and irrigating, created a diverse array of landscapes, which resulted in approximately half of the Mediterranean space being occupied by agriculture and the rest by forests (Blondel & Aronson 1999). This long-term interaction between man and nature has created many landscapes whose natural value is nowadays acknowledged.

Overall, it appears that human activities have been beneficial for many components of biological diversity, particularly in the Mediterranean basin (Blondel & Aronson 1999). As an example, several habitats with conservation value are clearly dependent on disturbance regimes and if left to natural recovering processes will evolve to other habitats dominated by shrubs or trees, often with lower conservation interest (European Commission 2003b), impoverishing habitat richness and the incidence of spots of conservation value at regional, national and European levels. Historically, such habitats have been maintained by human activities – livestock grazing, mowing, etc. – connected to traditional, low-intensity farming systems (LIFS). Thus they are the result of a historical background of rural practices (often resulting in what is called "semi-natural habitats"). Bignal & McCracken (1996) estimated that 42% of the habitats protected under the EU "Habitats" Directive (see below) occurring in the UK consist of managed farmland. Ostermann (1998) estimated that 28 of the 198 habitat types listed in this Directive could be threatened by the abandonment of LIFS. They are mostly grasslands, heaths and meadows. The same argument applies to a range of animals that usually require open land (e.g. steppe birds or sand-dwelling plants and invertebrates). This open land is often the result of farming practices that, if stopped or changed, will result in a loss of the habitat on which these species depend. Tucker (1997) showed that many bird species with unfavourable conservation status occur in low-intensity farming systems, including several globally threatened species occurring in the Mediterranean region such as the great bustard (*Otis tarda*), the lesser kestrel (*Falco naumanni*) and the Spanish imperial eagle (*Aquila adalberti*).

Species or habitats relying on low-intensity farming systems can be negatively affected by two main trends: agricultural intensification and land abandonment. Intensification is more common in northern Europe (e.g. Donald *et al.* 2001; Robinson & Sutherland 2002) and results, *inter alia*, in habitat simplification, drainage, introduction of irrigation crops, loss of fallow fields and increased use of agro-chemicals. Abandonment is a major trait in many

Mediterranean countries. Through natural vegetation regeneration and secondary succession, open fields become woody stands, ultimately leading to what is called "shrub encroachment". Abandonment is responsible for a substantial loss of small-scale patchiness, reducing openings and gaps towards a denser multilayered scrubland. In these circumstance natural forest recovery is facilitated. At the same time, there are several economic incentives for afforestation of former agricultural land (e.g. Fry 1989; Stoate *et al.* 2001; Suárez-Seoane *et al.* 2002). Both intensification and abandonment usually represent habitat degradation and loss for plants and animals currently considered of high conservation value and associated with low-intensity farming systems.

What Defines Low-Intensity Farming Systems

Beaufoy *et al.* (1994) and Bignal & McCracken (1996) defined a set of attributes characterising low-intensity farming systems (LIFS) in Europe. Such attributes, divided into livestock and crop-based systems, are all indicative of systems that have adapted their management techniques to cope with the natural environment constraints of the region. Important features of LIFS include a low nutrient input, low stocking density, low agro-chemical input, use of regional breeds of livestock, low degree of mechanisation, use of fallow in the crop rotation, low yield per hectare and absence of irrigation (Beaufoy *et al.* 1994). Based on these characteristics, these authors identified 3 broad types of LIFS found across Europe:

- *livestock systems*, occurring mainly in mountainous regions of Europe and also in Southern Europe. They range from sheep grazing in grasslands and scrublands in the Mediterranean region to cattle grazing in mountains. The traditional cork and holm oak open woodland (named "montados" in Portugal and "dehesas" in Spain) are included in this group. Livestock systems cover an important area in the Portuguese territory, shaping diverse vegetation types. The central granitic mountainous areas in Portugal are covered by vast scrublands rich in Ericaceae (*Erica* and *Calluna*), woody legumes (*Cytisus*, *Ulex* and *Genista*) and Cistaceae (*Cistus*, *Halimium* and *Tuberaria*) used for free-ranging livestock grazing, often in common land.
- *arable and permanent crop systems*, mostly concentrated in the Mediterranean region and ranging from extensive ricefields to the non-irrigated systems which use fallowing (in association with grazing) and create a pseudosteppe landscape of great importance for nature conservation. Permanent crops include olives, fruit and vines. In Portugal these systems occur mainly in the South part of the country.
- *mixed systems*, still occurring in several areas in Europe. They are small-scale, mostly subsistence, farming systems occurring in remote areas of the Mediterranean region and in mountains. They integrate crop production (cereals, vines, fruits) and livestock grazing, often in communal lands. In Portugal, they are common in the mountains.

Finally, these authors gave examples of several species of conservation concern associated to each system. They estimated that for Portugal, 60% of the Utilised Agricultural Area (UUA) in the country consists of LIFS.

A different approach was used by EEA (2004). Here the notion of "High nature value farmland" (HNVF) was used. Three types of HNVF were identified: (1) Farmland with a high proportion of semi-natural vegetation; (2) Farmland dominated by low intensity agriculture or a mosaic of semi-natural and cultivated land and small scale features; (3) Farmland supporting rare species or a high proportion of European or world populations. Using a farm system approach, this report identified the following types of HNVF (EEA 2004):

- *low intensity arable systems*; they might have livestock but it does not represent the main income source;
- *low intensity permanent crop systems*; e.g. olives and other permanent crops;
- *off-farm grazing systems*; with cattle, sheep or goats grazing outside the farm, for example on common land;
- *permanent grassland systems*; with cattle, sheep or goat systems where the main forage resource is grass from permanent or rough grassland;
- *arable grazing livestock systems*; with cattle, sheep or goat systems where the main forage resource is arable crops;
- *other systems*; mainly low intensity pigs or poultry systems.

For Portugal, this report estimated that 37% of the Utilized Agricultural Area (UUA) in the country is HNVF.

Setting the Scene: Linking Low-Intensity Farming Systems to European Nature Conservation Policies

The European Union nature conservation policy is regulated mainly by two directives: Council Directive 79/409/EEC on the conservation of wild birds (European Commission 1979) and Council Directive 92/43/EEC on the conservation of natural habitats and of wild fauna and flora (European Commission 1992). Both Directives identify *taxa* and habitats that should be given top priority for conservation in Europe. The latter Directive calls for the establishment of a network of designated sites, named Natura 2000, to maintain protected species (including birds) and habitats in a favourable conservation status. Many areas within Natura 2000 have low-intensity farming systems (EEA 2004), which suggest that part of their conservation interest relies on the existence of species and habitats dependent on disturbance regimes promoted by LIFS.

The overall objective of this paper is to explore the relationships between LIFS and species and habitats protected under EU Directives. Our rationale is: what is the role of LIFS in maintaining the habitat or species, and what would be the implications if current agricultural practices in LIFS were abandoned? Thus we concentrated on the degree of dependence, and on the consequences of abandonment, of LIFS, rather than on the impacts of agricultural intensification. We specifically aim to:

1. Define criteria to assess the degree of dependence of species and habitats listed in EU Directives on low-intensity farming systems. In spite of a great lack of scientific data to quantitatively assess the agricultural practices – biodiversity relationships (e.g. OECD 2001), we tried to use semi-quantitative criteria for linking habitats and species to agricultural practices.
2. Apply criteria to species and habitats occurring in Portugal and rank them on the basis of their degree of dependence on LIFS. Portugal is a South-European country for which we have more knowledge on agriculture-biodiversity relationships.
3. On the basis of the previous results, identify the main LIFS in Portugal holding more protected species and habitats. Natura 2000 sites with these LIFS should be given higher priority for agricultural management, and policies for keeping low-intensity farming practices in the site should be given top priority.

METHODS

Overall Approach

The baseline situation is the existence of the species and habitats. We do not address the role of low-intensity farming systems (LIFS) in creating new species populations, or new areas of habitat. We also do not focus on the impact of agricultural intensification on the habitat or species (intensification also affects species or habitats not dependent on low-intensity agriculture). Thus, our main focus is on the importance of maintaining low-intensity farming practices on sites already holding protected species and habitats (that is why they were selected for the Natura 2000 network).

There is a great lack of scientific knowledge for assessing species/habitats – agricultural practices interrelationships (OECD 2001). Thus we frequently used expert opinion, mainly for less well-known groups such as plants or habitats.

The overall approach was to classify (rank) species and habitats occurring in Portugal using variables expressing key concepts of dependence on LIFS, namely (a) *habitat* (for flora and fauna), (b) *food requirements* (for fauna), (c) *population changes* (for flora and fauna) and (d) *habitat representativity* (for habitats) and (e) *habitat representativity changes* (for habitats) in response to agricultural abandonment (Fig. 1). Two to three variables were used for each group (fauna, flora and habitats), and each species/habitat was given a rank (0-3) for each variable. Rank sums were then estimated; the higher the rank the more depend was the species/habitat on LIFS. Although variables were inter-correlated (e.g. species highly dependent on LIFS because it provides habitat are also expected to be negatively affected by abandonment), it was considered useful to evaluate each criterion separately, as it helped clarifying the type of dependence (particularly for fauna).

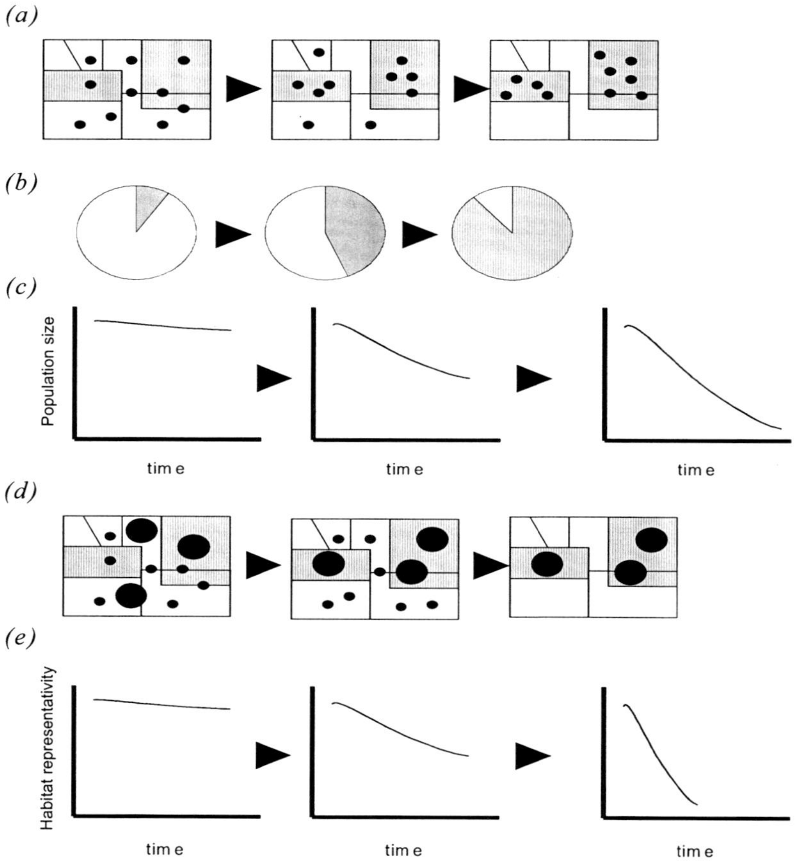

Figure 1. Illustration of key concepts to evaluate the degree of dependence of each species/ habitat on low-intensity farming systems (LIFS). *(a)* Degree of *dependence on habitat* (for flora and fauna); lower rank species (left) are habitat generalists, occurring either in LIFS (grey areas) and other habitats; medium rank species (centre) occur in higher densities in LIFS; higher rank species (right) are exclusive of habitats created by LIFS. Dots represent individuals. *(b)* Degree of *dependence on food resources* (for fauna); lower rank species (left) do not depend on food resources provided by LIFS (grey portions); medium rank species (centre) regularly use food resources provided LIFS; higher rank species (right) are highly dependent on food resources created, or highly promoted, by LIFS. *(c)* Degree of *population decline* (for fauna and flora); for lower rank species (left) their populations do not significantly decline as a response to LIFS abandonment (expressed as time since abandonment); for medium rank species (centre) their populations decline moderately (in years time-scale for plants) after LIFS abandonment; for higher rank species (right) the population strongly declines (in months time-scale for plants) after LIFS abandonment. *(d) Contribution of LIFS to habitat representativity*, defined as a measure of "how typical" a habitat is in comparison with the interpretation manual for habitats (see text); for lower rank habitats (left), their representativity is not influenced by LIFS (grey areas); for medium rank habitats (centre) habitat representativity is highly promoted by LIFS; for higher rank habitats (right) they occur exclusively (and with high representativeness) within LIFS. Dots represent habitat locations. The larger the symbols, the more representative is the habitat. *(e) Loss of habitat representativity*; for lower rank habitats (left), their characteristics (traits) do not vary significantly as a response to LIFS abandonment (expressed as time since abandonment); for medium rank habitats (centre) their characteristics change slowly (years time-scale) after LIFS abandonment; for higher rank habitats (right) their characteristics change quickly (months time-scale) after LIFS abandonment. For further details, see text.

Fauna

The analysis included only vertebrates (excluding marine mammals) listed in annex II of the “Habitats” Directive plus birds in the annex I of the “Birds” Directive. The knowledge on invertebrates is still too scarce to assess their relationship to agricultural uses. The degree of dependence of each species on LIFS was assessed using three variables, each with a 0-3 ranking system.

Table 1. Criteria for assessing the degree of vertebrate species dependence on single habitat, or mosaic of habitats, created by low-intensity farming systems (LIFS)

Criteria	Schematic representation	Weight factor
a) The species is a habitat generalist, not being associated to a single habitat or a landscape mosaic of habitats, created by LIFS; OR the species is a habitat specialist but does not depend on habitats created by LIFS.	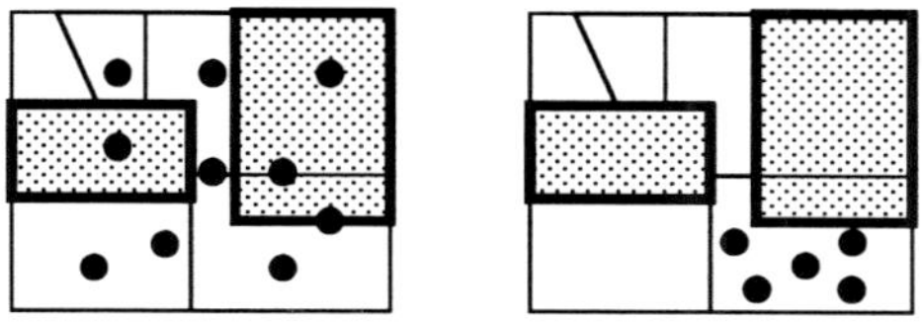	0
b) The species is a habitat generalist but usually occurs in higher population densities in habitat created by LIFS, or in a landscape mosaic including patches created by LIFS.	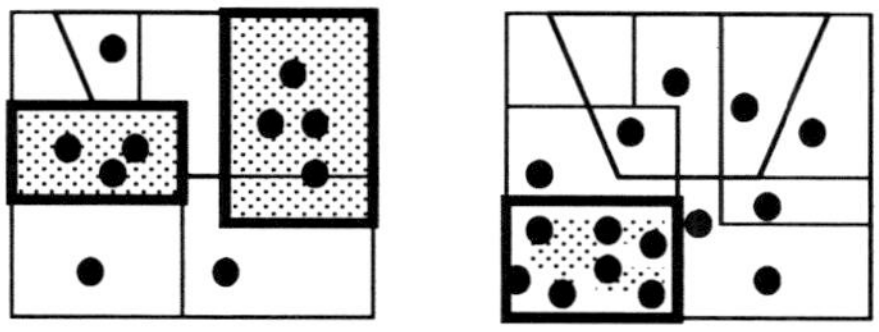	1
c) The species is a habitat specialist, occurring in a landscape mosaic where patches created by LIFS must exist. This includes e.g. species that breed in other habitat types (e.g. rocky areas or forests) but use LIFS habitats as feeding areas.	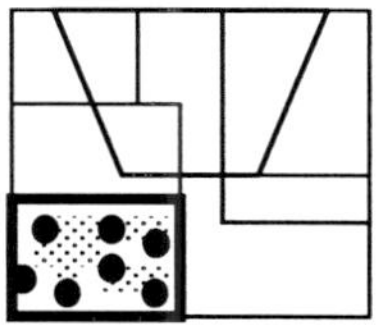	2
d) The species is a habitat specialist, using either a single habitat or a mosaic of habitats entirely created by LIFS.	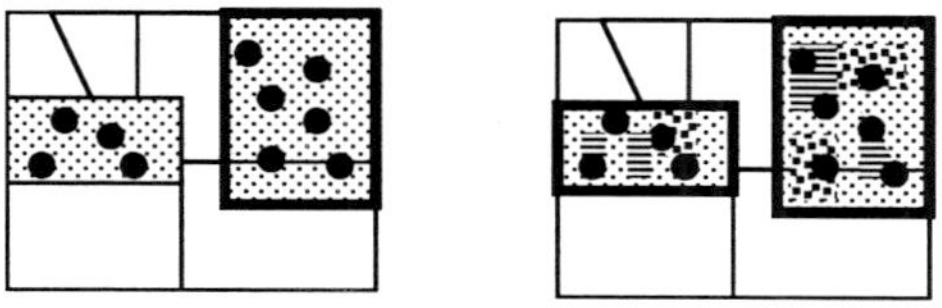	3

Note: Dotted areas correspond to LIFS (different patterns in *d)* represent mosaic of land uses); black dots represent individuals

The first variable related to the degree to which the species is dependent on a habitat, or landscape mosaic, partly or entirely created by low-intensity farming systems (LIFS) (Table 1). Highly dependent species exclusively use habitats created by LIFS and thus are highly prone to agricultural changes. Moderately dependent species use LIFS as feeding grounds during part of their annual cycle, although they can breed in e.g. forest or rocky areas (e.g. several species of raptors). Less dependent species do not relate to farmland habitats or occur in many habitats including some created by LIFS. Some species use old farm buildings (e.g. lesser kestrel) or farm ponds (e.g. amphibians) and these aspects were also taken into account.

Table 2. Criteria for assessing the degree of vertebrate species´dependence from food resources provided by low-intensity farming systems (LIFS)

Criteria	Schematic representation	Weight factor
a) The species does not depend on food resources provided by LIFS.	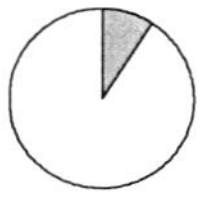	0
b) The species occasionally uses food resources provided by LIFS.	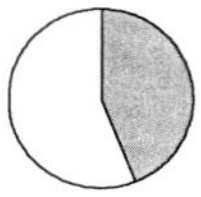	1
c) The species regularly uses food resources provided by LIFS.	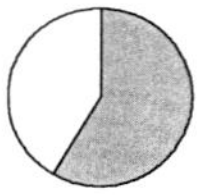	2
d) The species is highly specialized on food resources provided, or highly promoted, by LIFS.	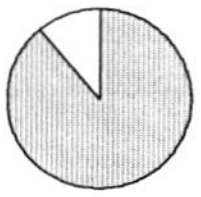	3

Note: The shadowed section of the circle represents the proportion of food resources obtained from LIFS

The second variable was the degree of dependence on food resources provided by LIFS (Table 2). Species were ranked according to the frequency of use of food resources provided or highly promoted by LIFS. Food resources range from seeds and arthropods in grasslands to livestock used by large carnivores or scavengers, and rabbits whose populations are promoted by the maintenance of grasslands.

The third variable assessed the degree to which the specie's population is negatively affected by agricultural abandonment of LIFS (Table 3). Abandonment includes both arable (end of cultivation) and livestock (end of livestock rearing) systems.

Table 3. Criteria for assessing the response of vertebrate species populations to abandonment of low-intensity farming systems (LIFS).

Criteria	Schematic representation	Weight factor
a) The species is not affected by agricultural abandonment in LIFS, or the population decline is not relevant	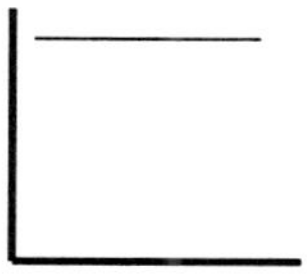	0
b) The species is moderately affected by agricultural abandonment in LIFS. A moderate population decline is expected, due to habitat loss and degradation, or decrease in food resource availability.	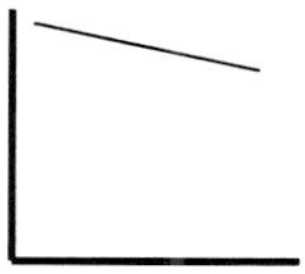	1
c) The species is strongly affected by agricultural abandonment in LIFS. A strong population decline is expected, due to habitat loss and degradation, or decrease in food resource availability. This increases the likelihood of population extinction.	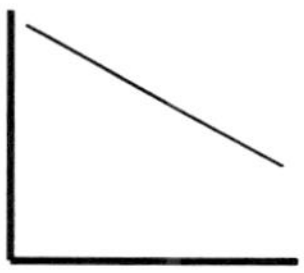	2
d) The species is extremely affected by agricultural abandonment in LIFS. A rapid population decline is expected, due to drastic losses in habitat and food resources. The likelihood of population extinction increases notoriously.	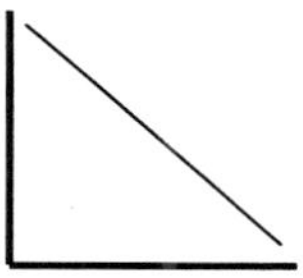	3

Note: The graphs represent population trends across time

Flora

The analysis included vascular plants listed in annex II of the "Habitats" Directive. The degree of dependence of each species on LIFS was assessed using two variables, one with a 0-3 ranking system and the other with a 0-2 ranking.

The first variable related to the degree to which the species is dependent on a habitat occurring in LIFS (Table 4). Highly dependent species occur exclusively on habitats created by LIFS. Other species might occur in higher population densities (but not exclusively) in LIFS-created habitats. Less dependent species do not occur in habitats related to LIFS.

Table 4. Criteria for assessing the degree of plant species dependence on habitat created by low-intensity farming systems (LIFS)

Criteria	Schematic representation	Weight factor
a) The species does not depend on habitats occurring in LIFS (either the species does not occur in LIFS habitats or does not depend on their management).	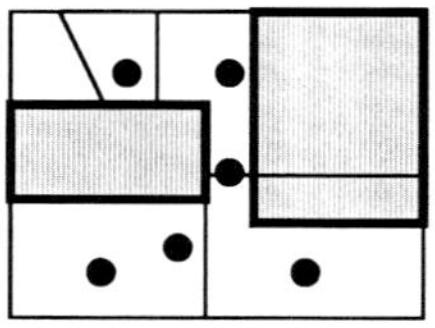	0
b) The species moderately depends on habitats occurring in LIFS. It occurs in higher population densities in other habitat types. It survives in less disturbed population nucleus from which it will effectively colonize agricultural/pastoral patches.	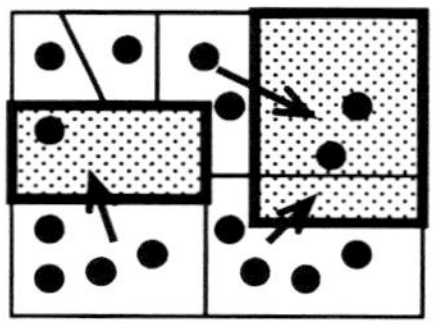	1
c) The species strongly depends on habitats occurring in LIFS, as it benefits from the disturbance regimes associated to them. The seed bank in the agricultural/pastoral patch is sufficient for the recolonization success after disturbance.	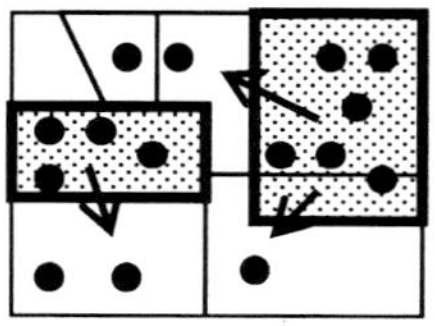	2
d) The species depends exceptionally on habitats occurring in LIFS, as it occurs exclusively in these habitats, using the largest number of micro-habitats available within the agricultural/pastoral patch.	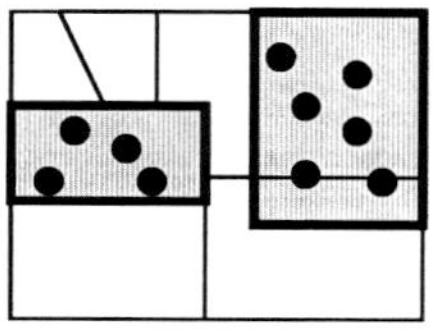	3

Note: Dotted areas correspond to LIFS; black dots represent individuals. Arrows represent movements during the recolonization process

The second variable expressed the expected rate of population decline after agricultural abandonment in LIFS (Table 5). Higher rates of decline expressed higher susceptibility to abandonment.

Table 5. Criteria for assessing the response of plant species populations to abandonment of low-intensity farming systems (LIFS)

Criteria	Schematic representation	Weight factor
a) The population status of the species is not changed in response to agricultural abandonment in LIFS.		0
b) The population of the species declines moderately after abandonment in LIFS. Notorious shifts in abundance within the agricultural patch occur only after a few years.	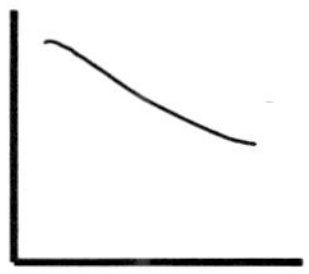	1
c) The population of the species declines rapidly after abandonment in LIFS. Notorious shifts in abundance and frequency occur within a few months (frequently in the following phenological cycle).	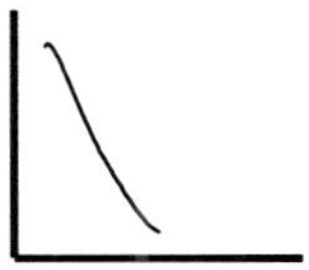	2

Note: The graphs represent population trends across time

Habitats

The analysis included habitats listed in annex I of the "Habitats" Directive. The degree of habitat dependence on LIFS was assessed using two variables, one with a 0-3 ranking system and the other with a 0-2 rank.

Firstly, the degree of dependence evaluated the importance of disturbances introduced by LIFS typical management on habitat representativity (Table 6). The degree of representativity gives a measure of 'how typical' a habitat type is, in comparison to the interpretation manual for habitats, which provides a list of relevant ecological and ecosystem elements and frequent species at European scale level (European Commission 2003a). A high level of dependence means that characteristics that define the habitat are a direct consequence of agricultural management. A low level of dependence means the habitat is not strongly influenced by LIFS management, or does not occur in farmland. Some habitats are marginal to farmland, but are moderately influenced by farming practices. The types of possible spatial relationships between habitats and the LIFS where they occur are shown in Fig. 2.

The second variable expressed the expected (common) rate of decline in habitat representativity after agricultural abandonment in LIFS (Table 7). This is expressed as deviation in relation to typical traits (e.g. species composition, species aggregation within communities) described in the Interpretation Manual. Higher rates of representativity loss represent higher susceptibility to abandonment.

Table 6. Criteria for assessing the degree of habitat dependence on low-intensity farming systems (LIFS) management

Criteria	Schematic representation	Weight factor
a) The habitat does not depend on LIFS.	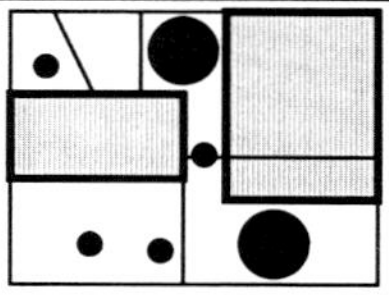	0
b) The habitat moderately depends on LIFS, as agricultural management contributes to habitat representativity.	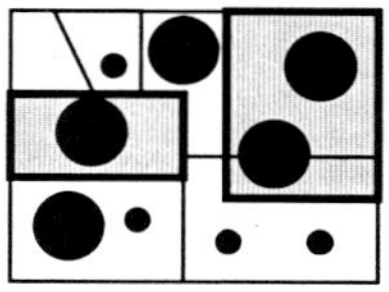	1
c) The habitat strongly depends on LIFS, as agricultural management promotes disturbance regimes clearly favoring habitat representativity.	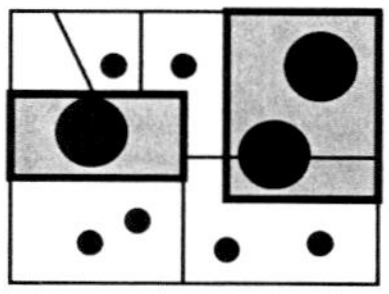	
d) The habitat depends exceptionally on LIFS, as it occurs exclusively as a response to agricultural management and disturbance regime typical of the system.	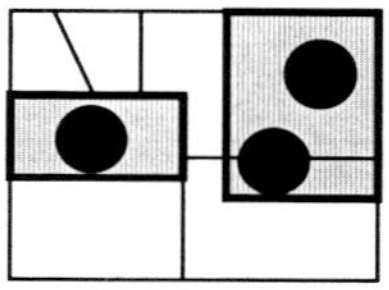	3

Note: Dotted areas correspond to LIFS; black dots represent habitat locations; black dot size is proportional to habitat representativity

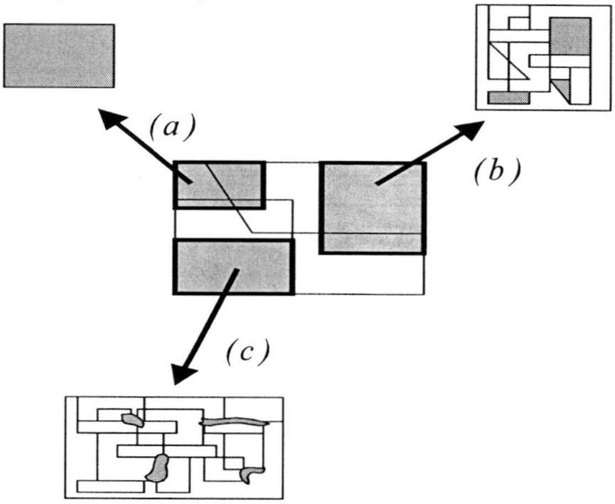

Figure 2. Possible spatial relationships between habitats listed in the Habitats Directive (92/43/EEC) and low-intensity farming systems (LIFS) (grey areas in central figure). *(a)* the habitat coincides entirely with a LIFS (e.g. cork oak woodland "montados" (habitat code 6310)); *(b)* the habitat is found in specific agricultural patches of the landscape mosaic created by the LIFS, (e.g. hay meadows (habitat code 6520) in mountain mixed farming systems); *(c)* the habitat is found in non-agricultural patches of the landscape mosaic created by the LIFS, but is influenced by LIFS management (e.g. Mediterranean temporary ponds (habitat code 3170) in arable crop systems).

Table 7. Criteria for assessing the response of habitats to abandonment of low-intensity farming systems (LIFS).

Criteria	Schematic representation	Weight factor
a) Habitat characteristics (representativity) do not vary significantly in response to agricultural abandonment in LIFS, original traits persisting during long periods of time.	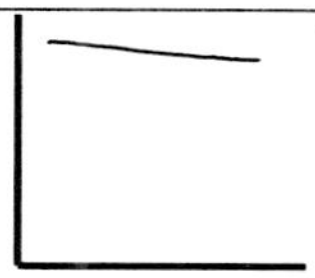	0
b) Habitat characteristics change slowly after abandonment in LIFS. Only after a few years shifts are notorious.	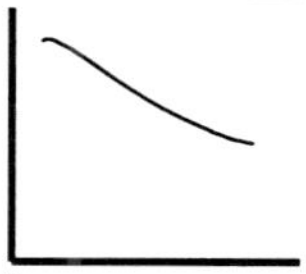	1
c) Habitat characteristics change quickly after abandonment in LIFS. After a few months shifts are notorious (frequently in the following phenological cycle).	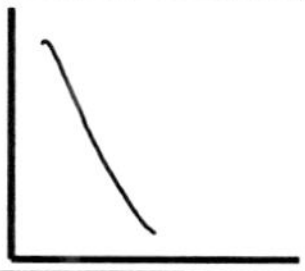	2

Note: The graphs represent loss of habitat representativity across time

RESULTS

Fauna

A total of 96 vertebrate species listed in both European Directives occur in Portugal. Of these, 45 were identified as having some kind of dependence on low-intensity farming systems (Table 8). These include 41 species of birds, 3 mammals (Iberian lynx, wolf and Cabrera's vole), 1 reptile (Schreiber's green lizard) and 1 amphibian (golden-stripped salamander). The large predominance of birds in this list is a consequence of both a better knowledge on the species ecology and relationships with farming systems (e.g. Pain & Pienkowski 1997), and a larger number of species potentially eligible through the "Birds" Directive.

Higher rank species include several ground-nesting birds associated to pseudosteppes (Suárez *et al.* 1997). This type of low-intensity arable system covers large areas of the Iberian Peninsula (over 4.5 million ha) and is characterised by a landscape mosaic including non-irrigated cereal crops, dry legumes, ploughed and fallow fields. A large group of birds depends entirely on this LIFS for habitat and food resources, such as the great bustard (*Otis tarda*), lesser kestrel (*Falco naumanni*), little bustard (*Tetrax tetrax*), calandra lark (*Melanocorypha calandra*), black-bellied sandgrouse (*Pterocles orientalis*) and pin-tailed sandgrouse (*Pterocles alchata*). Some species are associated with specific components (habitats) of this landscape mosaic whereas others use different components along their yearly biological cycle (e.g. Suárez et al. 1997; Delgado & Moreira 2000; Moreira *et al.* 2005). Both land abandonment and agricultural intensification are presumed to be detrimental for this group of steppe birds (e.g. Delgado & Moreira 2000; Moreira *et al.* 2005).

Table 8. Vertebrate species occurring in Portugal and showing some type of dependence on low-intensity farming systems (LIFS)

Vertebrate species	Group	Dependence habitat	Dependence food	Response to abandonment	Rank sum
Falco naumanni	B	3	3	3	9
Otis tarda	B	3	3	3	9
Tetrax tetrax	B	3	3	3	9
Grus grus	B	3	3	3	9
Melanocorypha calandra	B	3	3	3	9
Pterocles alchata	B	3	3	3	9
Pterocles orientalis	B	3	3	3	9
Lynx pardinus	M	2	3	2	7
Elanus caeruleus	B	2	2	3	7
Pluvialis apricaria	B	2	2	3	7
Pyrrhocorax pyrrhocorax	B	2	2	3	7
Coracias garrulus	B	2	2	2	6
Circus cyaneus	B	2	2	2	6
Circus pygargus	B	2	2	2	6
Glareola pratincola	B	2	2	2	6
Lanius collurio	B	2	2	2	6
Milvus milvus	B	2	2	2	6
Anthus campestris	B	2	2	2	6
Aquila chrysaetos	B	2	2	2	6
Asio flammeus	B	2	2	2	6
Burhinus oedicnemus	B	2	2	2	6
Gyps fulvus	B	2	2	2	6
Neophron percnopterus	B	2	2	2	6
Lullula arborea	B	2	2	2	6
Aegypius monachus	B	2	2	1	5
Aquila adalberti	B	2	2	1	5
Circaetus gallicus	B	2	2	1	5
Microtus cabrerae	M	2	2	1	5
Calandrella brachydactyla	B	2	2	1	5
Ciconia ciconia	B	1	2	2	5
Hieraaetus fasciatus	B	2	1	1	4
Falco biarmicus	B	2	1	1	4
Emberiza hortulana	B	1	1	2	4
Chioglossa lusitanica	A	1	1	1	3
Canis lupus	M	1	1	1	3
Bubo bubo	B	1	1	1	3
Milvus migrans	B	1	1	1	3
Ciconia nigra	B	1	1	1	3
Falco columbarius	B	1	1	1	3
Galerida theklae	B	1	1	1	3
Hieraaetus pennatus	B	1	1	0	2
Charadrius morinellus	B	1	1	0	2
Oenanthe leucura	B	1	0	1	2
Lacerta schreiberi	R	1	0	0	1
Falco peregrinus	B	0	1	0	1

Note: For each species, the degree of dependence for habitat and food, the response to land abandonment and the overall rank (rank sum) are shown. Group: B (bird), M (mammal), A (amphibian), R (reptile). Species are ranked by decreasing degree of overall dependence

Other group of species is also typical, but not exclusive, of pseudosteppes. Examples include the black-shouldered kite (*Elanus caeruleus*), common crane (*Grus grus*) golden plover (*Pluvialis apricaria*), hen harrier (*Circus cyaneus*), Montagu's harrier (*Circus pygargus*) and the roller (*Coracias garrulus*). These species also occur in regions with other LIFS such as montados (see below) and mountain pastoral systems.

Montados, a savanna-like wood pasture LIFS with evergreen *Quercus suber* or *Q. ilex*, (which are also a protected habitat; see 3.3) are very important for a large group of vertebrates. The above-mentioned black-shouldered kite preferentially selects this LIFS as breeding habitat. Most of the 60,000-70,000 common cranes wintering in Iberia use montados as the main habitat, where they feed on acorns (Diáz *et al.* 1996; Diáz *et al.* 1997). Montados are also the main habitat for several species as raptors including the red kite (*Milvus milvus*), short-toed eagle (*Circaetus gallicus*), booted eagle (*Hieraaetus pennatus*) and the Spanish imperial eagle (*Aquila adalberti*) (e.g. Diáz *et al.* 1997).

Other species rely on low-intensity pastoral systems mainly for food. This is the case of several vultures, which nest on rocky cliffs (usually in river valleys) but depend on carcasses of livestock, such as egyptian vulture (*Neophron percnopterus*), griffon vulture (*Gyps fulvus*) or the black vulture (*Aegypius monachus*) (Donázar et al. 1997). For the bonelli's eagle (*Hieraaetus fasciatus*), golden eagle (*Aquila chrysaetus*), eagle owl (*Bubo bubo*) and iberian lynx (*Lynx pardinus*), their main prey is rabbits (*Oryctolagus cuniculus*). Grasslands resulting from low-intensity pastoral systems promote rabbit populations, indirectly increasing food availability for these predators. The Action Plan for the highly threatened iberian lynx acknowledges that the species would benefit from pastoral management promoting both Mediterranean scrubland habitats and rabbit populations (Delibes *et al.* 2000). Wolves (*Canis lupus*) also use domestic livestock as a main food resource (e.g. Boitani 2000). Cabrera's vole (*Microtus cabrerae*) occurs near wetlands, often in nitrophilous plant communities (Fernandez-Salvador 2002), which are associated to pastures grazed by livestock. The chough (P*yrrhocorax pyrrhocorax*) is also associated with extensive pastoral systems where it feeds mainly on soil-living (often dung-associated) invertebrates in pastures grazed by livestock (e.g. Bignal & Curtis 1989; Blanco *et al.* 1998).

Two species depend on mixed mountain systems, the red-backed shrike (*Lanius collurio*) and the ortolan bunting (*Emberiza hortulana*). Both species occur in mountain regions, needing a mosaic of pastures, hayfields, hedgerows and scrubland promoted by this type of LIFS (e.g. Rufino 1989; Tucker & Heath 1994).

The golden-stripped salamander (C*hioglossa lusitanica)* and Schreiber's green lizard (*Lacerta schreiberi*) are also affected by human-made infrastructures in LIFS. Water mines, used to irrigate hay meadows, are preferred areas of occurrence for the amphibian (Ferrand et al. 2001), which also uses hay meadows as feeding areas. Stone walls associated to hay meadows and pastures near streams promote habitat quality for the lizard (Brito et al. 1996).

Table 9 depicts the species with higher rank, and presents further details on the type of dependence they show with LIFS.

Table 9. Summary of type of dependence of the top 25 vertebrate species more dependent on low-intensity farming systems (LIFS) occurring in Portugal

Vertebrate species	Type of dependence on LIFS
Falco naumanni (lesser kestrel)	depends on pseudosteppe habitat mosaic for habitat and food resources
Otis tarda (great bustard)	depends on pseudosteppe habitat mosaic for habitat and food resources
Tetrax tetrax (little bustard)	depends on pseudosteppe habitat mosaic for habitat and food resources
Grus grus (common crane)	winters in "montados" where it feeds on acorns; also uses pseudosteppe habitat mosaic
Melanocorypha calandra (calandra lark)	depends on pseudosteppe habitat mosaic for habitat and food resources
Pterocles alchata (pint-tailed sandgrouse)	depends on pseudosteppe habitat mosaic for habitat and food resources
Pterocles orientalis (black-bellied sandgrouse)	depends on pseudosteppe habitat mosaic for habitat and food resources
Lynx pardinus (iberian lynx)	rabbit (main prey) populations promoted by pastoral systems; these systems also contribute to a mosaic of Mediterranean scrubland and grassland, needed as habitat
Elanus caeruleus (black-shouldered kite)	depends on pseudosteppe habitat mosaic and "montado" for habitat and food resources
Pluvialis apricaria (golden plover)	occurs mainly in pseudosteppes, but also in other arable land and pastoral systems
Pyrrhocorax pyrrhocorax (chough)	depends on extensive pastoral systems where it feeds mainly on soil-living invertebrates
Coracias garrulus (roller)	occurs in higher densities in pseudosteppes
Circus cyaneus (hen harrier)	depends on pseudosteppe habitat mosaic for habitat and food resources, mainly during winter; also occurs in some pastoral systems in mountain areas, in a mosaic of scrubland, grassland and cereals, during the breeding season
Circus pygargus (montagu's harrier)	depends on pseudosteppe habitat mosaic for habitat and food resources; also occurs in some pastoral systems in mountain areas, in a mosaic of scrubland, grassland and cereals.
Glareola pratincola (pratincole)	occurs in higher densities in pseudosteppes
Lanius collurio (red-backed shrike)	depends on mosaic of pastures, hayfields, hedgerows and scrubland, in mountain areas
Milvus milvus (black kite)	depends mainly on food resources provided by extensive pastoral systems
Anthus campestris (tawny pipit)	occurs in higher densities in pseudosteppes
Aquila chrysaetos (golden eagle)	depends mainly on food resources provided by extensive pastoral systems
Asio flammeus (short-eared owl)	occurs in higher densities in agricultural land; takes advantage of food resources promoted by LIFS
Burhinus oedicnemus (stone curlew)	occurs in higher densities in pseudosteppes
Gyps fulvus (griffon vulture)	depends mainly on food resources provided by extensive pastoral systems
Neophron percnopterus (egiptian vulture)	depends mainly on food resources provided by extensive pastoral systems
Lullula arborea (woodlark)	occurs in higher densities in montados
Aegypius monachus (black vulture)	depends on food resources provided by extensive pastoral systems; preferred nesting habitat includes montados
Aquila adalberti (Spanish imperial eagle)	depends on food resources provided by extensive pastoral systems; preferred nesting habitat includes montados
Circaetus gallicus (short-toed eagle)	depends mainly on food resources provided by extensive pastoral systems
Microtus cabrerae (cabrera's vole)	occurs in higher densities near wetlands associated to pastures grazed by livestock
Calandrella brachydactyla (short-toed lark)	occurs in higher densities in pseudosteppes and pastoral systems
Ciconia ciconia (white stork)	often explores food resources provided by LIFS (e.g. pastures, rice fields)

Table 10. Plant species occurring in Portugal and showing some type of dependence on low-intensity farming systems (LIFS)

Plant species	Dependence habitat	Response to abandonment	Rank sum
Linaria ricardoi	3	1	4
Juncus valvatus	1	2	3
Melilotus segetalis ssp. *fallax*	1	2	3
Ononis hackelii.	2	1	3
Centaurea fraylensis	2	1	3
Narcissus pseudonarcissus ssp. *nobilis*	2	1	3
Linaria algarviana	2	1	3
Hyacinthoides vicentina	2	1	3
Festuca elegans	2	1	3
Narcissus scaberulus	1	1	2
Silene longicilia	1	1	2
Marsilea quadrifolia	1	1	2
Holcus setiglumis ssp. *duriensis*	1	1	2
Festuca sumilusitana	1	1	2
Festuca henriquesii	1	1	2
Festuca brigantina	1	1	2
Dianthus marizii	1	1	2
Centaurea micrantha ssp. *herminii*	1	1	2
Armeria pseudarmeria	1	1	2
Arabis sadina	1	1	2
Thymus camphoratus	1	0	1
Leuzea longifolia	1	0	1
Iberis procumbens ssp. *microcarpa*	1	0	1
Linaria ficalhoana	1	0	1
Jasione crispa ssp. *serpentinica*	1	0	1

Note: For each species, the degree of dependence from habitat, the sensitivity to land abandonment and the overall rank (rank sum) are shown. Species are ranked by decreasing degree of overall dependence.

Flora

A total of 72 plant species (excluding bryophytes) listed in the "Habitats" Directive occur in Portugal. There is much less knowledge on the relationships between plants and agricultural systems. Much of the results presented here are based on our own knowledge on species patterns of occurrence in the field, complemented with expert consultation. Of the 72 species, 25 were identified as having some kind of dependence on low-intensity farming systems (Table 10). Table 11 depicts the type of dependence they show with LIFS, as well as the best management guidelines to maintain their populations. The top priority species is *Linaria ricardoi*, a Portuguese endemism that occurs in dry cereal crops and fallow fields. This species strictly depends on disturbance promoted by ploughing and control of shrub encroachment. Then a group of 8 species follows, including (a) *Juncus valvatus* and *Melilotus segetalis* ssp. *fallax*, two species associated with wet grasslands and particularly prone to agricultural abandonment; (b) species strongly dependent on habitats promoted by grazing and control of shrub encroachment, including *Ononis hackelii*, *Linaria algarviana*, *Hyacinthoides vicentina*, *Festuca elegans*, *Narcissus pseudonarcissus* ssp. *nobilis* and *Centaurea fraylensis*. Then a large group of species moderately dependent on habitats occurring in LIFS includes (a) species associated with grazing in scrublands, such as *Narcissus scaberulus*, *Silene longicilia*, *Leuzea longifolia*, *Thymus camphoratus*, *Jasione crispa* ssp. *serpentinica*, *Dianthus marizii*, *Arabis sadina*, *Iberis procumbens* ssp. *microcarpa*, (b) species associated with grazed grasslands, such as *Festuca sumilusitana*, *Festuca henriquesii*, *Festuca brigantina*, and fallow land (*Holcus setiglumis* ssp. *duriensis*), (c) species that might occur in rice fields (*Marsilea quadrifolia*); (d) species associated with coastal grazed grasslands (*Armeria pseudarmeria* and *Linaria ficalhoana*).

Habitats

A total of 91 habitats listed in the "Habitats" Directive occur in Portugal. Of these, 19 were identified as having some kind of dependence on low-intensity farming systems (Table 12). They correspond mostly to intermediate vegetation succession stages, such as grasslands and scrublands.

Top priority habitats, in what concerns dependence on low-intensity farming systems (habitat codes given in brackets), are mesophile grasslands, namely mountain hay meadows (6520) and lowland hay meadows (6510). These habitats totally depend on farming management and their physiognomic and compositional characteristics disappear very fast after abandonment. Other habitat entirely dependent on LIFS is dehesas with evergreen *Quercus* spp. (6310), a type of sclerophillous grazed forest with a savanna-like structure, but here the effects of stopping traditional management take longer time (years) to be noticed. In Portugal they are named "montados" and cover large areas of the country. One additional habitat strongly depends on LIFS: semi-natural dry grasslands and scrubland facies on calcareous substrates (6210), which is an important orchid habit. Extensive grazing (mainly with sheep) is very important to maintain this habitat.

Table 11. Summary of relationships with LIFS and management prescriptions for the 25 plant species more dependent on low-intensity farming systems (LIFS) occurring in Portugal

Plant species	Relationships with LIFS	Burning	Grazing/ hay cutting	Mechanical shrub clearing	Plough-ing
Linaria ricardoi	Exclusively on cereal fields and fallow land		+	+	+
Juncus valvatus	Wet grasslands and hay meadows; shrub clearing at ca. 3+ year intervals			+	
Melilotus segetalis ssp. *fallax*	Natural wet grasslands associated with silage and hay			+	
Ononis hackelii	Xerophitic grasslands with cattle; ploughing at ca. 5+ year intervals		+	+	+
Centaurea fraylensis	Grazed scrublands			+	
Narcissus pseudonarcissus ssp. *nobilis*	Hay meadows		+		
Linaria algarviana	Semi-natural pastures, without fertilizers and addition of aloctonous species; shrub clearing at ca. 5+ year intervals		+	+	
Hyacinthoides vicentina	Semi-natural pastures, without fertilizers and addition of aloctonous species		+	+	
Festuca elegans	Grazed mountain grasslands and scrubland; might also benefit from burning to create pastures	+	+		
Narcissus scaberulus	Grazed scrublands	+	+		
Silene longicilia	Grazed scrublands	+	+		
Marsilea quadrifolia	Wet grasslands, rice fields			+	
Holcus setiglumis ssp. *duriensis*	Fallow land in rotation scheme and semi-natural pastures		+	+	
Festuca sumilusitana	Grazed grasslands	+	+		
Festuca henriquesii	Grazed montain grasslands	+	+		
Festuca brigantina	Ultrabasic grasslands and scrub clearings		+		
Dianthus marizii	Ultrabasic grasslands and scrub clearings	+			
Centaurea micrantha ssp. *herminii*	Grazed scrubland	+			
Armeria pseudarmeria	Grazed coastal grasslands and small-scale mixed farming	+	+	+	
Arabis sadina	Grazed scrublands; might also benefit from burning to create pastures	+	+	+	
Thymus camphoratus	Grazed scrubland; shrub clearing at ca. 15+ year intervals	+	+	+	
Leuzea longifolia	Grazed scrubland; shrub clearing at ca. 15+ year intervals			+	
Iberis procumbens ssp. *microcarpa*	Grazed scrubland; shrub clearing at ca. 15+ year intervals		+	+	
Linaria ficalhoana	Grazed coastal grasslands		+		+
Jasione crispa ssp. *serpentinica*	Ultrabasic scrublands	+	+		

Note: The specific management actions that might promote the species populations are shown.

Table 12. Habitats occurring in Portugal and showing some type of dependence on Low-intensity farming systems (LIFS)

Habitat	Habitat code	Dependence from LIFS	Response to abandonment	Rank sum
Lowland hay meadows (*Alopecurus pratensis, Sanguisorba officinalis*)	6510	3	2	5
Mountain hay meadows	6520	3	2	5
Dehesas with evergreen *Quercus* spp.	6310	3	1	4
Semi-natural dry grasslands and scrubland facies on calcareous substrates (Festuco Brometalia) (important orchid sites)	6210	2	1	3
Malcolmietalia dune grasslands	2230	1	1	2
Oligotrophic waters containing very few minerals generally on sandy soils of the West Mediterranean, with *Isoetes* spp.	3120	1	1	2
Natural euthrophic lakes with Magnopotamion or Hydrocharition-type vegetation	3150	1	1	2
Mediterranean temporary ponds	3170	1	1	2
Rivers with muddy banks with *Chenopodion rubri p.p.* and *Bidention p.p.* vegetation	3270	1	1	2
European dry heaths	4030	1	1	2
Mountain Cytisus purgans formations	5120	1	1	2
Thermo-Mediterranean and pre-desert scrub	5330	1	1	2
Pseudo-steppe with grasses and annuals of the Thero-Brachypodietea	6220	1	1	2
Species-rich *Nardus* grasslands, on siliceous substrates in mountain areas (and submountain areas in Continental Europe)	6230	1	1	2
Hydrophilous tall herb fringe communities of plains and of the montane to alpine levels	6430	1	1	2
Limestone pavements	8240	1	1	2
Molinia meadows on calcareous, peaty or clayey-silt-laden soils (Molinion caeruleae)	6410	1	0	1
Oro-Iberian *Festuca indigesta* grasslands	6160	1	0	1
Mediterranean tall humid grasslands of the Molinio-Holoschoenion	6420	1	0	1

Note: For each habitat, the degree of dependence, the sensitivity to land abandonment and the overall rank (rank sum) are shown. Species are ranked by decreasing degree of overall dependence.

The remaining habitat types are all moderately affected by LIFS. They are mostly affected by pastoral systems, which contribute to maintain their characteristics of intermediate stages of vegetation succession. They can be grouped into:

a) *Grassland habitats*. Examples include *Malcolmietalia* dune grasslands (2230), Pseudo-steppe with grasses and annuals of the *Thero-Brachypodietea* (6220), Species-rich *Nardus* grasslands, on silicious substrates in mountain areas (6230), Mediterranean tall humid grasslands of the *Molinio-Holoschoenion* (6420), and Limestone pavements (8240). The general trend in the absence of grazing (or wildfires) is for these habitats to become scrubland formations.

b) *Scrubland habitats*. Examples include Mountain *Cytisus purgans* formations (5120), European dry heaths (4030) and Thermo-Mediterranean and pre-desert scrub (5330). In the absence of grazing or wildfires, these habitats would progressively change to forests.

c) *Wetlands*. These include Natural eutrophic lakes with *Magnopotamion* or *Hydrocharition* – type vegetation (3150), Oligotrophic waters containing very few minerals generally on sandy soils of the West Mediterranean, with *Isoetes* spp. (3120), and Mediterranean temporary ponds (3170). The importance of livestock grazing for these habitats depends on habitat characteristics. For the former habitat, livestock droppings promote the eutrophic status of the habitat. For the other habitat types, livestock grazing prevents scrub encroachment.

Table 13 details the type of dependence each habitat shows with LIFS management.

DISCUSSION

The definition and application of some of the criteria used in the present study are subjective and prone to error due to lack of scientific evidence. Thus, the precise resulting rank order of *taxa* and habitats is potentially arguable. In spite of these drawbacks, we believe to have identified the main vertebrates, vascular plant species and habitats with unfavourable conservation status at European level and dependent on low-intensity farming systems (LIFS) occurring in Portugal. This study was the first attempt to quantify this dependence, and it showed that a significant part of the success in preserving biodiversity in the Portuguese Natura 2000 sites relies on maintaining farmers practising low-intensity agriculture in these regions. The proportion of *taxa* and habitats partly or totally dependent on LIFS is substantial, ranging from 20% for habitats to 47% in vertebrates.

Portugal shares habitats and species with many other Mediterranean countries. As an example, of the 142 habitats listed for the Mediterranean countries (Greece, Spain, France, Italy and Portugal) (EEA 1999), 82 occur in Portugal. The proportion of broad groups of habitats is also similar in Portugal and for all these countries (Fig. 3). Thus we think the observed importance of LIFS in Portugal can be extrapolated to the whole Mediterranean region.

Table 13. Habitats dependence on LIFS. Habitat names are abreviated (see Table 12 for complete names)

Habitat	Code	Influence from LIFS management
Lowland hay meadows	6510	Typical management of mountain hay meadows. Livestock densities and irrigation levels determine habitat representativeness.
Mountain hay meadows	6520	Typical management of mountain hay meadows. Livestock densities and irrigation levels determine habitat representativeness.
Dehesas with evergreen Quercus spp.	6310	Traditional management including shrub clearing in the undergrowth.
Semi-natural dry grasslands and scrubland facies on calcareous substrates	6210	Free ranging livestock grazing, mainly by goats and sheep. Fire, often used to promote shrub clearing lignivorous pastures, might be beneficial for the habitat.
Malcolmietalia dune grasslands	2230	Free ranging livestock grazing, mainly by goats and sheep. Management of coastal pine forests might benefit the habitat.
Oligotrophic waters containing very few minerals	3120	Moderate livestock densities are beneficial for the habitat, but both increased densities and end of pastoral systems may be detrimental. Management of coastal pine forests might benefit the habitat.
Natural euthrophic lakes	3150	Moderate livestock densities are beneficial for the habitat, as it constitutes a source of organic matter to the system. However, overgrazing in the margins might be detrimental.
Mediterranean temporary ponds	3170	Moderate livestock densities (especially in free ranging grazing) are beneficial for the habitat. Temporary overgrazing also admissible. Irregular burning beneficial.
Rivers with muddy banks	3270	Free ranging livestock grazing, promoting removal of shrub cover and increased organic matter in the soil, is beneficial for the habitat.
European dry heaths	4030	Livestock grazing, eventually associated to prescribed burning during Autumn to open pastures, beneficial for the habitat. Excessive occurrence of fire leads to decreased habitat representativity, due to dominance of Ericaceous.
Mountain Cytisus purgans formations	5120	Moderate livestock densities are beneficial for the habitat.
Thermo-Mediterranean and pre-desert scrub	5330	Free ranging livestock grazing is beneficial for the habitat.
Pseudo-steppe with grasses and annuals	6220	Free ranging livestock grazing, mainly by pigs and sheep, is beneficial for the habitat.
Species-rich Nardus grasslands	6230	Moderate livestock densities, mainly by sheep, are beneficial for the habitat.
Hydrophilous tall herb fringe communities of plains and of the montane to alpine levels	6430	Moderate livestock densities, mainly by sheep, are beneficial for the habitat, at least for some of the plant communities included in this habitat category.
Limestone pavements	8240	Moderate livestock densities plus prescribed fire to create pastures are beneficial for the habitat.
Molinia meadows on calcareous, peaty or clayey-silt-laden soils	6410	Livestock grazing. Fire, often used to promote shrub clearing and open pastures, might be beneficial for the habitat.
Oro-Iberian Festuca indigesta grasslands	6160	Moderate livestock densities are beneficial for the habitat.
Mediterranean tall humid grasslands	6420	Free ranging livestock grazing, eventually associated to prescribed burning during Autumn to open pastures, are beneficial for the habitat.

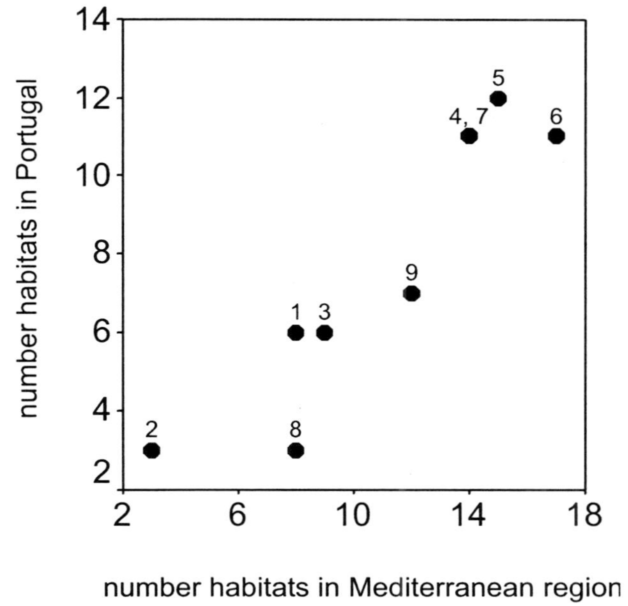

Figure 3 – Relationships between the number of habitats listed in the 92/43/EEC Directive for the whole Mediterranean area and the ones occurring in Portugal. Habitats were grouped according to the following major groups (numbers in figure): 1 - open sea and tidal habitats; 2 – sea cliffs and shingle or stony beaches; 3 – salt marshes, salt meadows and inland steppe habitats; 4 – sea dune habitats; 5 – standing and running water habitats; 6 – heath, scrub, matorral and phrygana habitats; 7 – grasslands, meadows and dehesas habitats; 8 – bogs and fens habitats; 9 – scree, rocky slopes and other rocky habitats. Forests are not shown due to large number of habitats (42 forest habitat types for the whole Mediterranean and 12 for Portugal). Based on EEA (1999).

One other conclusion of the present work is the need for further scientific research to relate agriculture to biodiversity. Even for better know *taxa*, such as birds, many aspects of the ecology of many species occurring in agricultural habitats, and its relation to agricultural management, are not known (e.g. Pain & Pienkowski 1997) and we felt many difficulties, even when consulting specialists, in linking species and habitat ecology to farming practices. This is a major drawback at both national and European levels, as agri-environmental policies have been used across Europe to promote an environmentally friendly agriculture. The rationale behind these policies is to compensate farmers financially for any loss of income associated with measures that aim to benefit the environment or biodiversity. There are currently agri-environment schemes in 26 European countries, and Kleijn & Sutherland (2003) estimated that 24 billion euros have been spent on these schemes in the European Union (EU) since 1994. However, the scientific bases and research designs of most studies were not adequate to assess the effectiveness of the schemes (Kleijn & Sutherland 2003). Thus, a much higher degree of involvement of ecologists in the development and evaluation of the European Union Common Agricultural Policy is claimed (Ormerod et al. 2003). On the basis of the current study, we suggest that priority research lines should include a better understanding of the effects of grazing, fire and responses to agricultural abandonment in habitats and species populations (particularly plants).

Why is it Extensive Agriculture Important for Biodiversity in the Mediterranean?

Disturbance is the key. Along centuries and millennia, species have adapted to both natural and human disturbances, such as fire, grazing, ploughing, cutting and shrub clearing. It may be even possible that human activities have increased habitat availability for species that would be otherwise much scarcer, or even absent in this region. Blondel & Aronson (1999) argue that the highest species diversity in the Mediterranean region is found in frequently, though moderately, disturbed sites. In their study on bird diversity in the Mediterranean, Covas & Blondel (1998) concluded that the highest diversity did not occur in primeval forests but rather in agro-sylvo-pastoral systems such as those that prevailed in many parts of the Mediterranean basin from the Middle ages to the beginning of the 20th century. These systems, covering large areas and entirely overlapping physiographic features such as mountains and plains, structuring important landscape corridors and imposing a renewed main primary ecology created upon a fine mosaic of interconnected habitats, resulted in a high global diversity and species turnover. Several habitats currently considered of conservation concern also depend on disturbance. They correspond mostly to intermediate phases of vegetation succession. However, disturbance should not occur too often and should cope with natural constraints. Thus, they became associated to LIFS, where management actions take place at regularly spaced time intervals. In contrast, in areas with intensive agriculture, disturbances might take place too often (ploughing, grazing) to preserve these habitats, or their representativity.

Lastly, it should be acknowledged that LIFS strongly contribute to maintain genetic diversity. Although this topic was not addressed in the present paper, many regional breeds associated to LIFS are spread across the Mediterranean, creating a diverse array of gene pools adapted to local environmental conditions. As an example, in such a small country as Portugal, we have 17 native races of cattle, 14 races of sheep, 5 races of goat and 2 races of pig (GPPAA 2002).

Important Low-Intensity Farming Systems in Portugal: Linking Biodiversity to Farming Systems

The results of the present study made it possible to identify four main LIFS in Portugal holding relevant natural values:

- *Pseudosteppes* – This LIFS includes dry grasslands and extensive cereal crops systems, which create a landscape mosaic of dry cereal crops, dry legumes and fallow land, usually grazed by sheep. In Portugal they occur mostly in the Alentejo region, with the most important area being Castro Verde (ca. 60,000 ha) (Delgado & Moreira 2000). The main natural value of pseudosteppes relies on vertebrates, specifically on bird species with unfavourable conservation status, such as the great bustard, little bustard, sandgrouse and lesser kestrel. Other natural values include plants (e.g. *Linaria ricardoi*) and a few habitats (Mediterranean temporary ponds and Pseudo-steppe with grasses and annuals). Pseudosteppes constitute a typically

Mediterranean arable system, and have their largest areas in Spain, where they cover ca. 4.5 million hectares (Suárez et al. 1997).

- *Montados* – This livestock system covers over 1 million hectares in Southern Portugal (Eden & Vieira 1995). More than a simple livestock system, montados constitute an agro-sylvo-pastoral system, used for crop cultivation, acorn production, livestock grazing and firewood, charcoal and cork extraction (Eden & Vieira 1995; Diáz et al. 1997). Diáz et al. (1997) define this system as "pasturelands populated by holm (*Quercus ilex*) and/or cork (*Quercus suber*) oaks, with an understorey of open grassland, cereal crops or Mediterranean scrub, commonly with a typical savanna appearance". Several threatened vertebrates are associated to montados, including woodlark, common crane, black vulture, Spanish Imperial eagle and black-shouldered kite. When the understorey is richer in woody plants forming a more or less continuous layer and offering a scrubland appearance, more than 30 species of vascular plants with conservation interest occur, such as *Linaria algaviana*, *Thymus lotocephalus*, *Euphorbia transtagana*, *Centaurea fraylensis*, *Plantago algarbiensis*, *Festuca duriotagana* and *Halimum verticilatum*. The Montados also constitute a listed habitat (6310 - Dehesas with evergreen *Quercus* spp.), and other habitats such as Mediterranean temporary ponds (3170) can also be found in this LIFS.
- *Mountain livestock systems* – they occur mostly in mountain areas of North and Central Portugal, although can also be found at lower altitudes. However, they share the characteristic of free-ranging grazing in pastures or scrubland. This LIFS is important for a wide range of habitats such as Mountain *Cytisus purgans* formations (5120), Species-rich *Nardus* grasslands (6230), Semi-natural dry grasslands and scrubland facies on calcareous substrates (6210), Oro-Iberian *Festuca indigesta* grasslands (6160),

  Mediterranean tall humid grasslands (6420), European dry heaths (4030) or Thermo-Mediterranean and pre-desert scrub (5330). Several vertebrate species also take advantage of these livestock systems, mainly using livestock as food resource (e.g. wolves and several species of vultures), but also profiting from food resources promoted by livestock (e.g. choughs and invertebrates taken from pastures). Some plant species are also typically associated to these systems, including *Festuca elegans, Festuca sumilusitana, Festuca henriquesii, Festuca brigantina, Centaurea micrantha* ssp. *herminii* and *Jasione crispa* ssp. *serpentinica*.
- *Mixed systems* – they constitute a mixture of pastures, hayfields, cereal fields, hedgerows, mostly in mountain regions. This creates a landscape mosaic where several types of habitats can be found, most notably lowland and mountain hay meadows (6510 and 6520). Other habitats associated with these systems include Hydrophilous tall herb fringe communities of plains and of the montane to alpine levels (6430), Mediterranean tall humid grasslands (6420), *Molinia* meadows on calcareous, peaty or clayey-silt-laden soils (6410), Oligotrophic waters containing very few minerals generally on sandy soils of the West Mediterranean (3120). The more characteristic plant species associated with these systems is *Narcissus pseudonarcissus* ssp. *nobilis*. Some bird species such as hen harrier, ortolan bunting and red-backed shrike are also representative of these landscape mosaics.

What Future For Low-Intensity Farming Systems in the Mediterranean?

Most of the LIFS identified as holding relevant natural values constitute economically marginal farming systems. As a consequence, across the Mediterranean region vast areas of these systems are being abandoned (e.g. Diáz et al. 1997; Suarez et al. 1997). Abandoned areas become scrublands, and then forests, through secondary succession. Additionally, subsidised afforestation schemes contribute to an increase of forest cover in abandoned areas (e.g. Pain & Pienkowski 1997). Alternatively, their transformation in monoculture forests, mostly dedicated to pine and eucalyptus growing is a regionally widespread feature (namely in Portugal). If the current trends hold, a large reduction in the geographic extent of LIFS-dominated landscapes is to be expected.

An increasing number of larger fires currently occur in the Mediterranean region, and the progressive abandonment of LIFS is a likely contributing factor to this trend (Lloret et al. 2002). Landscape heterogeneity due to agriculture, scrubland management, small-scale forest, as well as the management of rural pathways, stone walls and hedgerows, both created fuel connectivity breaks and limited fire spread. But abandonment leads to landscape homogenisation, which increases fuel connectivity at the landscape level and promotes uncontrolled fire spread. Fires further increase landscape homogenisation promoting even larger fires and creating scrubland-dominated landscapes highly prone to fire (Trabaud & Galtié 1996; Lloret et al. 2002).

At the ecosystem scale, this translates into simplified species aggregation patterns, reduced functional importance of biological sources of specialized keystone species, and increased spread of generalists. Disturbance size influences succession where long distance dispersive processes are important. Thus, larger fires may lead to less diverse and largely redundant ecosystems (Turner et al. 1998).

Thus, in the absence of agriculture, wildfires are expected to promote scrubland habitats and species. A future without extensive agriculture and small-scale forestry will probably bring simplified Mediterranean landscapes with vast areas of homogeneous scrublands, frequently burned by wildfires, few natural forests and even fewer areas with grasslands and other open habitats. The components of biodiversity that will be most affect are the ones associated with open habitats (e.g. Preiss et al. 1997), particularly the ones requiring more human intervention (e.g. the ones whose man-made disturbance regime can not be replaced by wildfires). The European Union has specific financial mechanisms for promoting habitat and species protection (such as the LIFE programme), but these have considerable budgetary constraints. Thus, they can only be used in specific areas, often for initial investments in habitat management (e.g. European Commission 2003b). These projects are not intended for medium or long-term management. As a consequence, without the financial capability to carry out habitat management in vast areas of the Natura 2000 network using the current nature conservation policies, the only possibility to maintain threatened species populations and habitats in a favourable conservation status will be through the maintenance of extensive agriculture and farmers working in the Mediterranean landscapes. Within the Natura 2000 network in each European country, sites in which the maintenance of LIFS is essential to preserve their natural value should be identified and given priority for the application of agri-environmental type policies.

REFERENCES

Beaufoy, G., Baldock, D. & Clark, J. (1994). The Nature of Farming. Low Intensity Farming Systems in nine European Countries. IEEP, London.

Bignal, E.M. & McCracken, D.I. (1996). Low-intensity farming systems in the conservation of the countryside. *Journal of Applied Ecology*, 33, 413-424.

Bignal, E. & Curtis, D.J. (eds.) (1989). Choughs and land-use in Europe. Scottish Chough Study Group, Argyll.

Blanco, G. Tella, J.L. & Torre, I. (1998). Tradicional farming and key foraging habitats for chough *Pyrrhocorax pyrrhocorax* in a Spanish pseudosteppe landscape. *Journal of Applied Ecology*, 35, 232-239.

Blondel, J. & Aronson, J. (1999). *Biology and wildlife of the Mediterranean region*. Oxford University Press, Oxford.

Boitani, L. (2000). *Action plan for the conservation of the wolves (Canis lupus) in Europe*. Convention on the conservation of European wildlife and natural habitats (Bern convention). Nature and environment, no. 113. Council of Europe Publishing.

Brito, J.C, Brito e Abreu, F., Paulo, O., Rosa, H. & Crespo, E. (1996). Distribuição e habitats do lagarto-de-água (*Lacerta schreiberi*) em Portugal: influência das zonas agrícolas. *Ciência e Natureza*, 2, 1-5.

Covas, R. & Blondel, J. (1998). Biogeography and history of the Mediterranean bird fauna. *Ibis*, 140: 395-407.

Delgado, A. & Moreira, F. (2000). Bird assemblages of an Iberian cereal steppe. *Agriculture, Ecosystems and Environment*, 78: 65-76.

Delibes, M., Rodrigeuz, A. & Ferreras, P. (2000). *Action plan for the conservation of the Iberian lynx (Lynx pardinus) in Europe*. Convention on the conservation of european wildlife and natural habitats (Bern convention). Nature and environment, no. 111. Council of Europe Publishing.

Diáz, M., González, E., Munoz-Pulido, R. & Naveso, M. (1996). Habitat selection patterns of common cranes *Grus grus* wintering in holm oak *Quercus ilex* dehesas of central Spain: effects of human management. *Biological Conservation*, 75: 119-123.

Diáz, M., Campos, P. & Pulido, J.F. (1997). The Spanish dehesas: a diversity in land-use and wildlife. In Pain, D. & Pienkowski, M. (Eds.) Farming and birds in Europe: The Common Agricultural Policy and its Implications for Bird Conservation. Academic Press, San Diego, pp. 178-209.

Donald, P. F., Green, R. E. and Heath, M. F. (2001). Agricultural intensification and the collapse of Europe's farmland bird populations. *Proc. R. Soc. Lond. B*. 268: 25-29.

Donázar, J., Naveso, M., Tella, J. & Campeón, D. (1997). Extensive grazing and raptors in Spain. In Pain, D. & Pienkowski, M. (Eds.) Farming and birds in Europe: The Common Agricultural Policy and its Implications for Bird Conservation. Academic Press, San Diego, pp. 117-149.

European Commission (1979). Council Directive 79/409/EEC on the conservation of wild birds. EC, Brussels.

European Commission (1992). Council Directive 92/43/EEC on the conservation of natural habitats and of wild fauna and flora. EC, Brussels.

European Commission (2003a). Interpretation Manual of European Union Habitats – EUR25. EC, Brussels.

European Commission (2003b). *Life and agri-environment supporting Natura 2000. Experience from the LIFE programme*. Life-focus, Luxembourg, 72 pp.

EEA (1999). Mediterranean region. Reference list of habitat types and species present in the region. Doc. Med/B/fin. 4.

EEA (2004). High nature value farmland. Characteristics, trends and policy challenges. EEA report, 1.

Fernandez-Salvador, R (2002). Microtus cabrera Thomas, 1906. *I*n: Palomo, L.J. & Gisbert, J. (ed.) *Atlas de los mamíferos de España*. DGCNA-MIMAM, SECEM, SECEMU, Madrid, p: 386-389.

Ferrand, N., Almeida, P., Gonçalves, H., Sequeira, F., Teixeira, J., Almeida, F. (2001). *Anfibios e Répteis de Portugal*, Guia FAPAS, Porto.

Fry, G.L.A. (1989). *Conservation in agricultural ecosystems*. In Spellerberg, I.F., Goldsmith, F.B. & Morris, M.G. (Eds.). The scientific management of temperate communities for conservation, pp. 415-443. Blackwell Science, Southampton.

GPPAA (2002). *Relações agricultura/floresta e ambiente*. Plano de acção 2000-2002. GPPAA, Ministério da Agricultura, do Desenvolvimento Rural e das Pescas.

Kleijn, D. & Sutherland, W. (2003). How effective are European agri-environment schemes in conserving and promoting biodiversity? *Journal of Applied Ecology*, 40: 947-969.

Lloret, F., Calvo, E., Pons, X. & Diáz-Delgado, R. (2002). Wildfires and landscape patterns in the East European Peninsula. *Landscape Ecology*, 17: 745-759.

Moreira, F., Morgado, R. & Arthur, S. (2005). Great bustard (*Otis tarda*) habitat selection in relation to agricultural use in southern Portugal. *Wildlife Biology,*124: 415-423.

OECD (2001). *Agriculture and Biodiversity: Developing Indicators for Policy Analysis*. Proceedings From an OECD Expert Meeting, Zurich, Switzerland, November 2001.

Ormerod, S.J., Marshall, E. J. P., Kerby, G. & Rushton, S. P. (2003). Meeting the ecological challenges of agricultural change: editors' introduction. *Journal of Applied Ecology*, 939-946.

Ostermann, O. (1998). The need for management of nature conservation sites designated under Natura 2000. *Journal of Applied Ecology*, 35, 968-973.

Pain, D. & Pienkowski, M. (1997). Conclusions: a future for farming and birds? In Pain, D. & Pienkowski, M. (Eds.) Farming and birds in Europe: The Common Agricultural Policy and its Implications for Bird Conservation. Academic Press, San Diego, pp. 358-388.

Pain, D. & Pienkowski, M. (Eds.) (1997) *Farming and birds in Europe: The Common Agricultural Policy and its Implications for Bird Conservation*. Academic Press, San Diego.

Preiss, E., Martin, J.L. & Debussche, M. (1997). Rural depopulation and recent landscape changes in a Mediterranean region: consequences to the breeding avifauna. *Landscape Ecology*, 51-61.

Robinson, R.A & Sutherland, W. (2002). Post-war changes in arable farming and biodiversity in Great Britain. *Journal of Applied Ecology*, 39, 157-176.

Rufino, R. (1989). Atlas das aves que nidificam em Portugal continental. ICN, CEMPA, Lisboa.

Stoate, C., Boatman, N. D., Borralho, R.J., Rio Carvalho, C., de Snoo, G. R. and Eden, P (2001). Ecological impacts of arable intensification in Europe. *Journal of Environmental Management,* 63, 337–365

Suárez, F., Naveso, M. & De Juana, E. (1997). *Farming in the drylands of Spain: birds of the pseudosteppes*. In Pain, D. & Pienkowski, M. (eds.) Farming and birds in Europe: The Common Agricultural Policy and its Implications for Bird Conservation. Academic Press, San Diego, pp. 297-330.

Suárez-Seoane, S., Osborne, P. & Baudry, J. (2002). Responses of birds of different biogeographic origins and habitat requirements to agricultural land abandonment in northern Spain. *Biological Conservation*, 105, 333–344.

Trabaud, L. & Galtié, J.F. (1996) Effects of fire frequency on plant communities and landscape pattern in the Massif des Aspres (southern France). *Landscape Ecology*, 215-224.

Tucker, G. (1997). *Priorities for bird conservation in Europe: the importance of the farmed landscape*. In Pain, D. & Pienkowski, M. (eds.) Farming and birds in Europe: The Common Agricultural Policy and its Implications for Bird Conservation. Academic Press, San Diego, pp. 79-116.

Tucker & Heath (1994) Birds in Europe. Their conservation status. BirdLife International. *BirdLife Conservation Series*, 3.

Turner, M.G, Baker, W.L., Peterson, C.J., Peet, R.K. (1998). Factors influencing succession: lessons from large, infrequent natural disturbances. *Ecosystems* 1: 511-523.

Vieira, L.M. & Eden, P. (1995). *The Portuguese montados*. In McCracken, Bignal, E.M. & Wenlock, S.E. (eds.) Farming on the edge: the nature of traditional farmland in Europe. Joint Nature Conservation Committee, Peterborough, 99-102.

ACKNOWLEDGEMENTS

Thanks are due to Ana Isabel Queiroz, António Mira, Ana Raínho, Pedro Beja, Jorge Capelo and Helena Cotrim for their comments and help. Part of this work was undertaken while carrying out a project for the Auditor de Ambiente do Ministério da Agricultura. F Moreira was partly funded by the post-doctoral grant SFRH/BPD/12213/03 from Fundação para a Ciência e Tecnologia.

In: Trends in Biodiversity Research
Editor: A. R. Burk, pp. 147-172

ISBN 1-59454-385-2

Chapter 6

THE FUNCTION OF NON-CROP HABITATS FOR SUSTAINABLE PEST CONTROL IN AGROECOSYSTEMS

F. J. J. A. Bianchi and W. van der Werf
Wageningen University, Department of Plant Sciences, Group Crop and Weed Ecology, Wageningen, The Netherlands

ABSTRACT

Intensive agricultural practices have resulted in a strong decline of biodiversity in agricultural landscapes, which may result in the deterioration of ecosystem functions, such as pest regulation by natural enemies. Non-crop habitats play an essential role in maintaining biodiversity and the biological control of pest populations in crops because these habitats are relatively undisturbed areas that provide essential (food) resources for natural enemies and their prey. The area, configuration and composition of non-crop habitats in the landscape are important factors that affect the pest regulation function. Simulations and empirical studies suggest that pest pressure decreases in a non-linear way with an increasing area of non-crop habitats in landscapes. This implies that the area of non-crop habitat should exceed a threshold value in order to acquire notable biological control. A fine-meshed distribution of non-crop habitats, which may be encountered in extensively managed, small-scale landscapes, allows an effective colonization of crops by natural enemies and is likely to result in improved crop protection. Forests and other robust undisturbed natural habitats are identified as habitats that are generally associated with improved impact of natural enemies and suppressed pest populations in surrounding crops. In conclusion, improving and expanding the area of non-crop habitats in agricultural landscapes has good potential to improve the pest regulation function in agroecosystems and may therefore contribute to a transition towards sustainable agriculture.

INTRODUCTION

Intensive Cropping Systems and Pest Problems

Intensive agriculture and expansion of agricultural land has enabled a rapid increase in food production. In the past 40 years, global cereal yield has doubled (FAO, 2001). This rise in agricultural production is made possible by high input of chemical fertilizer and pesticides, irrigation, use of high-yielding crop varieties and large-scale cultivation of monocrops. The global pesticide production increased linearly from the 1950's, exceeding 3 million tonnes per year in 2000. The global nitrogen fertilizer use shows a similar linear trend and exceeded 80 million tonnes per year in 2000 (Tilman et al., 2002). However, the management practices associated with intensive agriculture have undesirable side effects on human health, environment and ecosystem functioning. The heavy use of fertilizers may make crops vulnerable for attack by insect herbivores. Many agricultural pests, such as aphids, leafhoppers and planthoppers, have shown strong population increases in response to nitrogen fertilization (Honěk, 1994; Hasken & Poehling, 1995; Matson et al., 1997). Pest regulation by natural enemies is easily disrupted by pesticides (Matson et al., 1997; Tilman et al., 2002) and development of resistance against chemical pesticides in insect herbivores has become a serious problem (Clarke et al., 1997). The scaling-up of field sizes, removal of non-crop habitats and large-scale monocropping lead to simplified agroecosystems with only few and fragmented non-crop habitats left. These developments have contributed to a rapid decline of biodiversity in agroecosystems (Vandermeer et al., 1998; Donald et al., 2001; Benton et al., 2003), including the abundance and diversity of natural enemies that may control insect outbreaks (Kruess & Tscharntke, 1994; Thies & Tscharntke, 1999). At the present time, most biodiversity in intensively used areas is concentrated in non-crop habitats (Burel, 1996; Kleijn et al., 2001; Duelli & Obrist, 2003). The serious consequences of agricultural intensification on ecosystem services triggered the interest in more sustainable agricultural production systems. The use of ecologically based management strategies can increase the sustainability of agricultural production and mitigate crop damage without the negative environmental consequences that result from chemical pesticide use. This chapter will focus on strategies to sustain biological control of insect pests by improving the conditions for their natural enemies in the landscape.

Requisites for Natural Enemies

Natural enemies have been shown to successfully control arthropod pests in crops (Landis & van der Werf, 1997; Östman et al., 2001a; 2003; Schmidt et al., 2003; Cardinale et al., 2003). However, for a notable control of insect pests by their natural enemies, prerequisites for natural enemy survival and reproduction should be fulfilled. Many natural enemies depend on resources and favorable conditions needed for survival and reproduction that are not provided by crop habitats, such as alternative food sources, hibernation sites and shelter from environmental extremes, pesticides or disturbances (Landis et al., 2000). The most important requisites for natural enemies will be discussed below.

Alternative Food Sources

Many parasitoids and predators, such as syrphids, chrysopids, predatory bugs, coccinellids and predatory mites, depend on plant food sources besides hosts and prey. Nectar and pollen provided by flowers and trees form an essential part of the diet for a broad range of natural enemies. As crops do not provide these food items, or only during a limited period during the year, natural enemies rely on alternative habitats for these requisites. Presence of nectar and pollen may enhance the biological control by natural enemies in agricultural landscapes. For instance, nectar sources have been shown to increase the longevity and fecundity of parasitoids (Idris & Grafius, 1995; Baggen & Gurr, 1998; Wäckers, 2001). Long et al. (1998) demonstrated that coccinellids, parasitoids, syrphids and chrysopids dispersed from flowering plants to nearby crops. Indeed, crops adjoining flower-rich non-crop habitats may have higher natural enemy densities and lower pest densities than crops at further distance from non-crop habitats (White et al., 1995; Hickman & Wratten, 1996; Nicholls et al., 2001; Sengonca et al., 2002). However, natural enemies selectively use flowering plants (Cowgill et al., 1993; Wäckers, 2001) and insect herbivores may also benefit from flower-rich field margins (Baggen & Gurr, 1998; Baggen et al., 1999). This may explain why flower-rich field margins do not in all cases lead to suppressed pest populations.

Hibernation

Most natural enemies hibernate in non-crop habitats, as bare fields are unsuitable for hibernation. Carabid beetles, staphylinids, coccinellids, parasitoids are known to hibernate in woody or herbaceous non-crop habitats (Sotherton, 1985; Honěk; 1989; Corbett & Rosenheim, 1996). These habitats provide stable climatic conditions for hibernation. Thomas et al (1991) found densities of up to 1500 predators/m^2 in raised earth banks covered with grass tussocks. Consequently, field margins near arable fields may result in increased biological control because of an early colonization of fields by general predators (Dennis & Fry, 1992; Landis & van der Werf, 1997).

Microclimate

The microclimate in arable fields may be unfavorable for parasitoids. Laboratory experiments showed that the life span of some parasitoids is shorter at 24°C than at temperatures between 15 and 20°C (Rahim et al., 1991; Hailemichael & Smith, 1994). Dyer & Landis (1996) demonstrated that climatic conditions in agroecosystems impact the population dynamics of parasitoids. They showed that the longevity of parasitoids was prolonged in forests as compared to maize crops due to the moderate microclimate. Therefore, late successional non-crop habitats may function as refuge sites with a favorable microclimate for these natural enemies during warm periods of the day.

Alternative Prey and Hosts

Since crops are ephemeral habitats that support prey items for only a limited period during the year, natural enemies depend on prey and hosts in non-crop habitats for the rest of the year. Coccinellids are known to feed on aphids in non-crop habitats early and late in the season, when aphid densities in crops are low (Maredia et al., 1992; Leather et al., 1999). Low prey intake levels may impact reproduction rates of coccinellids (Xia et al., 1999) and may trigger long distance dispersal (Hodek et al., 1993), resulting in a local decrease of the ladybeetle population. Therefore, the prey availability on non-crop habitats is likely to impact the size of the natural enemy reservoir in agroecosystems. Wyss (1996) studied densities of natural enemies and alternative prey in orchards with and without weed strips. The higher densities of spiders, coccinellids and syrphids in orchards with weed strips could be explained by higher densities of alternative prey and by the presence of nectar and pollen in the weed strips (Wyss, 1995). Presence of alternative hosts may also boost densities of parasitoids (Corbett & Rosenheim, 1996). For instance, Maier (1981) found higher densities of parasitoids near blueberry, dogwood and winterberry, because these often support alternative prey.

Nesting Sites

Insectivorous birds, such as tits, wrens and robins, may contribute to the suppression of insect outbreaks (Getz & Brighty, 1986; Tremblay et al., 2001). Many bird species depend on non-crop habitats, such as hedges, hedgerows and woodlots. For instance, Johnson and Beck (1988) found in a literature survey that 29 bird species are directly dependent and 37 species moderately dependent on shelterbelts in agricultural landscapes in the USA. Twenty-eight species used shelterbelts for nesting. Accordingly, presence of wooded habitats may enhance pest control in crops by birds.

In conclusion, a wide range of natural enemies in agricultural landscapes depends on non-crop habitats. In particular, field margins, fallows, channels, hedgerows and woodlots provide important ecological functions for natural enemies, which may control pest outbreaks in crops.

Landscape Structure and Sustainable Pest Regulation

Intensively managed crops constitute a hostile environment for natural enemies because of frequent and intensive disturbances. On the other hand, non-crop habitats are considered valuable because these habitats provide important resources and desirable conditions for natural enemies. As a consequence, natural pest regulation by natural enemies is expected to be enhanced in landscapes with ample non-crop habitats as compared to landscapes with only limited non-crop habitats. Indeed, a number of studies report that pest pressure in diversified landscapes with crops intermingled with non-crop habitats (complex landscapes) is reduced as compared to landscapes mainly composed of crops (simple landscapes). Basedow (1990) measured pest and natural enemy densities in a small-scale, complex landscape composed of 7.5% non-crop habitats and a large-scale, simple landscape with only 1.7% of non-crop habitats in Germany. The complex landscape had during two years higher densities of natural enemies, resulting in a 14 and 18-fold reduction of aphid density in sugar beet as compared to the simple landscape. Schulze and Gerstberger (1993) describe a landscape characterized by hedgerows that provide nectar, pollen and alternative prey, which support high densities of parasitoids and predators. As a result, aphid populations are controlled by the natural enemy complex and this is one of the few regions in Germany where chemical aphid control is not necessary. Östman et al. (2001a) showed that aphid establishment was lower in landscapes with abundant field margins and perennial crops than in simple landscapes. However, after aphid establishment, the impact of ground-living natural enemies was less in landscapes with a high proportion of forests as compared to landscapes with more contiguous arable land.

Most likely, the natural enemies in complex landscapes spend more time in non-crop habitats, resulting in a reduced natural enemy density in crops. Thies and Tscharntke (1999) and Thies et al. (2003) found positive relationships between the area field margins, fallows, hedges and forest remnants and the percentage parasitism of rape pollen beetles in rape fields. Consequently, crop injury levels in rape fields were up to twice as high in simple landscapes as compared to complex landscapes.

Furthermore, there are a number of studies that compared the densities and activity of natural enemies in landscapes with varying structure, but that did not quantify effects of these natural enemies on pest densities. Thus, these studies do not show direct evidence of effects of landscape structure on pest suppression by natural enemies, although this is plausible. Marino & Landis (1996) found up to 5 times higher parasitism rates in small-scale, diversified landscapes as compared to large-scale, simple landscapes in the USA. However, in follow-up studies (Menalled et al., 1999; 2003) that repeated the experiment in multiple regions and in several years no consistent relationship was found between landscape structure and parasitism rates. These studies suggest distinct long-term host-parasitoid dynamics in complex and simple landscapes. Bianchi et al. (2005) reported higher predation rates of egg batches of the cabbage moth *Mamestra brassicae* in landscapes with abundant wood lots. Parasitism rates of egg batches by parasitoids were negatively correlated with the area of arable land. Ryszkowski et al. (1993) found 70% higher biomass of predators and parasitoids in landscapes containing 12% of non-crop habitats than in large-scale landscapes with no non-crop habitats in Poland. Šedivý (1995) reported 2.4 fold higher parasitism rates in wheat fields infested by leaf beetles in landscapes with ecological corridors than in landscapes without these structures. Finally, Schmidt et al. (2003) found twice as high parasitism rates of wheat aphids in complex landscapes as compared to simple landscapes. Although complex landscapes in most cases give rise to increased densities or activity of natural enemies, complex landscapes may also be subject to increased densities of colonizing aphids (Galecka, 1966; Thies et al, 2005). In both studies increased natural enemy impact counterbalanced the higher aphid colonization rate in complex landscapes, resulting in an overall comparable pest pressure in complex and simple landscapes.

The relation between landscape structure and pest regulation by natural enemies seems robust. In most cases, complex landscapes are subject to reduced pest pressure and have an increased natural enemy impact. Simple landscapes tend to have a reduced natural enemy complex and may have an increased risk of pest outbreaks as herbivores may be released from natural enemy control.

Arising Questions

Although there is good evidence of a general positive effect of non-crop habitats on pest regulation by natural enemies, there is only limited quantitative insight in this topic. For instance, little is known of about the minimal area requirement and the optimal spatial configuration of non-crop habitats to provide effective biocontrol. The area and spatial configuration of non-crop habitats are likely to affect pest regulation because many natural enemies move between crop and non-crop habitats at a seasonal basis (Wissinger, 1997). As many predators, such as carabid beetles and staphylinids, move on the ground, the colonization of crops early in the season is likely to take longer with increasing field size and increasing distance from hibernation to the fields, allowing pest populations more time for unrestricted growth. Other natural enemies, like parasitoids, may frequently commute between field margins to feed on nectar sources and crops to search for hosts (Siekmann et al., 2001). Consequently, crop areas near non-crop habitats providing nectar may be searched more intensively and may have higher levels of biological control than crop areas that are further away from nectar sources. Another unresolved issue is how the quality of non-crop elements affects biological control. We have little quantitative insight in how characteristics of non-crop habitats translate to pest reduction by natural enemies. For instance, it is unclear whether it is better from the perspective of pest regulation for field margins to provide nectar sources or to support alternative prey. Knowledge of which habitats or vegetation types are associated with enhanced pest regulation is crucial for the implementation of effective habitat management practices. As a first step in the process of the identification of advantageous habitats, the assessment of the theoretical potential of the benefit of habitat characteristics (e.g. the level of alternative prey or nectar supply) may be useful.

The theoretical questions, raised above, are relevant for habitat management practice, but they are difficult to answer with empirical studies. For such questions a modeling approach may be advantageous. Mathematical models offer the possibility to unravel the interactions between pests, natural enemies and landscape structure. Knowledge of the processes underlying natural pest control by natural enemies may thus be used to identify promising habitat management strategies.

THEORETICAL APPROACH

Model System

This section will focus on effects of the area, configuration and quality of non-crop habitats on pest regulation by natural enemies in agricultural landscapes using a modeling approach. The model system used is the ladybeetle-aphid system. We selected this system because aphids are an important group of pests of many agricultural crops and occur in crop and non-crop habitats. Aphids cause crop injury by feeding on the phloem, by the production of honeydew and also by transmission of plant viruses. Relatively few aphid species are regarded as agricultural pests. Most aphid species are restricted to host plants in non-crop habitats (Nentwig et al., 1998). Thus, aphids may act as harmful organisms that cause crop injury, or as beneficial organisms that may function as alternative prey for natural enemies that prey on aphid species that are important in agriculture. The natural enemy species under consideration is the seven-spotted ladybeetle, *Coccinella septempunctata*, which is a common predator that feeds on aphids in agricultural crops, but also depends on uncultivated habitats in the landscape for hibernation and alternative prey in periods when aphid densities in crops are low (Honěk, 1989). *C. septempunctata* is an attractive predator for modeling effects of pest regulation in relation to landscape structure because many aspects of their biology are well studied (Hodek & Honěk 1996; Xia et al., 1999; 2003; Van der Werf et al., 2000).

In the Temperate Zone, *C. septempunctata* has one generation per year. Adults hibernate in non-crop habitats and emergence in spring, after which they colonize crops (Honěk, 1982). The foraging behavior of *C. septempunctata* in aphid infested fields is characterized by short flights (Van der Werf et al., 2000). *C. septempunctata* shows extended residence times when situated in patches with prey (Ives et al., 1993), resulting in aggregation of ladybeetles in areas with high prey densities (Kareiva & Odell, 1987; Elliott & Kieckhefer, 2000). In summer, *C. septempunctata* deposits egg batches in patches with aphids. The larvae emerging from these egg batches feed on aphids in the vicinity of the egg batch because they have only a limited dispersal capacity. The larvae go through four larval stages and a pupal stage, after which they emerge as adults. The new generation of adults may disperse by flight and exploit aphid patches in various habitats during the rest of the growing season. In autumn, the adults move to non-crop habitats where they will hibernate.

Model Description

The simulation models presented in this section are described in detail in Bianchi and van der Werf (2003; 2004). The models describe the habitat use and population dynamics of a stage-structured population of *C. septempunctata* in a landscape. The landscape is composed of cells, each measuring 10 x 10 m^2. Each cell represents either crop or non-crop habitat. Crop habitats support pest aphids that may cause crop injury, whereas non-crop habitats support non-pest aphid populations that may function as alternative prey. Pest aphids colonize crops in spring. The number of aphids in crop and non-crop habitats increases rapidly in the course of the growing season. Ladybeetles hibernate in non-crop habitats. After emergence in spring, ladybeetles disperse in all directions according a rotated negative-exponential function (Fig. 1). Hence, the majority of ladybeetles taking off will move only over short distance, while a small fraction of the ladybeetles will move over somewhat longer distances. Not all ladybeetles in a cell are redistributed. The local aphid density in each cell determines the proportion of ladybeetles that disperse (Fig. 2). Low aphid densities result in high proportions of dispersing ladybeetles (short residence times), whereas high aphid densities result in low proportions of dispersing ladybeetles (long residence times). This description of foraging behavior results in ladybeetle aggregation in cells with high aphid densities. At a fixed date, each female ladybeetle deposits egg batches on its current location. The emergence of egg, the four larval and the pupal stages are simulated by shifting individuals from one stage to the following stage according to specific developmental rates for each stage (Fig. 3). Mortality is accounted for by removing individuals in each stage according to stage-specific relative mortality rates. During the immature stages, ladybeetle larvae and pupae remain in the cell where the eggs were deposited. Newly emerged adults disperse by flight and have the same dispersal characteristics as the previous ladybeetle generation (Figs. 1 and 2). For each cell, the number of aphids that are removed by the carnivorous larval and adult ladybeetle stages is recorded. Aphid predation rates are described by stage-specific Holling type II functional responses (Fig. 4). Thus, the model describes the control of aphid populations by carnivorous stages of ladybeetles explicitly in space during a single growing season.

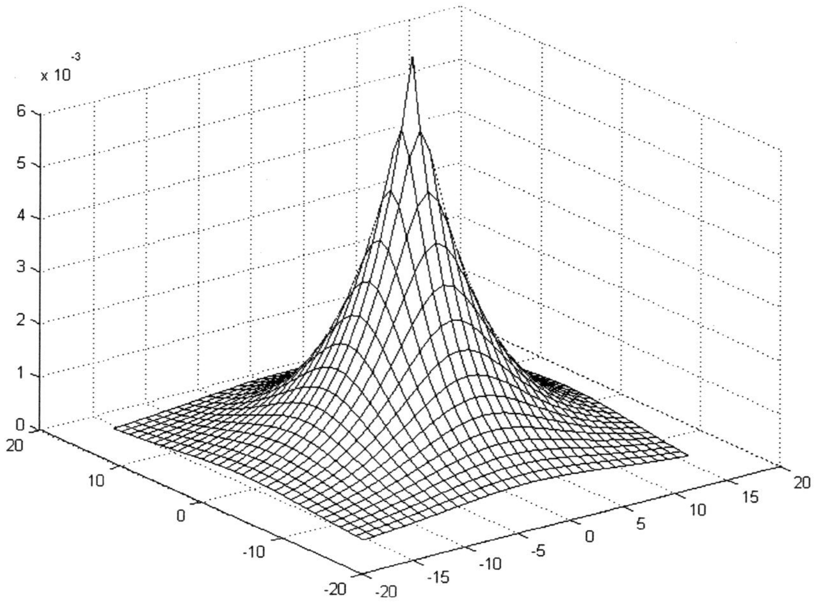

Figure 1. Spatial redistribution function for adults of *Coccinella septempunctata*.

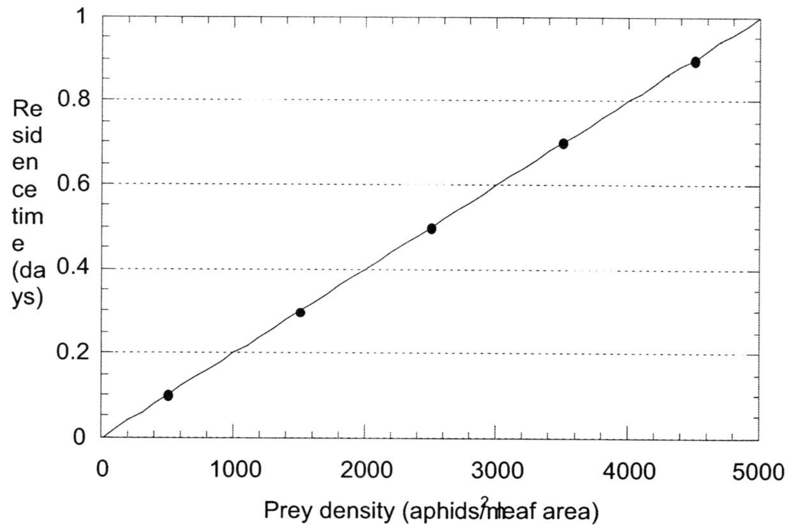

Figure 2. Relationship between the residence time of adults of *Coccinella septempunctata* and aphid density.

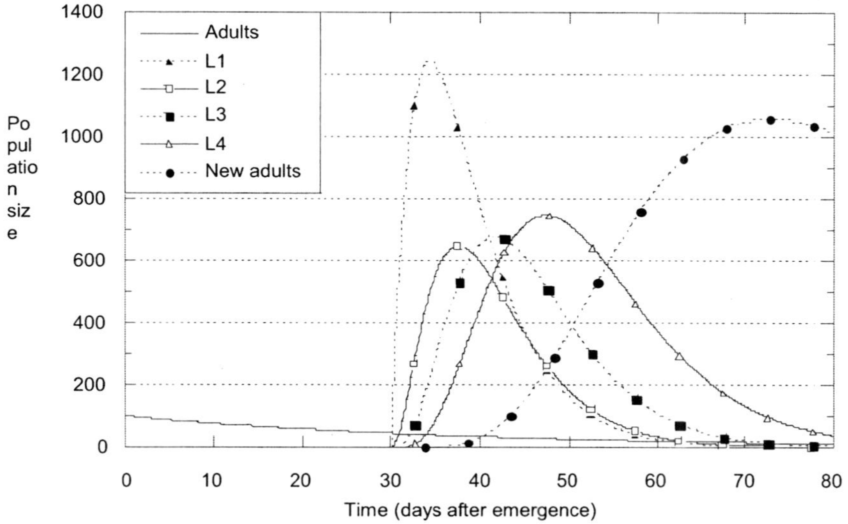

Figure 3. Population dynamics of carnivorous stages of *Coccinella septempunctata*. The initial population size is 100 adults of *C. septempunctata*. Thirty days after hibernation female *C. septempunctata* deposit egg batches.

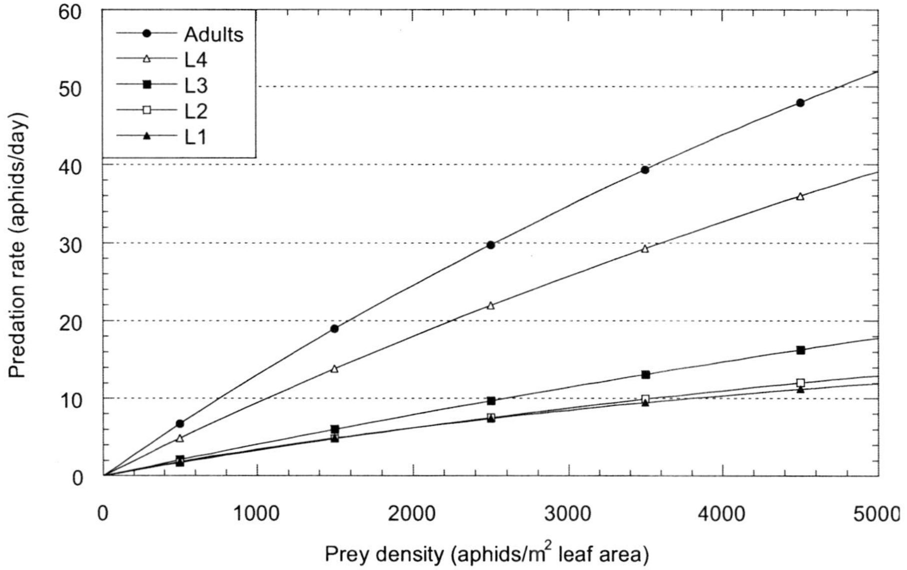

Figure 4. Relation between the predation rate of carnivorous stages of *Coccinella septempunctata* and aphid density (*Aphis gossypii*). Functional responses were derived using search rates derived from field experiments on cotton and handling times were determined at 20 °C on cotton leaves (Xia et al., 2003).

Area and Spatial Arrangement of Non-Crop Habitats

The effect of the area and spatial arrangement of non-crop habitats on pest control is studied in twelve landscapes consisting of crops and non-crops that differ in the proportion (1, 4, 9 and 16%) and fragmentation of the non-crop habitats (1, 4 or 16 elements; Fig. 5). The landscapes are composed of 40 × 40 cells that together cover 160,000 m^2 (400 × 400 m). At the start of the simulation, ladybeetles are evenly distributed over non-crop habitats, at a density of 10 ladybeetles/m^2. Thus, the initial number of ladybeetles is proportional to the area of non-crop habitat (16.000, 64.000, 144.000 and 256.000 for landscapes containing 1, 4, 9 and 16% non-crop habitats, respectively).

Both the proportion of non-crop habitats and the spatial distribution of non-crop habitats affected biological control by ladybeetles (Fig. 5 and 6). Landscapes with 1 and 4% of non-crop habitats (respectively 0.1 and 0.4 individuals per m^2, averaged over the landscape) were not able to provide adequate control. In these landscapes the mean density of aphids at the end of the growing season was always at least 3000 aphids/m^2 (Fig. 6). In contrast, landscapes with 9 and 16% hedgerows (respectively 0.9 and 1.6 individuals per m^2, averaged over the landscape) suppressed aphid densities to approximately 1000 aphids/m^2 or less at the end of the growing season. However, this level of aphid control was only achieved in landscapes with 4 or 16 hedgerow elements and not in the landscape elements in which the non-crop habitat was aggregated into a single square (Fig. 6).

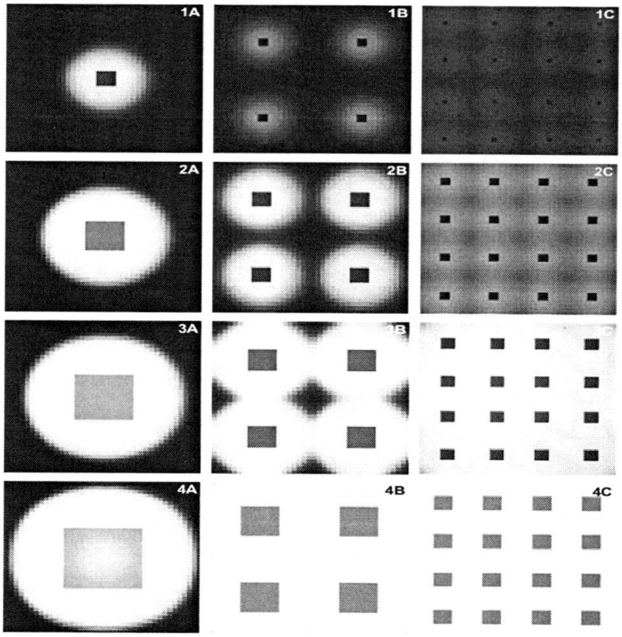

Figure 5. Spatial distribution of aphid density at the end of the growing season in 12 landscapes with 1%, 4%, 9% and 16% of non-crop habitats (from top to bottom) and increasing level of fragmentation (1, 4 and 16 non-crop habitats, left to right). White and black represent densities of 0 and 5000 aphids/m^2, respectively. (Reprinted from Environmental Entomology 32, Bianchi, F.J.J.A. & van der Werf, W. The effect of the area and configuration of hibernation sites on the control of aphids by *Coccinella septempunctata* (Coleoptera: Coccinellidae) in agricultural landscapes: A simulation study, pp. 1290-1304. Copyright (2003), with permission)

The fragmentation of non-crop habitats had hardly an effect on the level of aphid control in landscapes with 1 and 4% of non-crop habitats (Fig. 5 and 6). In these landscapes the initial number of ladybeetles was too low to provide adequate aphid control. However, in landscapes containing 9 and 16% non-crop habitats, the spatial distribution of non-crop habitats clearly affected aphid control. Landscapes with a single non-crop element had strongly suppressed aphid densities near the non-crop habitat and high aphids densities at further distance (Fig 5: 3A and 4A). In contrast, in landscapes with a fragmented distribution of non-crop habitats aphid populations were suppressed over the whole cropping area (Fig 5: 3C and 4C). Hence, best control was achieved in landscapes with a substantial area of non-crop habitat and where these habitats were evenly distributed over the landscape.

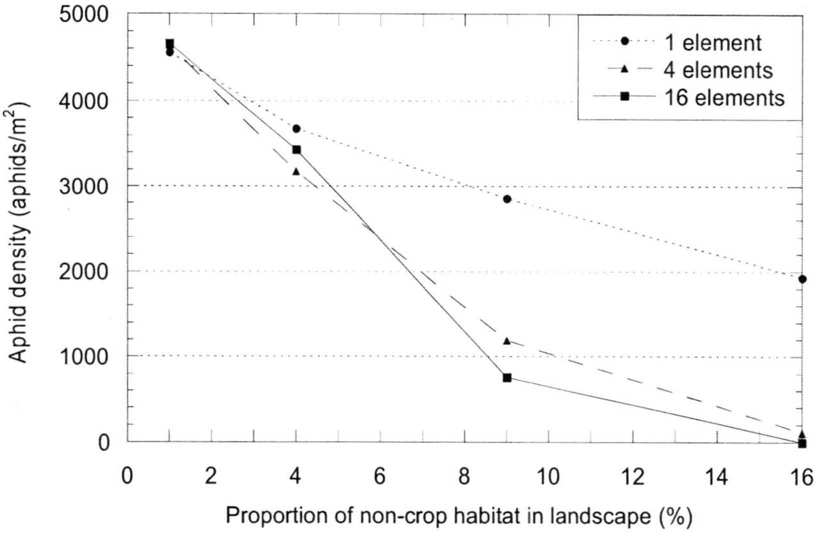

Figure 6. Density of aphids in crops at the end of the growing season in twelve landscapes with 1, 4, 9 and 16% of non-crop habitats divided into 1, 4 or 16 square elements. Landscapes with 1, 4, 9 to 16% non-crop habitats contained initial numbers of 16.000, 64.000, 144.000 and 256.000 *Coccinella septempunctata*, respectively, corresponding to 0.1, 0.4, 0.9 and 1.6 ladybeetles/m^2 over the whole landscape.

Quality of Non-Crop Habitats

The quality of non-crop habitats for biological control by ladybeetles will be evaluated in terms of supply of prey. We now consider a small-scale agricultural landscape composed of 90% crops and 10% non-crop habitats (Fig. 7). Non-crop habitats support non-pest aphids, whereas crops support pest aphids that infest crops. Both types of aphids have a distinct phenology and population dynamics. Aphid populations in non-crop habitats start to increase early March and reach a maximum density of 2500 aphids/m^2 (Fig. 8). Initial densities of aphids in non-crop habitats are 0, 1, 2, 5 or 10 aphids/m^2 reflecting non-crop habitats with increasing prey availability. Pest aphids colonize crops later in the growing season (mid May) and reach peak densities of 3500 aphids/m^2. Aphid densities in crops crash soon after reaching peak densities because of deterioration of crop quality for aphid development (Williams et al., 1999). Ladybeetles are initially present in non-crop habitats at densities of 10 ladybeetles per square meter. These ladybeetles emerge in the end of March, after which they remain 30 days in non-crop habitats feeding on non-pest aphids. Thirty days after emergence (Julian date 150) the ladybeetles start to disperse into the crops (Fig. 8).

Fecundity of ladybeetles increases with prey intake (Xia et al., 1999). Therefore, we assume that reproduction of female ladybeetles depends linearly on the number of aphids eaten between emergence (end of March) and the time of reproduction (end of June; Fig. 9). Ladybeetles have a minimum requirement of aphids to enable reproduction (Ives, 1981; Xia et al., 1999) and reproduction reaches a plateau at high prey availability (Xia et al., 1999).

Initial densities of non-pest aphids in non-crop habitats of 0, 1, 2, 5 or 10 aphids/m^2 resulted in increasing levels of prey availability. At the emergence date of *C. septempunctata* (Julian date 120) densities of aphids in non-crop habitats were 0, 340, 600, 1100 and 1530 aphids/m^2, respectively (Fig. 8). In the scenario under consideration, ladybeetles depended strongly on aphids in non-crop habitats (Fig. 10). In absence of prey in non-crop habitats prey intake levels of ladybeetle females were not sufficient to acquire the threshold value of 500 aphids needed for reproduction. With increasing levels of prey availability in non-crop habitats ladybeetle reproduction increased up to 135 eggs per female at an initial density of 10 aphids/m^2. These differences in reproduction affect the effectiveness of ladybeetles as biological control agents. When no ladybeetle reproduction took place, the aphid load in crops exceeded 10^6 aphid-days/m^2 (Fig. 11). With increasing reproduction rates of ladybeetles, the aphid load in crops declined with 31% to almost 7×10^5 aphid-days/m^2. These simulations show that, at parameter settings representing real systems, prey availability in non-crop habitats may boost biological control by predators and reduce crop injury.

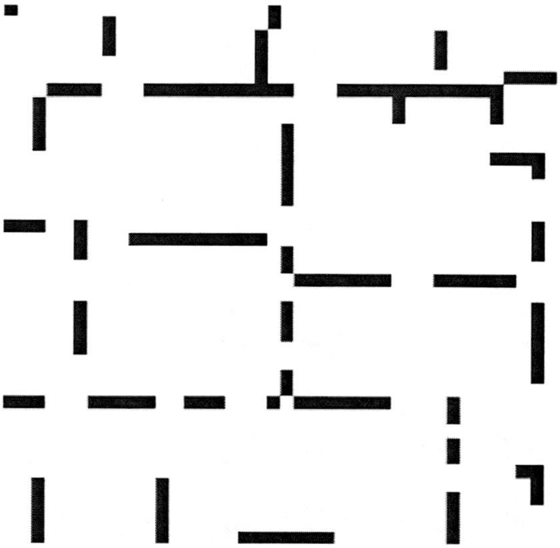

Figure 7. Landscape map used for the simulation of the effect of prey availability in non-crop habitats on biological control by *Coccinella septempunctata*. The landscape (400 x 400 m) is built up from 10 x 10 m^2 cells consisting of crops (white) and non-crop habitats (black). (Reprinted from Ecological Modelling 171, Bianchi, F.J.J.A. & van der Werf, W. Model evaluation of the function of prey in non-crop habitats for biological control by ladybeetles in agricultural landscapes, pp.177-193. Copyright (2004), with permission from Elsevier)

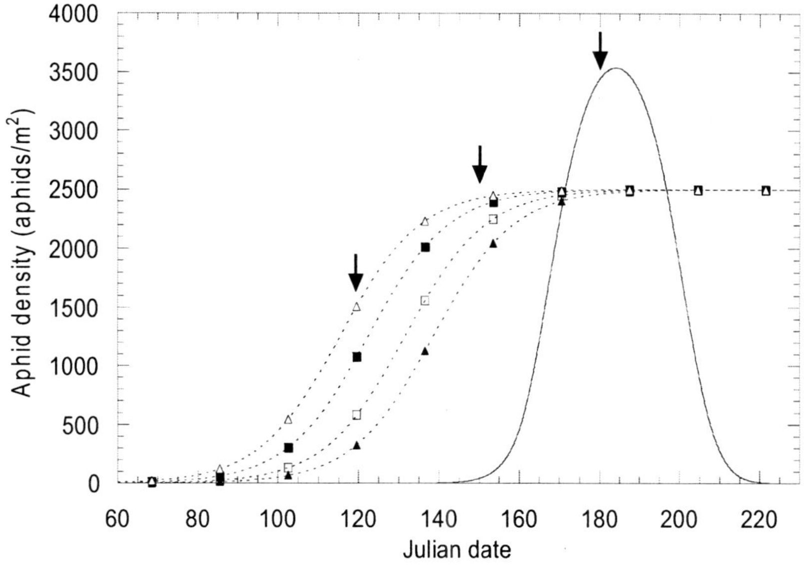

Figure 8. Population dynamics of pest aphids in crops (solid line) and non-pest aphids in non-crop habitats (dashed lines) at initial densities of 1 (▲), 2 (□), 5 (■) and 10 (Δ) aphids/m^2 ground area in absence of *Coccinella septempunctata*. Arrows indicate emergence in non-crop habitats (Julian date 120), colonization of crops (Julian date 150) and reproduction of *C. septempunctata* (Julian date 180), consecutively.

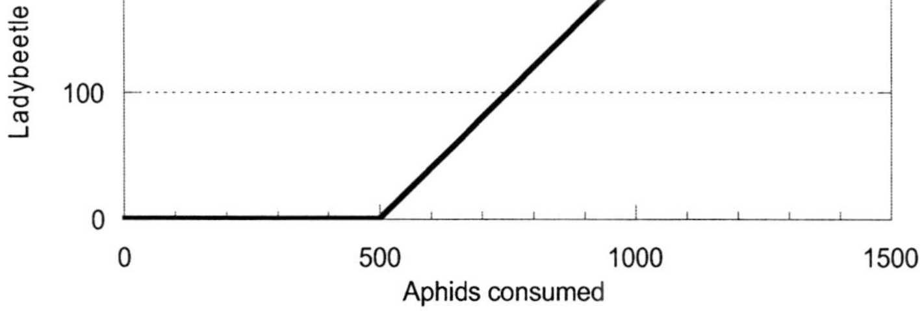

Figure 9. Relation between the number of eggs deposited by *Coccinella septempunctata* and the number of aphids consumed between emergence and reproduction. (Reprinted from Ecological Modelling 171, Bianchi, F.J.J.A. & van der Werf, W. Model evaluation of the function of prey in non-crop habitats for biological control by ladybeetles in agricultural landscapes, pp.177-193. Copyright (2004), with permission from Elsevier)

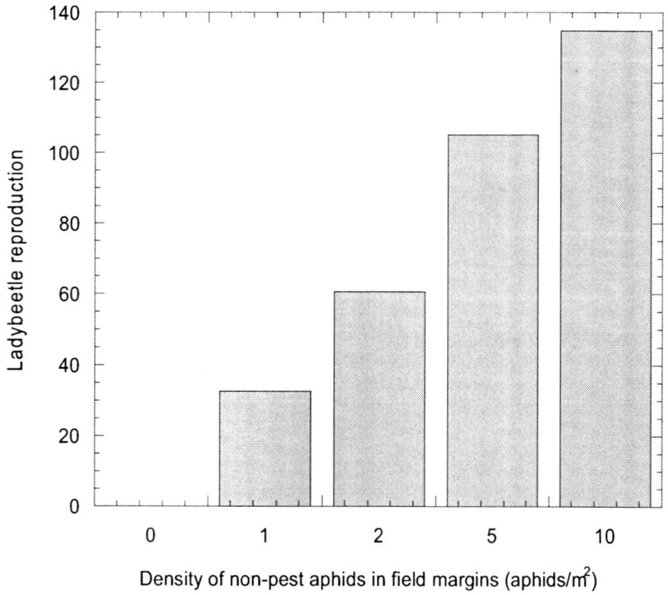

Figure 10. Reproduction per female *Coccinella septempunctata* as function of the initial density of non-pest aphids in non-crop habitats.

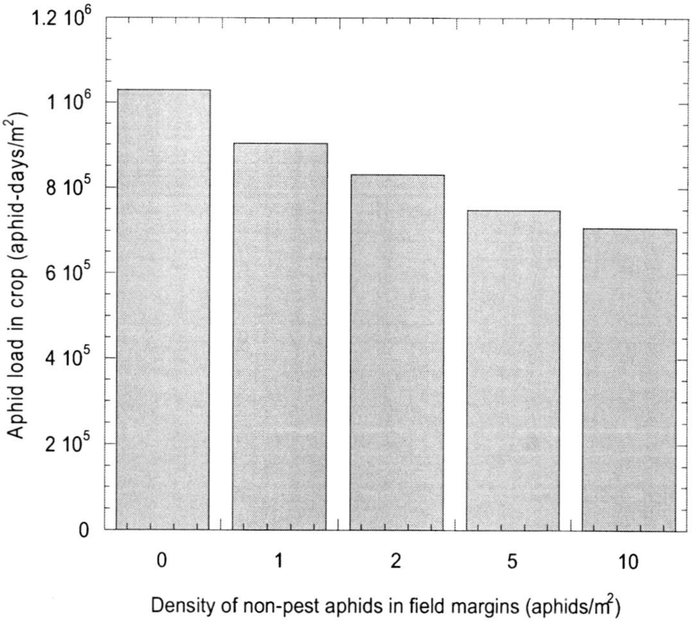

Figure 11. Aphid load of pest aphids in crops as function of the initial density of non-pest aphids in non-crop habitats.

EMPIRICAL EVIDENCE

Area of Non-Crop Habitats

In this section the outcome of simulations are confronted with empirical data. Simulations indicate that pest regulation by predators improves with increasing area of non-crop habitat in agricultural landscapes (Fig. 6). This finding corresponds with most empirical studies that compared pest regulation by natural enemies in landscapes with different areas of non-crop habitats (Basedow, 1990; Šedivý, 1995; Thies & Tscharntke, 1999; Den Belder et al, 2002; Thies et al., 2003; Schmidt et al., 2003; Bianchi et al., 2005), but not all (Menalled et al., 1999; 2003). In the studies of Thies & Tscharntke (1999) and Thies et al. (2003) a wide variety of landscapes were considered (15 in both studies), ranging from 3-65% and 3-50% non-crop habitats, respectively. Both studies reported positive logistic relationships between the area of non-crop habitat and the percentage parasitism in rape fields. Furthermore, crop injury levels were found to decrease with increasing area of non-crop habitats in the landscape. Our simulations of ladybeetle-aphid interactions likewise resulted in a decrease of aphid pressure as the area of non-crop habitats in the landscape increased, especially when non-crop habitats were distributed in 4 and 16 elements (Fig. 6). Therefore, simulated natural enemy-pest interactions in a simple spatially explicit simulation model reflected the complex multitrophic interactions in diversified landscapes well. As the model assumed a proportional increase of the number of predators with landscapes having 1, 4%, 9% and 16% non-crop habitat, this may also hold true for real landscapes. Thus, the combination of simulation and empirical studies suggests that the density of natural enemies increases proportionally with the area of non-crop habitat in agricultural landscapes, leading to a non-linear response of pest pressure.

Spatial Arrangement of Non-Crop Habitats

Simulations suggest that fragmentation of non-crop habitats may boost biological control, provided that the area of non-crop habitats is sufficiently large (Fig 5). Figure 5 can be interpreted as the change in landscape structure observed from large-scale (Fig. 5; 1A) to small-scale agricultural landscapes (Fig. 5; 4C). Large-scale agricultural landscapes have large fields and small non-crop habitats between the fields, resulting in large distances between the non-crop habitats. Small-scale agricultural landscapes have small field sizes and a dense network of field edges, which often are composed of non-crop habitats. Thus, the arable fields in small-scale landscapes have high perimeter-to-area ratios and the non-crop habitats are typically located near one another (Landis, 1994). Landscapes with high perimeter-to-area ratios are likely to have long non-crop/arable interfaces, which may result in an effective colonization of fields by natural enemies from adjoining non-crop habitats. Positive relationships between perimeter-to-area ratios of cultivated fields and natural enemy impact and pest suppression have been reported by Bommarco (1998) and Östman et al. (2001a; 2001b). Bommarco (1998) reported an almost three fold higher fecundity of predatory carabid beetles in landscapes that had small fields, high perimeter-to-area ratios and a high percentage of perennial crops as compared to simple landscapes. Östman et al. (2001b) found a positive relationship between the perimeter-to-area ratios of cultivated fields and the condition of predatory carabid beetles, which corresponds with the findings of Bommarco (1998). In another study, Östman et al. (2001a) found a reduced establishment and survival of aphids in landscapes with increasing perimeter-to-area ratios. Likewise, Bianchi et al. (2005) found a relationship between pest control by predators and the perimeter of non-crop habitats at a scale of 0.3 km. Predation rates of egg batches of the cabbage moth, *M. brassicae*, in Brussels sprout crops were positively correlated with the length of forest edges, which are known to function as hibernation sites for many predatory beetles (Sotherton, 1985). Finally, isolation of non-crop habitats may disrupt the community structure of natural enemies. Kruess & Tscharntke (1994) showed that the abundance and diversity of parasitoids controlling insect herbivore populations in clover were reduced with increasing distance between clover habitats. As a consequence, herbivore populations in isolated habitats were released from parasitoid control and initiated pest problems. Thus, a dense network of non-crop habitats not only enables an effective colonization of fields by natural enemies, but may also provide a robust habitat network for meta-populations of natural enemies.

Quality of Non-Crop Habitats

The simulation study suggests that properties of non-crop habitats, such as the availability of alternative prey, may result in enhanced pest control. This outcome is in line with an empirical study by Östman (2004), who found a positive correlation of aphid removal by generalist predators and alternative prey abundance in spring barley. A number of empirical studies focused on the identification of habitat types associated with enhanced crop protection by natural enemies (Elliott et al. 1998; 2002a; 2002b; Thies & Tscharntke, 1999; Den Belder et al., 2002; Bianchi et al., 2005). Elliott et al. (1998) found that the density of 6 species of predators in wheat fields (1 species of damsel bug, 1 chrysopid and 4 ladybeetle species) was positively correlated with unmanaged grasslands and forests. Results of another study by Elliott et al. (2002b), where the abundance of 4 ladybeetle species in corn were related to landscape variables, were less unequivocal. Two species responded in a variable way to pasture/grassland, whereas the abundance of one species was positively correlated with forests. The abundance of another ladybeetle species was positively correlated with unmanaged grassland. Yet in another study by Elliot et al. (2002) the density of 5 predator species (1 damsel bug, 1 chrysopid and 3 ladybeetle species) were related to landscape variables. Specific predator species responded in variable ways to wetlands and unmanaged grasslands, whereas one ladybeetle species was negatively correlated to the area of forests in the surrounding landscape. Bianchi et al. (2005) found that predation rates of *M. brassicae* eggs in Brussels sprout, which are most likely eaten by predatory carabid beetles, staphylinids, earwigs and larvae of chrysopids, were positively correlated with the area of woody habitats (forests area at and length of tree lines) in the surrounding landscape. Forests were also identified as an important landscape factor associated with reduced thrips pressure (Den Belder et al., 2002). All the above-mentioned studies related biological control to landscape factors using regression analysis. Since the existence of such a relationship provides only indirect evidence for causality, these results should be interpreted with care. This is for instance illustrated by two studies of Elliot et al. (2002a; 2002b) where the density of ladybeetle species (*Hippodamia convergens*) in alfalfa and cornfields were negatively and positively influenced by unmanaged grassland, respectively. Direct evidence of favorable non-crop habitats for biological control are provided by studies that quantified natural enemy impact in both crop and non-crop habitats. Thies & Tscharntke (1999) found that parasitism rates of rape pollen beetles (*Meligethes aeneus*) were enhanced in rape plots established in old fallows and to a somewhat lesser extent in old field margin strips, as compared to plots in rape crops. The enhancing effect of old fallows and field margins on pest control in rape fields was confirmed by measurements conducted at the landscape level. Landis & Haas (1992) studied interactions between the parasitoid *Eriborus terebrans* and the European cornborer *Ostrinia nubilalis*, which is considered a pest in corn. During the first generation of *E. terebrans* and *O. nubilalis* higher parasitoid densities were found near wooded edges and herbaceous edges than in the field interior. During the second generation, no consistent pattern was observed. This study suggests that wooded and herbaceous non-crop habitats play an important role in the population build up of this parasitoid over successive generations. The general trend in the presented studies is that robust non-crop habitats like forests and fallows/unmanaged grasslands play an important role in control of pest populations in agricultural landscapes.

IMPLICATIONS FOR PRACTICE

The relation between biodiversity, landscape structure and pest regulation in crops is extremely complex. The many specific interactions between crop and non-crop habitats, insect herbivores, natural enemies and the physical environment result in variable success of conservation biological control. Despite this variability some rules of thumb for effective biological control by indigenous natural enemies may be formulated.

Pest suppression by natural enemies requires a minimal area of non-crop habitats and a fine-meshed distribution of these habitats over the landscape. The quantification of the minimal area requirement for non-crop habitats is difficult, but as an indication improved pest control has been observed in a small-scale landscape consisting of 7.5% non-crop habitat (Basedow, 1990). An important aspect for the implementation of habitat management is that the expected benefit of an additional non-crop habitat depends on the area of non-crop habitat that is already present in a landscape, given the non-linear relationship between pest pressure and the area of non-crop habitat. In landscapes that hardly have non-crop habitats the expected benefit of adding a small area of non-crop habitats may be limited, whereas adding additional non-crop habitats in landscapes that already have some non-crop habitats may result in attaining the threshold area needed for effective biological control.

Pest regulation by natural enemies acts at many levels of scale, up to the landscape level. Since natural enemies and insect herbivores move within landscapes, requisites for natural enemies should at least be fulfilled at the landscape scale. This implies that for effective habitat management aiming at improved biological control collaboration between farmers and other landscape users and managers is essential.

New non-crop habitats can best be established in a fine-meshed network in the landscape because the highest levels of biological control are usually in the close proximity of these habitats (Nicholls et al., 2001; Bowie et al., 1999; Dennis & Fry, 1992; Landis and Haas, 1992). Such fine-grained networks are easier to establish in small-scale landscapes than in large-scale landscapes. In large-scale landscapes the distance between non-crop habitats and field interior may be problematic. Establishment of non-crop areas within fields, e.g. beetle banks (Thomas et al., 1991), may solve this problem of scale.

The size of non-crop habitats is likely to affect the potential conservation of natural enemies, as larger habitats are less vulnerable to disturbances. Fertilization and pesticide applications have been shown to affect the composition of bordering non-crop habitats (Kleijn & Snoeijing, 1997; De Snoo & van der Poll, 1999; Kleijn & Verbeek, 2000), and the abundance and diversity of generalist predators (McAdam et al., 1994; Haughton et al., 1999). Further, newly established non-crop habitats may need several years before they provide optimal pest control because these habitats need time to be colonized by herbivores and natural enemies and develop favorable vegetation (Denys & Tscharntke, 2002).

The composition of the vegetation in new non-crop habitats is essential for the biological control levels that can be realized. As both pest insects and natural enemies selectively use nectar sources, plant species may have a positive, neutral or even a negative effect on pest control in neighboring crops. Preferably, plant species are selected that provide requisites for natural enemies during their whole life cycle, without enhancing potential pest populations (Nentwig et al., 1998).

Using the concept of conservation biological control, pest populations are not eradicated, but only suppressed by their natural enemies. Without the presence of insect herbivores that occasionally may reach a pest status, high densities of natural enemies can not be maintained. The suppression of insect herbivores by natural enemies holds the risk that economic crop injury levels are sometimes exceeded. Therefore, conservation biological control should not be considered as a stand alone method, but should be complemented with additional measures, such as traditional biological control (Landis et al., 2000).

Concluding Remarks

There is a growing concern about the consequences of modern agricultural production systems on the functioning of the world's terrestrial and aquatic ecosystems. A restriction of the input of agrochemicals, less intensive management practices and diversification of agroecosystems may solve much of the current problems in intensively used areas. New studies provide a solid body of evidence that the pest regulation function is generally enhanced in complex agricultural landscapes as compared to simple landscapes. Hence, habitat management at the landscape scale may contribute to the transition from intensive towards sustainable agriculture and may not only enhance biological control, but also contribute to the conservation of biodiversity, and increase the aesthetic and recreational value of agricultural landscapes.

REFERENCES

Baggen, L.R. & Gurr, G.M. 1998. The influence of food on *Copidosoma koehleri* (Hymenoptera: Encyrtidae), and the use of flowering plants as a habitat management tool to enhance biological control of potato moth, *Phthorimaea operculella* (Lepidoptera: Gelechiidae). *Biol. Control, 11*, 9-17.

Baggen, L.R., Gurr, G.M. & Meats, A. (1999). Flowers in tri-trophic systems: Mechanisms allowing selective exploitation by insect natural enemies for conservation biological control. *Entomol. Exp. Appl., 91*, 155-161.

Basedow, T. (1990). On the impact of boundary strips and of hedges on aphid predators, aphid attack and the necessity of insecticide applications in sugar beets. *Gesunde Pflanzen, 42*, 241-245.

Benton, T.G., Vickery, J.A. & Wilson, J.D. (2003). Farmland biodiversity: is habitat heterogeneity the key? *TREE, 18*, 182-188.

Bianchi, F.J.J.A. & van der Werf, W. (2003). The effect of the area and configuration of hibernation sites on the control of aphids by *Coccinella septempunctata* (Coleoptera: Coccinellidae) in agricultural landscapes: a simulation study. *Environ. Entomol., 32*, 1290-1304.

Bianchi, F.J.J.A. & van der Werf, W. (2004). Model evaluation of the function of prey in non-crop habitats for biological control by ladybeetles in agricultural landscapes. *Ecol. Modelling, 171*, 177-193.

Bianchi, F.J.J.A., van Wingerden, W.K.R.E., Griffioen, A.J., van der Veen, M., van der Straten, M.J.J., Wegman, R.M.A. & Meeuwsen, H.A.M. (2005). Landscape factors affecting the control of *Mamestra brassicae* by natural enemies in Brussels sprout. *Agric. Ecosyst. Environ., in press.*

Bommarco, R. (1998). Reproduction and energy reserves of a predatory carabid beetle relative to agroecosystem complexity. *Ecol. Appl., 8*, 846-853.

Bowie, M.H., Gurr, G.M., Hossain, Z., Baggen, L.R. & Frampton, C.M. (1999). Effects of distance from field edge on aphidophagous insects in a wheat crop and observations on trap design and placement. *Int. J. Pest. Manage., 45*, 69-73.

Burel, F. (1996). Hedgerows and their role in agricultural landscapes. *Crit. Rev. Plant Sci., 15*, 169-190.

Cardinale, B.J., Harvey, C.T., Gross, K. & Ives, A.R. (2003). Biodiversity and biocontrol: emergent impacts of a multi-enemy assemblage on pest suppression and crop yield in an agroecosystem. *Ecol. Letters, 6*, 857-865.

Clarke, J.H., Clark, W.S. & Hancock, M. (1997). Strategies for the prevention of development of pesticide resistance in the UK - Lessons for and from the use of herbicides, fungicides and insecticides. *Pestic. Sci., 51*, 391-397.

Corbett, A. & Rosenheim, J.A. (1996). Impact of a natural enemy overwintering refuge and its interaction with the surrounding landscape. *Ecol. Entomol., 21*, 155-164.

Cowgill, S.E., Wratten, S.D. & Sotherton, N.W. (1993). The selective use of floral resources by the hoverfly *Episyrphus balteatus* (Diptera: Syrphidae) on farmland. *Ann. Appl. Biol., 122*, 223-231.

Den Belder, E., Elderson, J., van den Brink, W.J. & Schelling, G. (2002). Effect of woodlots on thrips density in leek fields: a landscape analysis. *Agric. Ecosyst. Environ., 91*, 139-145.

Dennis, P. & Fry, G.L.A. (1992). Field margins: can they enhance natural enemy population densities and general arthropod diversity on farmland? *Agric. Ecosyst. Environ., 40*, 95-115.

Denys, C. & Tscharntke, T. (2002). Plant-insect communities and predator-prey ratios in field margin strips, adjacent crop fields, and fallows. *Oecologia, 130*, 315-324.

De Snoo, G.R. & van der Poll, R.J. (1999). Effect of herbicide drift on adjacent boundary vegetation. *Agric. Ecosyst. Environ., 73*, 1-6.

Donald, P.F., Green, R.E. & Heath, M.F. (2001). Agricultural intensification and the collapse of Europe's farmland bird populations. *Proc. R. Soc. Lond. B., 268*, 25-29.

Duelli, P. & Obrist, M.K. (2003). Regional biodiversity in an agricultural landscape: the contribution of seminatural habitat islands. *Basic Appl. Ecol., 4*, 129-138.

Dyer, L.E. & Landis, D.A. (1996). Effects of habitat, temperature, and sugar availability on longevity of *Eriborus terebrans* (Hymenoptera: Ichneumonidae). *Environ. Entomol., 25*, 1192-1201.

Elliott, N.C., Kieckhefer, R.W., Lee, J.H. & French, B.W. (1998). Influence of within-field and landscape factors on aphid predator populations in wheat. *Landsc. Ecol., 14*, 239-252.

Elliott, N.C. & Kieckhefer, R.W. (2000). Response by coccinellids to spatial variation in cereal aphid density. *Popul. Ecol., 42*, 81-90.

Elliott, N.C., Kieckhefer, R.W., Michels, Jr., G.J. & Giles, K.L. (2002a). Predator abundance in alfalfa fields in relation to aphids, within-field vegetation, and landscape matrix. *Environ. Entomol., 31*, 253-260.

Elliott, N.C., Kieckhefer, R.W. & Beck, D.A. (2002b). Effect of aphids and the surrounding landscape on the abundance of Coccinellidae in cornfields. *Biol. Control, 24*, 214-220.

Food and Agriculture Organization of the United Nations. (2001). FAO Statistical databases.

Galecka, B. (1966). The role of predators in the reduction of two species of potato aphids, *Aphis nasturtii* Kalt. and *A. frangulae* Kalt. *Ekologia Polska, Seria A, 16*, 245-274.

Getz, L.L. & Brighty, E. (1986). Potential effects of small mammals in high-intensity agricultural systems in East-Central Illinois, USA. *Agric. Ecosyst. Environ., 15*, 39-50.

Hailemicheal, Y. & Smith, Jr., J.W. (1994). Development and longevity of *Xanthopimpla stemmator* (Hymenoptera: Ichneumonidae) at constant temperatures. *Ann. Entomol. Soc. Am., 87*, 874-878.

Hasken, K.H. & Poehling, H.M. (1995). Effects of different intensities of fertilisers and pesticides on aphids and aphid predators in winter wheat. *Agric. Ecosyst. Environ., 52*, 45-50.

Haughton, A.J., Wilcox, A., Chaney, K. & Boatman, N.D. (1999). The effects of different rates of glyphosate on non-target invertebrates in field margins. *Asp. Appl. Biol., 54*, 185-190.

Hickman, J.M. & Wratten, S.D. (1996). Use of *Phacelia tanacetifolia* strips to enhance biological control of aphids by hoverfly larvae in cereal fields. *J. Ec. Entomol., 89*, 832-840.

Hodek, I. & Honěk, A. Ecology of Coccinellidae. Dordrecht: Kluwer Academic Publishers; 1996.

Hodek, I., Iperti, G. & Hodková, M. (1993). Long-distance flights in Coccinellidae (Coleoptera). *Eur. J. Entomol., 90*, 403-414.

Honěk, A. (1982). The distribution of overwintered *Coccinella septempunctata* L. (Col., Coccinellidae) adults in agricultural crops. *Z. Ang. Entomol., 94*, 311-319.

Honěk, A. (1989). Overwintering and annual changes of abundance of *Coccinella septempunctata* in Czechoslovakia (Coleoptera, Coccinellidae). *Acta Entomol. Bohemoslov., 86*, 179-192.

Honěk, A. (1994). The effect of plant quality on the abundance of *Metopolophium dirhodum* (Homoptera: Aphididae) on maize. *Eur. J. Entomol., 91*, 227-236.

Idris, A.B. & Grafius, E. (1995). Wildflowers as nectar sources for *Diadegma insulare* (Hymenoptera: Ichneumonidae), a parasitoid of diamondback moth (Lepidoptera: Yponomeutidae). *Environ. Entomol., 24*, 1726-1735.

Ives, P.M. (1981). Feeding and egg production of two species of coccinellids in the laboratory. *Can. Entomol., 113*, 999-1005.

Ives, A.R., Kareiva, P. & Perry, R. (1993). Response of a predator to variation in prey density at three hierarchical scales: lady beetles feeding on aphids. *Ecology, 74*, 1929-1938.

Johnson, R.J. & Beck, M.M. (1988). Influences of shelterbelts on wildlife management and biology. *Agric. Ecosyst. Environ., 22/23*, 301-335.

Kareiva, P. & Odell, G. (1987). Swarms of predators exhibit "preytaxis" if individual predators use area-restricted search. *Am. Nat., 130*, 233-270.

Kleijn, D. & Snoeijing, G.I.J. (1997). Field boundary vegetation and the effects of agrochemical drift: Botanical change caused by low levels of herbicide and fertilizer. *J. Appl. Ecol., 34*, 1413-1425.

Kleijn, D. & Verbeek, M. (2000). Factors affecting the species composition of arable field boundary vegetation. *J. Appl. Ecol., 37*, 256-266.

Kleijn, D., Berendse, F., Smit., R. & Gilissen, N. (2001). Agri-environment schemes do not effectively protect biodiversity in Dutch agricultural landscapes. *Nature, 413*, 723-725.

Kruess, A. & Tscharntke, T. (1994). Habitat fragmentation, species loss, and biological control. *Science, 264*, 1581-1584.

Landis, D.A. Arthropod sampling in agricultural landscapes: ecological considerations. In: Pedigo L.P. & Buntin G. D., editors. *Handbook of sampling methods for arthropods in agriculture*. Boca Raton: CRC Press, 1994; 15-31.

Landis, D.A. & Haas, M.J. (1992). Influence of landscape structure on abundance and within-field distribution of European corn borer (Lepidoptera: Pyralidae) larval parasitoids in Michigan. *Environ. Entomol., 21*, 409-416.

Landis, D.A. & van der Werf, W. (1997). Early-season predation impacts the establishment of aphids and spread of beet yellows virus in sugar beet. *Entomophaga, 42*, 499-516.

Landis, D.A., Wratten, S.D. & Gurr, G.M. (2000). Habitat management to conserve natural enemies of arthropod pests in agriculture. *Annu. Rev. Entomol., 45*, 175-201.

Leather, S.R., Cooke, R.C.A., Fellowes, M.D.E. & Rombe, R. (1999). Distribution and abundance of ladybirds (Coleoptera: Coccinellidae) in non-crop habitats. *Eur. J. Entomol., 96*, 23-27.

Long, R.F., Corbett, A., Lamb, C., Reberg-Horton, C., Chandler, J. & Stimmann, M. (1998). Beneficial insects move from flowering plants to nearby crops. *California Agric., 52*, 23-26.

Maier, C.T. (1981). Parasitoids emerging from puparia of *Rhagoletis pomonella* (Diptera: Tephritidae) infesting hawthorn and apple in Connecticut. *Can. Entomol., 113*, 867-870.

Maredia, K.M., Gage, S.H., Landis, D.A. & Scriber, J.M. (1992). Habitat use patterns by the seven-spotted lady beetle (Coleoptera: Coccinellidae) in a diverse agricultural landscape. *Biol. Control, 2*, 159-165.

Marino, P.C. & Landis, D.A. (1996). Effect of landscape structure on parasitoid diversity and parasitism in agroecosystems. *Ecol. Appl., 6*, 276-284.

Matson, P.A., Parton, W.J., Power, A.G. & Swift, M.J. (1997). Agricultural intensification and ecosystem properties. *Science, 277*, 504-509.

McAdam, J.H., Bell, A.C. & Henry, T. Field margin flora and fauna changes in response to grassland management practices. In: Boatman, N., editor. *Field margins: integrating agriculture and conservation*. Farnham: British Crop Protection Council; 1994; 153-160.

Menalled, F.D., Marino, P.C., Gage, S.H. & Landis, D.A. (1999). Does agricultural landscape structure affect parasitism and parasitoid diversity? *Ecol. Appl., 9*, 634-641.

Menalled, F.D., Costamagna, A.C., Marino, P.C. & Landis, D.A. (2003). Temporal variation in the response of parasitoids to agricultural landscape structure. *Agric. Ecosyst. Environ., 96*, 29-35.

Nentwig, W., Frank T. & Lethmayer, C. Sown weed strips: artificial ecological compensation areas as an important tool in conservation biological control. In: Barbosa, P., editor. *Conservation biological control.* San Diego: Academic press; 1998; 133-153.

Nicholls, C.I., Parrella, M. & Altieri, M.A. (2001). The effects of a vegetational corridor on the abundance and dispersal of insect biodiversity within a Northern California organic vineyard. *Landsc. Ecol., 16*, 133-146.

Östman, Ö., Ekbom, B. & Bengtsson, J. (2001a). Landscape heterogeneity and farming practice influence biological control. *Basic Appl. Ecol., 2*, 365-371.

Östman, Ö., Ekbom, B., Bengtsson, J. & Weibull, A.C. (2001b). Landscape complexity and farming practice influence the condition of polyphagous carabid beetles. *Ecol. Appl., 11*, 480-488.

Östman, Ö., Ekbom, B. & Bengtsson, J. (2003). Yield increase attributable to aphid predation by ground-living polyphagous natural enemies in spring barley in Sweden. *Ecol. Economics, 45*, 149-158.

Östman, Ö. (2004). The relative effects of natural enemy abundance and alternative prey abundance on aphid predation rates. *Biol. control, 30*, 281-287.

Rahim, A., Hashmi, A.A. & Khan, N.A. (1991). Effects of temperature and relative humidity on longetivity and development of *Ooencyrtus papilionis* Ashmead (Hymenoptera: Eulophidae), a parasite of the sugarcane pest, *Pyrilla perpusilla* Walker (Homoptera: Cicadellidae). *Environ. Entomol., 20*, 774-775.

Ryszkowski, L., Karg, J., Margarit, G., Paoletti, M.G. & Zlotin, R. Above-ground insect biomass in agricultural landscapes of Europe. In: Bunce, R.G., Ryszkowski, L. & Paoletti, M.G., editors. *Landscape ecology and agroecosystems*. Boca Raton: Lewis Publishers; 1993; 71-82.

Schmidt, M.H., Lauer, A., Purtauf, T., Thies, C., Schaefer, M. & Tscharntke, T. (2003). Relative importance of predators and parasitoids for cereal aphid control. *Proc. R. Soc. Lond. B., 270*, 1905-1909.

Schulze, E.D. & Gerstberger, P. Functional aspects of landscape diversity: a Bavarian example. In: Schulze E.D. & Mooney, H.A., editors. *Biodiversity and ecosystem function.* Berlin: Springer Verlag; 1993; 453-466.

Šedivý, J. (1995). Hymenopterous parasitoids of cereal leaf beetle *Oulema galleciana* Heyd. *Ochr. Rostl., 31*, 227-235.

Sengonca, C., Kranz, J. & Blaeser, P. (2002). Attractiveness of three weed species to polyphagous predators and their influence on aphid populations in adjacent lettuce cultivations. *J. Pest. Science, 75*, 161-165.

Siekmann, G., Tenhumberg, B. & Keller, M.A. (2001). Feeding and survival in parasitic wasps: sugar concentration and timing matter. *Oikos, 95*, 425-430.

Sotherton, N.W. (1985). The distribution and abundance of predatory Coleoptera overwintering in field boundaries. *Ann. Appl. Biol., 106*, 17-21.

Thies, C. & Tscharntke, T. (1999). Landscape structure and biological control in agroecosystems. *Science, 285*, 893-895.

Thies, C., Steffan-Dewenter, I. & Tscharntke, T. (2003). Effects of landscape context on herbivory and parasitism at different spatial scales. *Oikos, 101*, 18-25.

Thies, C., Roschewitz, I. & Tscharntke, T. The landscape context of cereal aphid-parasitoid interactions. *Proc. Royal Soc. London B., 285*, 893-895.

Thomas, M.B., Wratten, S.D. & Sotherton, N.W. (1991). Creation of "island" habitats in farmland to manipulate populations of beneficial arthropods: predator densities and emigration. *J. Appl. Ecol., 28*, 906-917.

Tilman, D., Cassman, K.G., Matson, P.A., Naylor, R. & Polasky, S. (2002). Agricultural sustainability and intensive production practices. *Nature, 418*, 671-677.

Tremblay, A., Mineau, P. & Stewart, R.K. (2001). Effects of bird predation on some pest insect populations in corn. *Agric. Ecosyst. Environ., 83*, 143-152.

Vandermeer, J., van Noordwijk, M., Anderson, J., Ong, C. & Perfecto, I. (1998). Global change and multi-species agroecosystems: Concepts and issues. *Agric. Ecosyst. Environ., 67*, 1-22.

Van der Werf, W., Evans, E.W. & Powell, J. (2000). Measuring and modelling the dispersal of *Coccinella septempunctata* (Coleoptera: Coccinellidae) in alfalfa fields. *Eur. J. Entomol., 97*, 487-493.

Wäckers, F. L. (2001). A comparison of nectar- and honeydew sugars with respect to their utilization by the hymenopteran parasitoid *Cotesia glomerata. J. Insect Physiol., 47*, 1077-1084.

White, A.J., Wratten, S.D., Berry, N.A. & Weigmann, U. (1995). Habitat manipulation to enhance biological control of Brassica pests by hover flies (Diptera: Syrphidae). *J. Econ. Entomol., 88*, 1171-1176.

Williams, I.S., van der Werf, W., Dewar, A.M. & Dixon, A.F.G. (1999). Factors affecting the relative abundance of two coexisting aphid species on sugar beet. *Agr. For. Entomol., 1*, 119-125.

Wissinger, S.A. (1997). Cyclic colonization in predictably ephemeral habitats: a template for biological control in annual crop systems. *Biol. control, 10*, 4-15.

Wyss, E. (1995). The effects of weed strips on aphids and aphidophagous predators in an apple orchard. *Entomol. Exp. Appl., 75*, 43-49.

Wyss, E. (1996). The effects of artificial weed strips on diversity and abundance of the arthropod fauna in a Swiss experimental apple orchard. *Agric. Ecosyst. Environ., 60*, 47-59.

Xia, J. Y., van der Werf, W. & Rabbinge, R. (1999). Temperature and prey density on bionomics of *Coccinella septempunctata* (Coleoptera: Coccinellidae) feeding on *Aphis gossypii* (Homoptera: Aphididae) on cotton. *Environ. Entomol., 28,* 307-314.

Xia, J. Y., Rabbinge, R. & van der Werf, W. (2003). Multistage functional responses in a ladybeetle-aphid system: scaling up from the laboratory to the field. *Environ. Entomol., 32*, 151-162.

In: Trends in Biodiversity Research
Editor: A. R. Burk, pp. 171-192
ISBN 1-59454-385-2

Chapter 7

IMPACTS OF MULTI-NUTRIENT FERTILIZATION WITH OTHER NUTRIENTS ON UNDERSTORY VEGETATION CA AND P CONCENTRATIONS AND THE CA/P RATIO

Curtis L. VanderSchaaf*
Department of Forestry, Virginia Tech University, Blacksburg, Virginia

ABSTRACT

Multi-nutrient fertilization can be an effective management tool to enhance conifer production and economic returns in the inland Northwest. Given that a greater emphasis has been placed on multiple-resource management, it is important to quantify how these silvicultural treatments for overstory vegetation affect understory vegetation to provide a picture of overall ecosystem health, and for wildlife habitat and range quality. This chapter reports on the response of understory vegetation Ca and P concentrations following the addition of other nutrients through multi-nutrient fertilization treatments. Vegetation was separated into three lifeforms (grasses and grass-likes, forbs, and shrubs). A selected number of individual species were also analyzed.

Based on this study, P concentrations appear to be more affected by multi-nutrient fertilization with other nutrients than Ca concentrations across all lifeforms. Optimum animal growth is highly dependent on these two nutrients. However, the proper ratio between them is also important because extreme amounts of Ca can interfere with P metabolism. Ca/P ratios showed variability across lifeforms and sites following treatment.

Keywords: Fertilization; Inland Northwest; Understory Vegetation; Wildlife Habitat.

* Fax +5402313698, E-mail cvanders@vt.edu; Telephone – (540) 382-6268

INTRODUCTION

Most forests in the inland Northwest are nutrient deficient and overstory conifers respond with increases in growth (Shaffii et al. 1989, Moore et al. 1991, Garrison et al. 2000) and changes in nutrient concentrations following fertilization (Garrison et al 2000, Moore et al. 2004). However, information regarding the impacts of multi-nutrient fertilization with other nutrients on understory vegetation calcium (Ca) and phosphorus (P) concentrations and the Ca/P ratio in the inland Northwest is minimal. Determining response of these two nutrients following fertilization with other nutrients is important to determine impacts on nutrient cycling and how changes in concentration can affect wildlife habitat and rangeland quality (VanderSchaaf et al. 2004). These results may lead some natural resource managers to apply Ca and P when fertilizing stands in this region.

Nutrient status of forage and browse has a large effect on overall health of both domestic and wild animals, reproductive success, physical development, and wild animal population size (Shomon et al. 1969, Verme 1979, Wood 1986, Holechek et al. 1995). Nutrient content is also highly related to vegetation palatability (Verme 1979). Palatability increases following fertilization since animals prefer fertilized vegetation to unfertilized (Oh et al 1970, Anderson et al. 1974, Geist et al. 1974, Verme 1979, Brockley 1996, Nams et al. 1996, Kimball et al 1998).

Calcium is important in animals for overall growth, bone strength (Ullrey et al. 1973, Wood 1986, McDonald et al. 1988, Underwood and Suttle 1999), fertility (Underwood and Suttle 1999), and antler development (Ullrey et al. 1973). This nutrient is usually not limiting to animals (Ullrey et al. 1973, Holechek et al. 1995). Phosphorus is the most limiting nutrient to grazing animal productivity throughout the world (Holechek et al. 1995). Defiency of this nutrient results in abnormalities in bones and teeth, poor growth, and impairment of fertility (Wood 1986, McDonald et al. 1988, Underwood and Suttle 1999). In general, greater concentrations of Ca and P produce healthier vegetation for wild and domestic animals but the proper ratio between Ca and P is also important. The Ca/P ratio is used as a measure of wildlife habitat and rangeland quality (Ullrey et al. 1973, Ullrey et al 1975, Holechek et al. 1995) and is significant because extreme amounts of Ca can interfere with P metabolism (Severson 1982).

Studies of non-seeded or non-planted understory vegetation in conifer stands have reported the results of fertilization with other nutrients on Ca and P concentrations. Results from *Pseudotsuga menziesii* (Mirbel) Franco dominated stands on the western side of the Cascades in Washington were reported for the shrub *Gaultheria shallon* Pursh following nitrogen (N) and sulphur (S) fertilization (Prescott et al. 1993). The treatments had little effect on Ca and P concentrations. Based on their published Ca and P concentrations (the authors did not analysis the Ca/P ratio in their paper), the lack of response by these nutrients also had little effect on the Ca/P ratio. In South Carolina, Wood (1986) studied the impacts of N and P fertilization on several understory shrubs in *Pinus taeda* L. and *Pinus palustris* stands. Fertilization was shown to decrease Ca concentrations. Since P was included in the fertilizer blend, I present no summary of his findings for this nutrient. Wood and Tanner (1985) presented results from N and P fertilization treatments in *Pinus elliottii* plantations in Florida for two shrubs; *Acer rubrum* and *Ilex glabra.* Although not statistically significant, Ca concentrations generally decreased. Little information could be found on non-seeded or non-planted herbaceous vegetation Ca and P concentration response following fertilization with other nutrients.

The objective of this study was to determine whether Ca and P concentrations and the Ca/P ratio would change following application of multi-nutrient fertilizer blends containing other nutrients in conifer stands throughout the inland Northwest.

METHODS

Site Descriptions

Four sites were included in this study; one each in Idaho and Washington and two in Oregon. These study sites were selected because they are representative of operationally fertilized mid-elevation conifer forests in central Idaho, central Washington, and northeastern Oregon (Table 1). Elevations ranged between 670 m for the Goldendale, WA mixed-conifer site to 1245 m for the New Meadows, ID *Pinus ponderosa* Dougl. location, where the Wallowa, OR mixed-conifer site had an elevation of 1219 m and the Wallowa, OR *Pinus ponderosa* Dougl. plantation had an elevation of 1128 m. Precipitation amounts during the sampling period were; Goldendale, WA mixed-conifer site - 8.5 cm, New Meadows, ID *Pinus ponderosa* Dougl. site - 31.4 cm, both Wallowa, OR sites – 30.8 cm (NOAA 1998). A variety of overstory tree densities and species compositions, and both Douglas-fir and grand fir habitat series were sampled. Overstory tree species composition included natural, second-growth, mixed-conifers as well as a *Pinus ponderosa* Dougl. plantation. At the Wallowa, OR mixed-conifer site the dominant overstory species were *Abies grandis* (Dougl.) Forbes, *Pseudotsuga menziesii* (Mirbel) Franco, and *Picea engelmannii* Perry with all three species having relatively the same proportion of basal area. The study sites did not have any sort of overstory tree cutting within the last 10 years. Grazing was excluded from the study sites except for a light amount at the New Meadows, ID *Pinus ponderosa* Dougl. location. For species examined during this study, nomenclature is consistent with Hitchcock and Cronquist (1973).

Study Design

The study areas were designed to be fertilizer trials within much larger operational fertilization areas where the size of experimental areas ranged from 10 to 120 ha. The fertilizer and control treatments were randomly assigned to study stands within a site to the extent possible, given operational constraints. Aerial photographs were used to help determine the exact locations of the fertilized units and boundaries were marked for each treatment location. Fertilizers were applied aerially by helicopter and containers were placed throughout each treatment area to collect fertilizer. Collected fertilizer was then weighed to monitor and ensure even distribution throughout the study site. The fertilizer blends and treatment dates for each stand are provided in Table 1. Phosphorus concentrations and the Ca/P ratio are not presented for the Wallowa, OR mixed-conifer and Wallowa, OR *Pinus ponderosa* Dougl. sites because this nutrient was included in the fertilizer blend.

Table 1. Selected site, stand, and treatment characteristics at the experimental locations.

Site	Dominant Overstory Species	Treat	Basal area[1] (m^2/ha)	Crown competition factor[1] (%)	Habitat type series[2]	Treatment date	Multi-nutrient fertilizer blend (kg/ha)
Goldendale, WA	*Pseudotsuga menziesii* (Mirbel) Franco &	M	15.3	59	Douglas-fir	Spring 1997	B 5.5, Cu 11, K 220, Mo 1, N 220, S 88, Zn 11
	Pinus ponderosa Dougl.	C	14.9	62			
New Meadows, ID	*Pinus ponderosa* Dougl.	M	17.9	64	Douglas-fir	Fall 1996	B 11, Cu 11, K 220, Mo 1, N 220, S 88, Zn 11
		C	16.3	57			
Wallowa, OR	Mixed-conifer	M	14.4	67	Grand fir	Fall 1995	B 11, Cu 11, K 220, Mo 1, N 220, P 110, S 99, Zn 11
		C	14.2	70			
	Pinus ponderosa Dougl.	M	9.1	34		Fall 1995	B 11, Cu 11, K 220, Mo 1, N 220, P 110, S 99, Zn 11
		C	9.1	34			

M – multi-nutrient fertilization.

C – control.

[1] Includes all tree species.

[2] After Steele et al. 1981 and Johnson and Clausnitzer 1992.

Nutrient concentration analyses were mostly conducted on understory vegetation obtained from plots developed to measure understory vegetation annual production. Therefore, first, a description of how overstory vegetation basal area and annual understory vegetation production were measured is given followed by a description of how nutrient concentrations of this vegetation were obtained. For a greater explanation of how understory vegetation annual production was measured refer to VanderSchaaf (1999) or VanderSchaaf et al (2002).

One hundred meter transects were established in both control and fertilized areas, with 13 m^2 sub-plots located every 10 meters along a transect for a total of 11 sub-plots. The physical arrangement of the various study sites differed resulting in variable numbers of transects per site. Eight to 10 transects were placed in each stand to minimize variability within a transect as well as to capture variation across the treatment unit.

Three life forms were sampled: shrubs, forbs, and grasses and grass-likes (*Carex geyeri* Boott), using the 13 m^2 sub-plots following protocols described in Moeur (1985). The grasses and grass-like lifeform will further be referred to as grasses. Sampling occurred in mid and late summer of 1998. The exact sampling date differed by site to make plant phenological development stage similar between sites. Sampling was conducted during the period of maximum understory production and again at the end of the growing season. Vegetation sampling plots were marked with a PVC pipe in the center. Variable radius overstory tree plots were centered on the vegetation plots to measure overstory tree density and species composition. Average basal area per ha and crown competition factor (CCF) (Krajieck et al 1961) were calculated as the average of the transects for each treatment (Table 1). Understory vegetation annual production was measured using a modification of the comparative yield method developed by Haydock and Shaw (1975).

At each permanent understory sample plot, two separate components were involved in estimating annual production based on the comparative yield method (Haydock and Shaw 1975): destructive (clipping and weighing) and non-destructive (ocular estimates) plots. Nutrient concentration analyses were conducted on the vegetation that was clipped during the destructive component. Clipped plots were selected based on the most common species within a site and therefore not all life forms were necessarily represented per site and treatment combination. Additionally, at each 13 m^2 quadrat, the dominant species was recorded based on percent cover measurements (only if at least one species occurred with a minimum of 5% cover). See VanderSchaaf (1999) or VanderSchaaf et al (2000) for percent cover sampling methodology. The closest plant(s) of this dominant species was located and clipped to obtain a minimum of 2 grams green weight. All harvested material was stored in plastic bags, placed in a cooler, transported back to the laboratory, and then oven dried at 70 degrees Centigrade for 48 hours (Erixson 1993).

Understory vegetation species analyzed at the Goldendale, WA mixed-conifer site included but were not limited to the grass *Festuca occidentalis* Hook., the forb *Apocynum androsaemifolium* L., the shrubs *Arctostaphylos nevadensis* Gray and *Ceanothus velutinus* Dougl. while the species analyzed at the New Meadows, ID *Pinus ponderosa* Dougl. site included but were not limited to the grass-like *Carex geyeri* Boott, the forb *Achillea millefolium* L., and the shrubs *Symphoricarpos albus* (L.) Blake, *Salix scouleriana* Barratt, and *Ceanothus velutinus* Dougl. Comparisons between multi-nutrient fertilized and non-fertilized individual species can be conducted (at least three observations per treatment) for *Festuca occidentalis* Hook. and *Arctostaphylos nevadensis* Gray for mid-summer, and

Apocynum androsaemifolium L. and *Arctostaphylos nevadensis* Gray for late-summer at the Goldendale, WA mixed-conifer site while at the New Meadows, ID *Pinus ponderosa* Dougl. site, *Carex geyeri* Boott for mid-summer and *Carex geyeri* Boott and *Symphoricarpos albus* (L.) Blake for late-summer can be analyzed. The understory vegetation species analyzed within a lifeform at both Wallowa, OR sites included but were not limited to the grass *Deschampsia* sp., the forb *Thermopsis* sp., and the shrubs *Symphoricarpos albus* (L.) Blake and *Salix scouleriana* Barratt. The shrub *Lonicera* sp. was also analyzed at the Wallowa, OR mixed-conifer site. No individual species had at least three observations per treatment at the two Wallowa, OR sites. With the exception of the individual species analyses, vegetation was grouped by lifeform when clipped without recording the species that composed the clipped vegetation. Therefore, when I say the analyses were not limited to, I mean that I can only identify with certainty that those species mentioned above were included in the overall lifeform analyses for a particular site.

Chemical Analysis

Oven-dried vegetation were ground by site, sampling period, treatment, and lifeform in a Wiley mill (Intermountain Forest Tree Nutrition Cooperative 1988) with the exception of individual species that were ground by site, sampling period, and treatment in a Wiley mill. Phosphorus and Ca concentrations were determined by inductively coupled plasma (ICP) emission with digested plant tissue. Both procedures were completed by Scotts Laboratories in Allentown, Pa.

Statistical Analysis

Concentration of individual nutrients was the dependent variable in this analysis. Nutrient concentrations were computed and analyzed separately for shrubs, forbs, and grasses and were averaged within each site, sampling period, and treatment. These averaged data were then used in subsequent statistical analyses. The experiment was designed for using Analysis of Variance (ANOVA), and statistical comparisons between fertilizer treatments were conducted using PROC GLM of the Statistical Analysis System (SAS Institute Inc. 1985). Homogeneity of variance was examined using the Brown-Forsythe test (Brown and Forsythe 1974), and normality was checked using the Kolmogorov-Smirnov test. For those analyses that did not meet the homogeneity of variance or normality assumptions, natural logarithmic transformations were conducted on the dependent variable. The assumptions were then checked again. Least-squares means were used and adjusted using the Tukey-Kramer test. Simple t-tests were conducted for the individual species nutrient concentration analyses. All reported individual species concentrations are in their original units. The significance level chosen for all statistical tests was 0.10.

RESULTS

Overall ANOVA results are reported first for P concentrations and the Ca/P ratio since these variables were analyzed only at the Goldendale, WA mixed-conifer and the New Meadows, ID *Pinus ponderosa* Dougl. sites. Significant two-way interactions for P concentration were observed for the treat*period and site*treat interactions for grasses and the site*treat interaction for shrubs. Phosphorus concentrations of forbs and shrubs showed significant main effects for site and treatment. However, only grasses showed a significant sampling period main effect for P concentration. The only significant two-way interactions for the Ca/P ratio was the site*treat interaction for both grasses and shrubs. All lifeforms showed a significant main effect for site but only shrubs had a significant main effect for treatment. Significant sampling period main effects for the Ca/P ratio were observed for forbs and shrubs.

Calcium concentrations were analyzed across all four sites since this nutrient was not part of the multi-nutrient fertilizer blend at any of the four sites. Significant two-way interactions for Ca concentrations were only observed for the site*treat interaction for forbs and the site*period interaction for shrubs. Shrubs and grasses showed a significant main effect for site, no lifeform showed a significant main effect for treatment, and sampling period showed significant main effects for forbs and shrubs.

Variability was observed among and between sites across lifeforms following treatment (Figure 1). The Goldendale, WA mixed-conifer site showed significantly lower shrub Ca and P concentrations and Ca/P ratios for all lifeforms while the New Meadows, ID *Pinus ponderosa* Dougl. site had the highest concentrations in all shrub and grass analyses.

In order to account for higher order interactions, analyses were conducted between treatments by site and sampling period for each lifeform (Figure 2). Phosphorus concentration changes showed variable results following multi-nutrient fertilization with other nutrients. Decreases in P concentration were seen for forbs in mid-summer at the New Meadows, ID *Pinus ponderosa* Dougl. site, forbs in late-summer and grasses in mid-summer at the Goldendale, WA mixed-conifer site, shrubs in both mid-summer and late-summer at the New Meadows, ID *Pinus ponderosa* Dougl. site, and shrubs in late-summer at the Goldendale, WA mixed-conifer site. An increase in P concentration was observed for grasses at the New Meadows, ID *Pinus ponderosa* Dougl. site in mid-summer following treatment. All other understory vegetation analyses showed no statistically significant change in P concentration. In general, overlooking statistical significance, P concentrations decreased following treatment. All Ca analyses showed no statistically significant change except for forbs during mid-summer at the New Meadows, ID *Pinus ponderosa* Dougl. site.

Although not always statistically significant, forbs and shrubs generally showed increases in the Ca/P ratio following multi-nutrient fertilization with other nutrients. All grass analyses showed decreases.

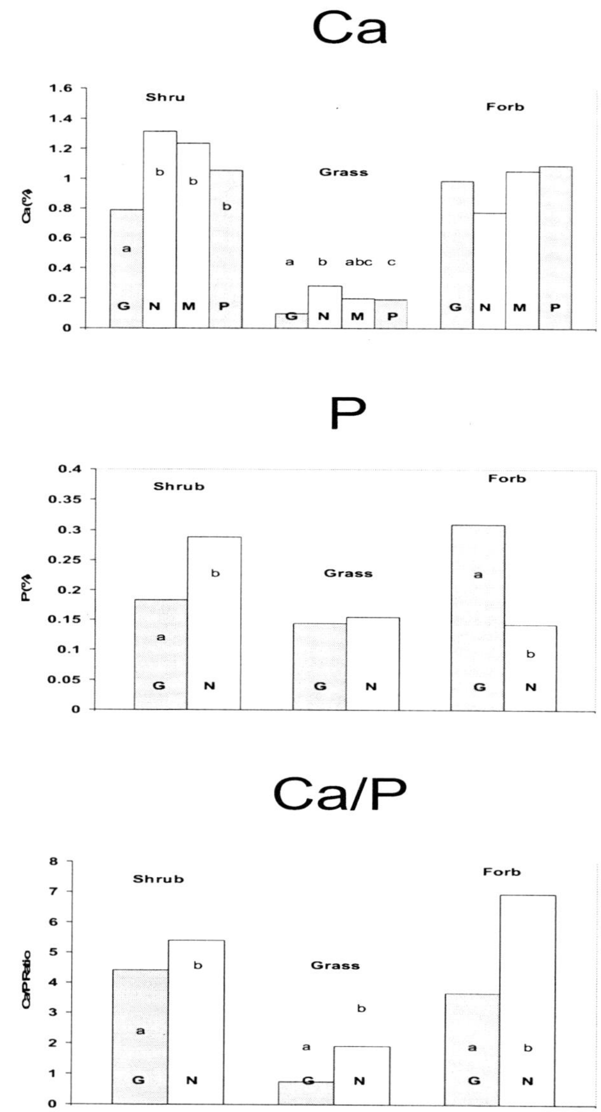

Figure 1. Concentrations by site for three lifeforms following operational multi-nutrient fertilization (n = 75). Where: G: Goldendale, WA mixed-conifer site; N: New Meadows, ID *Pinus ponderosa* Dougl. site; M: Wallowa, OR mixed-conifer site, P: Wallowa, OR *Pinus ponderosa* Dougl. plantation; Grass: grasses and grass-likes (i.e. *Carex geyeri* Boott). Mean values with different letters for a lifeform and nutrient combination significantly differ at the 0.10 level.

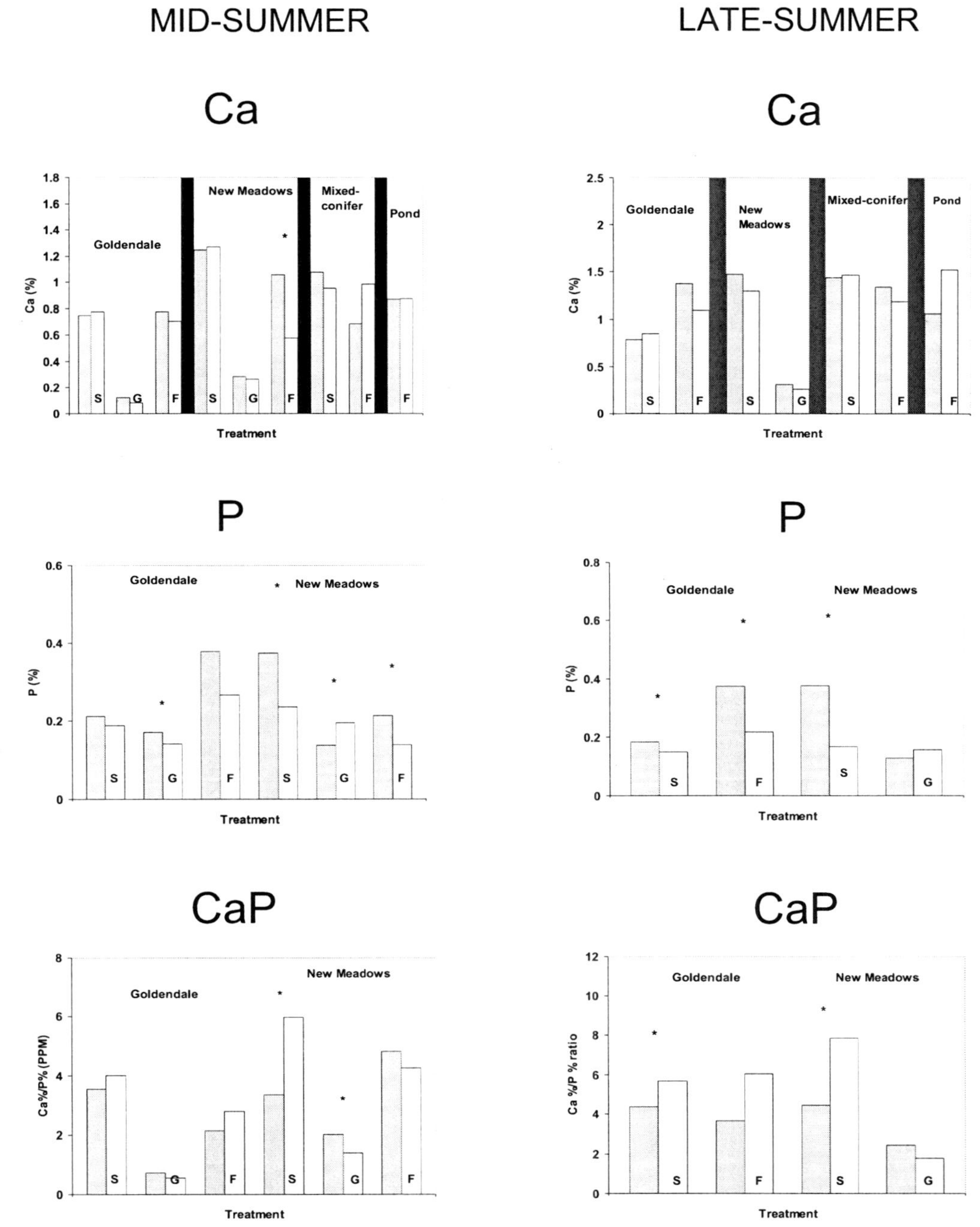

Figure 2. Concentrations by nutrient and sampling period (Mid and Late-summer) for three lifeforms (S - shrubs, G - grasses and grass-likes, F- forbs) following operational multi-nutrient fertilization (n = 75). Where: gray bars are the controls, white bars are the multi-nutrient fertilized concentrations, Goldendale: Goldendale, WA mixed-conifer site, New Meadows: New Meadows, ID *Pinus ponderosa* Dougl. site, Mixed-conifer: Wallowa, OR mixed-conifer site, and Pond: Wallowa, OR *Pinus ponderosa* Dougl. plantation. An asterisk above a site, sampling period, nutrient, and lifeform combination indicates the means were significantly different at the 0.10 level. Black bars are used to more clearly separate sites.

Individual species nutrient concentrations and Ca/P ratios showed variability following treatment (Tables 2 and 3). All species at the Goldendale, WA mixed-conifer site showed significant decreases in P concentrations for both periods following treatment while *Symphoricarpos albus* (L.) Blake showed a decrease at the New Meadows, ID *Pinus ponderosa* Dougl. site. *Carex geyeri* Boott showed an increase in P concentration following treatment during mid-summer. Calcium concentration significantly decreased in *Arctostaphylos nevadensis* Gray during mid-summer at the Goldendale, WA mixed-conifer site and in *Symphoricarpos albus* (L.) Blake and *Carex geyeri* Boott during late-summer at the New Meadows, ID *Pinus ponderosa* Dougl. site. All other Ca analyses showed no significant difference. Ca/P ratios decreased for *Arctostaphylos nevadensis* Gray during mid-summer at the Goldendale, WA mixed-conifer site and *Carex geyeri* Boott during late-summer at the New Meadows, ID *Pinus ponderosa* Dougl. site. Significant increases in the Ca/P ratio were observed at the Goldendale, WA mixed-conifer site for *Arctostaphylos nevadensis* Gray during late-summer and for *Festuca occidentalis* Hook. *Symphoricarpos albus* (L.) Blake at the New Meadows, ID *Pinus ponderosa* Dougl. site also showed a significant increase.

Table 2. Nutritive concentrations by species following operational multi-nutrient fertilization at the Goldendale, WA mixed-conifer site

Nutrient	Species	Mid-summer		Late-summer	
		C	M	C	M
Ca%	*Apocynum androsaemifolium* L.	-	-	1.520a	1.286a
	Festuca occidentalis Walt.	0.047a	0.057a	-	-
	*Arctostaphylos nevadensis*Gray	0.749a	0.559b	0.826a	0.849a
P%	*Apocynum androsaemifolium* L.	-	-	0.408a	0.277b
	Festuca occidentalis Walt.	0.170a	0.135b	-	-
	Arctostaphylos nevadensis Gray	0.212a	0.179b	0.188b	0.151b
Ca/P ratio	*Apocynum androsaemifolium* L.	-	-	3.8a	5.1a
	Festuca occidentalis Walt.	0.3a	0.4b	-	-
	Arctostaphylos nevadensis Gray	3.6a	3.1b	4.4a	5.7b

M – multi-nutrient fertilization.

C - control. Means within a sampling period, nutrient, and species combination with different letters are significantly different at the 0.10 level.

DISCUSSION

Changes in P concentration were seen at sites where P was not applied in the multi-nutrient fertilizer blends (Figure 2 and Tables 2 and 3). Phosphorus analyses showed a significant increase in concentration for grasses at the New Meadows, ID *Pinus ponderosa* Dougl. site in mid-summer while all other significant differences were decreases. Grasses showed more variability in P uptake, while forbs and shrubs either did not change concentration or decreased concentration. Prescott et al. (1993) also found that P did not significantly change following fertilization with N and S. Perhaps, additional amounts of other nutrients caused those nutrients to be taken up rather than P by the present understory composition at the Goldendale, WA mixed-conifer and the New Meadows, ID *Pinus ponderosa* Dougl. sites.

Table 3. Nutritive concentrations by species following operational multi-nutrient fertilization at the New Meadows, ID *Pinus ponderosa* Dougl. site

Nutrient	Species	Mid-summer		Late-summer	
		C	M	C	M
Ca%	*Carex geyeri* Boott	0.283a	0.289a	0.351a	0.276b
	Symphoricarpos albus (L.) Blake	-	-	1.640a	1.363b
P%	*Carex geyeri* Boott	0.147a	0.218b	0.132a	0.191a
	Symphoricarpos albus (L.) Blake	-	-	0.500a	0.182b
Ca/P ratio	*Carex geyeri* Boott	1.9a	1.4a	2.7a	1.6b
	Symphoricarpos albus (L.) Blake	-	-	3.3a	7.7b

M – multi-nutrient fertilization.
C - control. Means within a sampling period, nutrient, and species combination with different letters are significantly different at the 0.10 level.

Although concentrations provide useful information about uptake of nutrients, contents provide information about whether concentrations decreased due to lower plant uptake or due to greater plant production resulting in dilution (Timmer and Stone 1978). Therefore, nutrient contents were estimated by lifeform for a particular site, sampling period, and treatment for both P and Ca using concentrations presented in this chapter and understory vegetation production from VanderSchaaf et al. (2002). No statistical analyses were conducted. All P contents increased following multi-nutrient fertilization except for shrubs at the New Meadows, ID *Pinus ponderosa* Dougl. site for both sampling periods. Therefore, with the exception of shrubs at the New Meadows, ID *Pinus ponderosa* Dougl. site, it appears that plants in the fertilized areas probably did not decrease uptake rates of P, but rather that increased production by the plants resulting from greater availability of other nutrients produced dilution of P.

Phosphorus is the most limiting nutrient to grazing animal productivity throughout the world (Holechek et al. 1995). Ullrey et al. (1975) found that 0.28% P would allow for optimum development of *Odocoileus virginianus* fawns, while Magruder et al (1957) found that *Odocoileus virginianus* bucks could survive on 0.25% P, and Holechek and Herbel (1986) found that 0.10-0.15% P is needed for cattle maintenance and that 0.25% P is necessary for lactating cattle. Multi-nutrient fertilization with other nutrients resulted in some decreases in P concentrations. Nonetheless, all vegetation met the maintenance requirements for cattle regardless of treatment but more control areas met the minimum requirements of 0.28% for *Odocoileus virginianus* fawns and 0.25% for *Odocoileus virginianus* bucks and lactating cattle than the fertilized areas. Perhaps P should have been applied at these sites to produce healthier forage.

Calcium concentrations showed some decreases for all lifeforms in response to multi-nutrient fertilization with other nutrients across both sampling periods (Figure 2) but most analyses were not statistically significant. Concentrations of individual species appear to respond quite variably regardless of lifeform (Tables 2 and 3). Wood (1986) and Prescott et al (1993) showed decreases in Ca concentration following fertilization with other nutrients in shrubs. Apparently, multi-nutrient fertilization with nutrients other than Ca does not have much impact on Ca concentrations. Content of Ca following multi-nutrient fertilization increased at most sites across both sampling periods except for late-summer at the Wallowa, OR mixed-conifer site. Therefore, when concentrations decreased, dilution probably occurred in most cases.

Ullrey et al. (1973) recommended that *Odocoileus virginianus* fawns have a minimum of 0.40% of calcium in their forage but for *Odocoileus virginianus* adults the recommended amount is 0.10 to 0.20% (Verme and Ullrey 1972). The only vegetation that did not meet the requirement for fawns was grasses regardless of treatment and all vegetation met the requirements for adults except for grasses fertilized in mid-summer at the Goldendale, WA mixed-conifer site (Figure 2 and Tables 2 and 3).

The Ca/P ratio is used as a measure of wildlife habitat and rangeland quality (Ullrey et al. 1973, Ullrey et al 1975, Holechek et al. 1995). The recommended ratio for ruminants is somewhere between 1:1 and 7:1 (Wise et al 1963, Ullrey et al 1973, Wood 1986), and the optimum is about 2:1 (Maynard & Loosli 1969, Thill et al 1987). All locations, lifeforms, and individual species analyses, have reasonable Ca/P ratios except for grasses in mid-summer at the Goldendale, WA mixed-conifer site (Figure 2 and Tables 2 and 3). The low Ca/P ratio in grasses at the Goldendale, WA mixed-conifer site does not seem to be related to fertilization since a low ratio was found in both treatments. The other lifeforms at this site showed ratios that were reasonable or optimum. Perhaps Ca fertilization at the Goldendale, WA mixed-conifer site would improve grazing quality of grasses. *Symphoricarpos albus* (L.) Blake at the New Meadows, ID *Pinus ponderosa* Dougl. site during late-summer is bordering on poor quality because of a drastic reduction in P following fertilization (Table 3). Generally, fertilization did not seem to increase or reduce the Ca/P ratio and in this sense does not seem to greatly enhance or decrease wildlife habitat and rangeland quality. Additionally, despite a few changes in the Ca/P ratio following treatment, almost all vegetation is within the recommended ratios for ruminants.

Differences in Ca and P concentrations and the Ca/P ratio were observed between sites (Figure 1). This was also observed for nutrients applied in the fertilizer blends at these sites as well (VanderSchaaf et al. 2004). In general, the Goldendale, WA mixed-conifer site showed the lowest concentrations and Ca/P ratios. This site is a Douglas-fir habitat type (Table 1) and on average has the lowest amount of precipitation (NOAA 1998). These factors probably result in lower nutrient demanding understory vegetation species compositions (Grime 1977, Chapin et al. 1986, Meerts 1997). Nutrient demand is assumed to be greatest when trees are young and around the time of crown closure (Turner et al. 1978, Edmonds et al. 1989, Garrison and Moore 1998). Crown closure is assumed to begin when the CCF is near 100 (Krajieck et al 1961). With the exception of perhaps the Wallowa, OR *Pinus ponderosa* Dougl. plantation, overstory tree density is probably not a factor in explaining nutrient concentration differences between sites. However, overstory vegetation stand age may contribute to differences in understory vegetation nutrient concentrations among all sites. The Wallowa, OR *Pinus ponderosa* Dougl., Wallowa, OR mixed-conifer, New Meadows, ID *Pinus ponderosa* Dougl., and the Goldendale, WA mixed-conifer sites are 14, 30, 68, and 85 years old; respectively. Therefore, although overstory density is less at the Wallowa, OR *Pinus ponderosa* Dougl. plantation, perhaps reducing nutrient uptake/requirements by the overstory vegetation, nutrient demand maybe greater at this site because of its younger age. It cannot definitively be determined what the nutrient demand status is of these sites based on the data collected during this study, but potential factors accounting for differences of understory vegetation nutrient concentrations among the sites can be identified.

The New Meadows, ID *Pinus ponderosa* Dougl. site is also a Douglas-fir habitat type but precipitation on average is greater here relative to the Goldendale, WA mixed-conifer site (NOAA 1998). Additionally, this site is dominated by *Pinus ponderosa* Dougl., while the Goldendale, WA mixed-conifer site is composed of *Pinus ponderosa* Dougl. and *Pseudotsuga menziesii* (Mirbel) Franco. As mentioned in VanderSchaaf et al. (2002, 2004), overstory species compositions may play a role in understory vegetation response following fertilization. Several studies have found that *Pseudotsuga menziesii* (Mirbel) Franco has greater Ca and P demands than *Pinus ponderosa* Dougl. (Powers 1983, Webster and Dobkowski 1983, Garrison and Moore 1998, Garrison et al. 2000, Moore et al. 2004). This may explain to some degree the increases in concentrations observed at the New Meadows, ID *Pinus ponderosa* Dougl. site relative to the Goldendale, WA mixed-conifer site for most analyses.

Comparisons among all four sites were only conducted for Ca concentrations. Studies have shown that *Picea engelmannii* Perry and *Pseudotsuga menziesii* (Mirbel) Franco have equal nutrient requirements for Ca but slightly higher requirements than *Abies grandis* (Dougl.) Forbes, and that *Pinus ponderosa* Dougl. has the lowest demand (Van den Driessche 1974, Powers 1983, Webster and Dobkowski 1983, Garrison and Moore 1998, Garrison et al. 2000, Moore et al. 2004). VanderSchaaf (1999) and VanderSchaaf et al. (2002, 2004) proposed that understory vegetation plants under more shade-intolerant overstory species (i.e. *Pinus ponderosa* Dougl.) may have greater nutrient amounts available to them following fertilization than under more shade-tolerant overstory species (i.e. *Abies grandis* (Dougl.) Forbes) because of differences in nutrient demand between the overstory species. Based on this study, no site has greater nutrient concentrations across all lifeforms (Figure 1). There does not appear to be a substantial difference in Ca concentrations between the two Wallowa, OR sites. Perhaps, different overstory species compositions don't have a drastic effect on understory vegetation Ca concentrations following multi-nutrient fertilization with other nutrients.

When comparing differences among sites, one obvious factor is species selection. Not all species were sampled at a site; therefore, results basically only apply to those species sampled. Perhaps a stronger effort should have been made to sample the same species at all sites. However, as evidenced in VanderSchaaf (1999), these four sites have different understory species compositions brought about by differences in site fertility, aspect, precipitation, soil moisture, etc. (Grime 1977, Flanagan and Van Cleve 1983, Chapin et al. 1986, Knoepp and Swank 1997, Meerts 1997, Trettin et al. 1999). Therefore, it may have been difficult to achieve that goal.

Individual species analyses in these stands can provide us with more specific information on nutrient dynamics of Ca and P following multi-nutrient fertilization with other nutrients. For instance, nutrient concentrations of understory species can provide us information about the relative contributions of individual species to specific nutrient cycles (Turner et al. 1978). See VanderSchaaf et al. (2004) for discussion about multi-nutrient fertilization effects on boron (B), copper, potassium (K), molybdenum, N, S, and zinc concentrations of individual species. Multi-nutrient fertilization produced a decrease in P concentration for *Apocynum androsaemifolium* L. (Table 2). This species decreased in cover following the fertilization treatment (VanderSchaaf 1999). Since it is not a highly palatable plant by cattle and wildlife, the multi-nutrient fertilization response probably has little impact on animal habitat quality. *Festuca occidentalis* Hook. is a semi-palatable plant to cattle (Holechek et al. 1982). Calcium concentrations changed little but P concentration decreased following fertilization. This produced an increase in the Ca/P ratio although the effect had little impact on improving animal habitat. As mentioned earlier, the recommended ratio between Ca and P for ruminants is somewhere between 1:1 and 7:1 (Wise et al 1963, Ullrey et al 1973, Wood 1986), and the optimum is about 2:1 (Maynard & Loosli 1969, Thill et al 1987). This understory species, based on Ca and P concentrations and the Ca/P ratio, appears to provide very poor nutrition for animals regardless of treatment at this site. *Festuca occidentalis* Hook. was found to be responsive to multi-nutrient fertilization on this site (VanderSchaaf 1999, VanderSchaaf et al. 2000). *Arctostaphylos nevadensis* Gray is an ericaceous shrub whose berries are eaten by wildlife (Johnson Jr. 1993) but is probably not a highly foraged plant by deer. Perhaps the lack of P and Ca in the fertilizer blend resulted in these nutrient concentrations decreasing. These decreases dropped the Ca/P ratio closer to the optimum value of 2:1 (Maynard & Loosli 1969, Thill et al 1987) during mid-summer but since Ca did not change much during late-summer the Ca/P ratio increased. This appears to have reduced nutritional quality for wildlife and cattle. Studies have shown that *Arctostaphylos* species (Nams et al. 1993, VanderSchaaf 1999, VanderSchaaf et al. 2000) and other ericaceous shrubs are not responsive to fertilization in terms of growth (Prescott et al. 1993), particularly following N fertilization (Prescott et al. 1993).

Carex geyeri Boott has been reported to be an important grazing plant for elk (Johnson Jr. 1993, Stubbendieck et al. 1997), cattle (Holechek et al. 1982, Uresk and Paintner 1985, Stubbendieck et al. 1997), and deer (Stubbendieck et al. 1997). However, Skovlin and Vavra (1979) found little use of this species by *Odocoileus hemionus hemionus* and variable use by *Cervus canadensis nelsoni*. Multi-nutrient fertilization with other nutrients resulted in little change for Ca concentration during mid-summer but an increase in P concentration which decreased the Ca/P ratio (Table 3). During late-summer, the fertilization treatment produced decreases in Ca concentration and a non-significant increase in P which decreased the Ca/P ratio. Despite these changes in the Ca/P ratio, regardless of treatment, *Carex geyeri* Boott appears to be a highly nutritious plant for wildlife and cattle throughout the growing season at the New Meadows, ID *Pinus ponderosa* Dougl. site. Unfortunately, this species decreased in percent cover following multi-nutrient fertilization on this site (VanderSchaaf 1999, VanderSchaaf et al. 2000). However, two other sites analyzed in conjunction with this study (no nutrient analyses were conducted on these sites) showed a small degree of positive response in percent cover following multi-nutrient fertilization (VanderSchaaf 1999) and Riegel et al. (1991) also showed a positive growth response following N-only fertilization.

Another study presented nutrient concentrations of unfertilized *Carex geyeri* Boott plants (Riegel et al. 1992). Overstory basal area ranged from 10 m^2/ha to 24.9 m^2/ha on their site which was dominated by *Pinus ponderosa* Dougl. located in northeastern Oregon. All of the Ca concentrations reported in this chapter are lower than theirs. Phosphorus concentrations following treatment with other nutrients are close to their values with the maximum value in this study exceeding theirs. The unfertilized P concentrations in this study are lower than their lowest values. Therefore, multi-nutrient fertilization with other nutrients may increase P concentration in *Carex geyeri* Boott. Perhaps genetic differences in this species from one site to another, a different understory species composition, dilution effects, or differences in elevations (1060 m for their site and 1245 m for the New Meadows, ID *Pinus ponderosa*

Dougl. site) played a role in producing variation in nutrient concentrations between their study and this one. However, all concentration values are within a reasonable range of one another. This suggests that we may get a good idea of the variation in *Carex geyeri* Boott Ca and P concentrations in northeastern Oregon and central Idaho using these two studies. Based on published results of Ca and P concentrations from Riegel et al. (1992), this study and theirs show similar values for the Ca/P ratio close to the optimum value near 2:1 (Maynard & Loosli 1969, Thill et al 1987). Therefore, based on this measure, *Carex geyeri* Boott appears to be a nutritious plant for animals in northeastern Oregon and central Idaho *Pinus ponderosa* Dougl. forests.

Symphoricarpos albus (L.) Blake is a common plant throughout the inland Northwest (Holechek et al. 1982, Johnson Jr. 1993, VanderSchaaf 1999, VanderSchaaf et al. 2000). Mixed results have been seen in terms of palatability by cattle (Holechek et al. 1982, Johnson Jr. 1993, Stubbendieck et al. 1997), but it is an important plant for deer (Stubbendieck et al. 1997), particularly in the winter (Johnson Jr. 1993). It is an important food and cover plant for song and game birds as well (Stubbendieck et al. 1997). No increases in nutrient concentrations were observed following multi-nutrient fertilization (Table 3). Since production of this species was increased following fertilization at this site (VanderSchaaf 1999, VanderSchaaf et al. 2000), dilution may account for decreases in concentrations. Three other studies have reported nutrient concentrations for this species (Turner et al. 1978, Severson 1982, Riegel et al. 1992). Severson (1982) reported Ca concentrations for this species located on unfertilized sites in the Black Hills of South Dakota and Wyoming under an overstory composition of *Populus tremuloides*, *Pinus ponderosa* Dougl., and *Picea glauca*. The Ca concentration value reported in that study of 1.24% is similar to the fertilized value presented in Table 3. Turner et al. (1978) conducted nutrient concentration analyses on this species in an unfertilized 22-year-old Douglas-fir stand on a site west of the Cascades in Washington. They found a Ca concentration (1.64%) very similar to the control presented in this chapter. Riegel et al. (1992) reported similar values to the control in this study and to that of Turner et al. (1978) during their first year of measurement (1.54 – 1.69%). However, data from their second year of measurement is below the fertilized value found in this study and the value in Severson (1982). Riegel et al. (1992) also found a relatively wide range in P concentration from one year to the next. Their first year data were greater than the control presented in this chapter but their second year data were lower than the control. Turner et al. (1978) found a P concentration value lower than the control value. However, both of these other studies report concentration values ranging from 187% to 412% greater than the multi-nutrient fertilized value found in this study. Based on this study and the results from Turner et al. (1978) and Riegel et al. (1992), multi-nutrient fertilization with other nutrients may have a greater impact on P concentration than Ca concentration in this species. Consistent with the findings of Turner et al. (1978), *Symphoricarpos albus* (L.) Blake generally showed greater Ca and P concentrations relative to other understory species (Tables 2 and 3). VanderSchaaf et al. (2004) also found this to be true for nutrients applied in the multi-nutrient fertilization treatment; B and K. Thus, this species maybe an important "nutrient sink" for the cycles of B, Ca, K, and P in conifer stands throughout the Pacific Northwest - however, based on this study, fertilization with other nutrients may affect the uptake of Ca and P.

The Ca/P ratio was greatly changed following treatment in *Symphoricarpos albus* (L.) Blake (Table 3). Based on published results of Ca and P concentrations, data from Turner et al. (1978) had a value of 4.56 for the Ca/P ratio while Riegel et al. (1992) had values ranging from 2.24 to 2.59. Unlike Ca and P concentrations, data from Riegel et al. (1992) showed that the Ca/P ratio was much less variable from year to year. As Ca concentration changed in a particular direction so did P concentrations. Following treatment, the Ca/P ratio is bordering on being non-healthy (Wise et al 1963, Ullrey et al 1973, Wood 1986) at the New Meadows, ID *Pinus ponderosa* Dougl. site. If P concentrations are greatly reduced following treatment with other nutrients, this may produce an unhealthy ratio between Ca and P in *Symphoricarpos albus* (L.) Blake. Perhaps the application of P in multi-nutrient fertilizer blends may improve the quality of this plant for animals.

CONCLUSIONS

Multi-nutrient fertilization with other nutrients can impact Ca and P concentrations in conifer stands throughout the inland Northwest. For understory vegetation species sampled on these sites, P concentrations appear to be more affected than Ca concentrations across all lifeforms. Generally, the Ca/P ratio seems little affected by fertilization with nutrients other than Ca and P but in some cases the ratio was greatly affected. This study confirms previous findings that response of nutrient concentrations is highly variable depending on many site-specific factors.

REFERENCES

Anderson, B.L., Pieper, R.D., Howard, V.W., 1974. Growth response and deer utilization of fertilized browse. *J. Wildl. Manage.* 38, 525-530.

Brockley, R.P. 1996. Lodgepole pine nutrition and fertilization: a summary of B.C. Ministry of Forests research results. For. Can. And B.C. Min. For., Victoria, B.C. *FRDA* Rep. No. 266.

Brown, M.B., Forsythe, A.B., 1974. Robust tests for the equality of variances. *Journal of the American Statistical Association* 69, 364-367.

Chapin, F.S., III., Vitousek, P.M., Van Cleve, K., 1986. The nature of nutrient limitation in plant communities. *Am. Nat.* 127, 48-58.

Edmonds, R.L., Binkley, D., Feller, M.C., Sollins, P., Abee, A., Myrold, D.D. 1989. Nutrient cycling: effects on productivity of Northwest forests. In: Perry, D.A., Meurisse, R., Thomas, B., Miller, R., Boyle, J., Means, J., Perry, C.R., Powers, R.F. (Eds.). *Maintaining the long-term productivity of Pacific Northwest forest ecosystems.* Timber Press. pp. 17-35.

Erixson, J.A. 1993. *Estimating shrub production and utilization in northern Idaho.* Masters Thesis, University of Idaho, Moscow, ID.

Flanagan, P.W., Van Cleve, K., 1983. Nutrient cycling in relation to decomposition and organic-matter quality in taiga ecosystems. *Can. J. For. Res.* 13, 795-817.

Garrison, M.T., Moore, J.A., 1998. Nutrient Management: A summary and review.Intermountain Forest Tree Nutrition Cooperative, *Supplemental Report* No. 5. University of Idaho Moscow, ID, 47 pp.

Garrison, M.T., Moore, J.A., Shaw, T.M., Mika, P.G., 2000. Foliar nutrient and growth response of mixed-conifer stands on the Okanogan and Umatilla National Forests to three fertilization treatments. *For. Ecol. Manage.* 132, 183-198.

Geist, J.M., Edgerton, P.J., Strickler, G.S,. 1974. Yukky to Yummy-with fertilizers. *Rangemans Journal* 1, 39-41.

Grime, J.P. 1977. Evidence for the existence of three primary strategies in plants and its relevance to ecological and evolutionary theory. *The American Naturalist* 111, 1169-1194.

Haydock, K.P., Shaw, N.H., 1975. The comparative yield method for estimating dry matter yield of pasture. Australian *J. of Experimental Agriculture and Animal Husbandry* 15, 663-670.

Hitchcock, C.L., Cronquist, A., 1973. *Flora of the Pacific Northwest.* University of Washington Press. Seattle, Washington.

Holechek, J.L., Herbel, C.H., 1986. Supplementing range livestock. *Rangelands* 8, 29-33.

Holechek, J.L., Vavra, M., Skovlin, J., Krueger, W.C., 1982. Cattle diets in the Blue Mountains of Oregon II. Forests. *Journal of Range Management* 35, 239-242.

Holechek, J.L., Pieper, R.D., Herbel, C.H., 1995. *Range Management.* Prentice Hall. Upper Saddle River, New Jersey.

Intermountain Forest Tree Nutrition Cooperative. 1988. *Foliage weighing and drying procedures*. p 3.

Johnson, Jr. C.G. 1993. Common Plants of the Inland Pacific Northwest. *USDA Forest Service Publication* R6-ERW-TP051-93. 389 pp.

Johnson, Jr. C.G., Clausnitzer, R.R., 1992. Plant associations of the Blue and Ochoco mountains. *USDA For. Serv. Pub.* R6-ERW-TP-036-92, 162 pp.

Kimball, B.A., Turnblom, E.C., Nolte, D.L., Griffin, D.L., Engeman, R.M., 1998. Effects of thinning and nitrogen fertilization on sugars and terpenes in Douglas-fir vascular tissues: implications for black bear foraging. *For. Sci.* 44, 599-602.

Knoepp, J.D., Swank, W.T., 1997. Forest management effects on surfact soil carbon and nitrogen. *Soil Sci. Soc. Am. J.* 61, 928-935.

Krajicek, J.E., Brinkman, K.A., Gingrich, S.F., 1961. Crown competition – a measure of density. *For. Sci.* 7, 35-42.

Magruder, N.D., French, C.E., McEwen, L.C., Swift, R.W., 1957. Nutritional requirements of white-tailed deer for growth and antler development II. *Bull.* 628. Pennsylvania State Univ., University Park, PA. 21 p.

Maynard, L.A., Loosli, J.K, 1969. *Animal Nutrition.* McGraw-Hill Book Company. New York, New York.

McDonald, P., Edwards, R.A, Greenhalgh, J.F.D., 1988. *Animal Nutrition.* Longman Scientific and Technical. New York, New York.

Meerts, P. 1997. Foliar macronutrient concentrations of forest understorey species in relation to Ellenberg's indices and potential relative growth rate. *Plant and Soil* 189, 257-265.

Moeur, M., 1985. Cover: a user's guide to the CANOPY and SHRUBS extension of the Stand Prognosis Model. *General Technical Report INT-190.* Ogden, UT: U.S. Department of Agriculture, Forest Service, Intermountain Research Station; 49 pp.

Moore, J.A., Mika, P.G., VanderPloeg, J.L., 1991. Nitrogen fertilizer response of Rocky Mountain Douglas-fir by geographic area across the inland Northwest. *West. J. Appl. For.* 6, 94-98.

Moore, J.A., P.G. Mika, T.M. Shaw, and M.I. Garrison-Johnston. 2004. Foliar nutrient characteristics of four conifer species in the Interior Northwest United States. West. *J. Appl. For.* 19: 13-24.

Nams, V.O., Folkard, N.F.G, Smith, J.N.M., 1993. Effects of nitrogen fertilization on several woody and nonwoody boreal forest species. *Canadian Journal of Botany* 71, 93-97.

Nams, V.O., Folkard, N.F.G, Smith, J.N.M., 1996. Nitrogen fertilization stimulates herbivory by snowshoe hares in the boreal forest. *Canadian Journal of Zoology* 74, 196-199.

NOAA. 1998. Climatic data for 1998. Available on the web at *http://noaa.ncdc.gov.*

Oh, J.H., Jones, M.B, Longhurst, W.M., Connolly, G.E., 1970. Deer browsing and rumen microbial fermentation of Douglas-fir as affected by fertilization and growth stage. *For. Sci.* 16, 21-27.

Powers, R.F. 1983. Forest fertilization research in California. P. 388-397 *in* IUFRO symp. On forest site and continious productivity. Ballard, R., and S.P. Gessel (eds.). USDA *For. Serv. Gen. Tech. Rep.* PNW-163.

Prescott, C.E., Coward, L.P.,Weetman, G.F., Gessel, S.P., 1993. Effects of repeated nitrogen fertilization on the ericaceous shrub, salal (Gaultheria shallon), in two coastal Douglas-fir forests. *For. Ecol. Manage.* 61, 45-60.

Riegel, G.M., Miller, R.F., Krueger, W.C., 1991. Understory vegetation response to increasing water and nitrogen levels in a *Pinus ponderosa* forest in Northeastern Oregon. *Northwest Science* 65:10-15.

Riegel, G.M., Miller, R.F., Krueger, W.C., 1992. Competition for resources between understory vegetation and overstory *Pinus ponderosa* in Northeastern Oregon. *Ecological Applications* 2, 71-85.

SAS Institute, Inc., 1985. *Statistical analysis system's user's guide basics*, version 5 edition. SAS Institute Inc., Cary, N.C.

Severson, K.E. 1982. Production and nutritive value of aspen understory, Black Hills. *J. Range Manage.* 35: 786-789.

Shaffii, B., Moore, J.A., Olson, J.R., 1989. Effects of nitrogen fertilization on growth of grand fir and Douglas-fir stands in northern Idaho. *West. J. Appl. For.* 4, 54-57.

Shomon J.J., Ashbaugh, B.L., Tolmon, C.D., 1969. *Wildlife habitat improvement.* National Audubon Society.

Skovlin, J., Vavra, M., 1979. Winter diets of elk and deer in the Blue Mountains of Oregon, U.*S. Dep. Agr. Forest Serv. PNW Forest and Range Exp. Sta. Res. Pap.* PNW-260. 21 p.

Steele, R., Pfister, R.D., Ryker, R.A., Kittams, J.A., 1981. Forest Habitat Types of Central Idaho. *USDA For. Ser. Gen.Tech.* Rep. INT-114.

Stubbendieck, J., Hatch, S.L., Butterfield, C.H., 1997. *North American Range Plants.* University of Nebraska Press. Lincoln, NE.

Thill, R.E., Martin, Jr., A., Morris, Jr., H.F., McCune, E.D., 1987. Grazing and burning impacts on deer diets on Louisiana pine-bluestem range. *J. Wildl. Manage.* 51: 873-880.

Timmer, V.R., Stone, E.L., 1978. Comparative foliar analysis of young balsam fir fertilized with nitrogen, phosphorus, potassium, and lime. *Soil Sci. Soc. Am. J.* 42, 125-130.

Trettin, C.C., Johnson, D.W., Todd Jr., D.E., 1999. Forest nutrient and carbon pools at Walker Branch watershed: changes during a 21-year period. *Soil Sci. Soc. Am. J.* 63, 1436-1448.

Turner, J., Long, J.N., Backiel, A., 1978. Under-storey nutrient content in an age sequence of Douglas-fir stands. *Annals of Botany* 42, 1045-1055.

Ullrey, D.E., Youatt, W.G., Johnson, H.E., Fay, L.D., Schoepke, B.L., Magee, W.T., Keahey, K.K., 1973. Calcium requirements of weaned white-tailed deer fawns. *J. Wildl. Manage.* 37: 187-194.

Ullrey, D.E., Youatt, W.G., Johnson, H.E., Cowan, A.B., Fay, L.D., Covert, R.L., Magee, W.T., Keahey, K.K., 1975. Phosphorus requirements of weaned white-tailed deer fawns. *J. Wildl. Manage.* 39: 590-595.

Underwood, E.J., Suttle, N., 1999. *The mineral nutrition of livestock.* CABI Pub., New York, NY. 3rd Ed.

Uresk, D.W., and W.W. Paintner. 1985. Cattle diets in a ponderosa pine forest in thenorthern Black Hills. *J. Range. Manage.* 38: 440-442.

Van den Driessche, R., 1988. Response of Douglas-fir (*Pseudotsuga menziesii* (Mirb.) Franco) to some different fertilizers applied at planting. *New Forests* 2: 89-110.

VanderSchaaf, C.L. 1999., *Operational fertilization effects on under-story vegetation.* MS Thesis. University of Idaho. 157 pp.

VanderSchaaf, C.L., Moore, J.A., Kingery, J.L., 2000. The effect of multi-nutrient fertilization on understory plant diversity. *Northwest Science* 74, 316-324.

VanderSchaaf, C.L., Moore, J.A., Kingery, J.L., 2002. The effect of multinutrient fertilization on understory vegetation annual production. *West. J. Appl.* For. 17, 147-153.

VanderSchaaf, C.L., Moore, J.A., Kingery, J.L., 2004. The effect of multinutrient fertilization on understory vegetation nutrient concentrations in inland Northwest conifer stands. *For. Ecol. Manage.* 190: 201-218.

Verme, L.J., 1979. Wildlife nutrition. In: Teague, R.D., Decker, E. (eds.) *Wildlife Conservation*. The Wildlife Society, Washington D.C. pp. 117-122.

Verme, L.J., Ullrey, D.E., 1972. Feeding and nutrition of deer. *In*: *The Digestive Physiology and Nutrition of Ruminants*. Vol. 3, D.C. Church, Ed., Dep. Animal Sci. Oregon State Univ., Corvallis, OR. 350 p.

Webster, S.R., Dobkowski, A. 1983. Concentrations of foliar nutrients for trees and the dosage frequency of fertilizer trials. *Weyerhaeuser Res. Rep. No. 1*, Project 050-3920/3. 25 p.

Wise, M.B., Ordoveza, A.L., Barrick, E.R., 1963. Influence of variations in dietary calcium:phosphorus ratio on performance and blood constituents of calves. *J. Nutr.* 79: 79-84.

Wood, G. W., 1986. Influences of forest fertilization on South Carolina deer forage quality. *South. J. Appl. For.* 10, 203-206.

Wood, G.W., Tanner, G.W., 1985. Browse quality response to forest fertilization and soils in Florida. *Journal of Range Management* 38, 432-435.

ACKNOWLEDGEMENTS

I would like to thank Dr. James A. Moore and Dr. James L. Kingery of the University of Idaho for their help in preparing this chapter. Nancy Loewenstein of Auburn University provided helpful comments. This research was supported by the Boise Cascade Corporation. I would also like to thank the Intermountain Forest Tree Nutrition Cooperative Members for additional support.

INDEX

A

B

C

D

E

F

G

H

I

K

L

M

N

O

P

R

S

T

U

V

W

Z